The Freeman Library of Laboratory Separates

Freeman Laboratory Separates are self-bound, self-contained exercises. They are 8½ inches by 11 inches in format and are punched for a three-ring notebook. Separates may be ordered in any assortment or quantity at 75¢ each. Thus the instructor can construct an entire manual tailored to the design of the course, or select Separates to broaden the coverage of the laboratory manual in use.

Order Separates by number. Students' sets are collated and packaged by the publisher before shipment to the bookstore.

Each exercise in this manual is available as a Separate (see below). On the facing page are listed other Freeman Laboratory Separates in Biology.

LABORATORY OUTLINES IN BIOLOGY, 846, 501–538
75¢ each
by ABRAMOFF and THOMSON
*(Also available as a bound manual,
LABORATORY OUTLINES IN BIOLOGY III)*

846. Use and Care of the Microscope
501. Cell Structure and Function
502. Cellular Reproduction
503. Plant Anatomy: Roots and Stems
504. Plant Anatomy: Leaves and Flowers
505. Vertebrate Anatomy: External Anatomy, Skeleton, and Muscles
506. Vertebrate Anatomy: Digestive, Respiratory, Circulatory, and Urogenital Systems
507. Movement of Materials Through Cell Membranes
508. Biologically Important Molecules: Proteins
509. Carbohydrates and Lipids
510. Photosynthesis

511. Carbohydrate Metabolism
512. Cellular Respiration
513. Transport in Biological Systems
514. Biological Coordination in Plants
515. Biological Coordination in Animals
516. Mendelian Genetics
517. Biochemical Genetics
518. Fertilization and Early Development of the Sea Urchin
519. Fertilization and Early Development of the Frog
520. Early Development of the Chick
521. Plant Growth and Development
522. Plant Development: Hormonal Regulation
523. Plant Development: Effect of Light
524. Kingdom Monera: Phyla Schizophyta and Cyanophyta
525. Kingdom Protista: Phyla Euglenophyta, Flagellata, Ciliata, Sarcodina, Sporozoa, and Gymnomycota
526. Kingdom Fungi
527. Kingdom Plantae: Phyla Chlorophyta, Phaeophyta, and Rhodophyta
528. Kingdom Plantae: Phylum Bryophyta
529. Kingdom Plantae: Phylum Tracheophyta
530. Kingdom Animalia: Phyla Porifera and Cnidaria
531. Kingdom Animalia: Phylum Platyhelminthes
532. Kingdom Animalia: Phylum Aschelminthes and Parasites of the Frog
533. Kingdom Animalia: Phylum Mollusca
534. Kingdom Animalia: Phylum Annelida
535. Kingdom Animalia: Phyla Onycophora and Arthropoda
536. Kingdom Animalia: Phylum Echinodermata
537. Kingdom Animalia: Phyla Hemichordata and Chordata
538. Appendixes for Separates 846; 501–537

W. H. FREEMAN AND COMPANY
660 Market Street, San Francisco, California 94104
20 Beaumont Street, Oxford, England OX1 2NQ

A 104-page instructor's handbook for use with this manual
will be sent to instructors free of charge on request.

LABORATORY OUTLINES
IN BIOLOGY-III

Peter Abramoff / Robert G. Thomson

MARQUETTE UNIVERSITY

W. H. FREEMAN AND COMPANY
San Francisco

Project Editor: Judith Wilson
Copy Editor: Linda Purrington
Designer: Robert Ishi
Production Coordinator: Linda Jupiter
Illustration Coordinator: Cheryl Nufer
Artist: Donna Salmon
Compositor: Graphic Typesetting Service
Printer and Binder: Webcrafters, Incorporated

1 2 3 4 5 6 7 8 9 0   WC   0 8 9 8 7 6 5 4 3 2

Contents

APPENDIXES

Preface

In this third edition of Laboratory Outlines in Biology, we adhere to our basic philosophy that the laboratory experience is an integral part of the biology curriculum and should be complementary—not subservient—to the lectures. Laboratory studies constitute an essential part of a liberal education in that, if properly presented, they encourage ingenuity and accuracy and enable the student to gain insight into how conclusions reached by scientists proceed logically from observation and experiment. Further, laboratory study allows the student to become intensely and personally involved in the knowledge acquired, conveys something of the meaning, scope, and excitement of biology as a significant perspective from which to view the world, and introduces the complexity and diversity of living organisms and their relationships to one another.

More exercises are included in this edition than are generally used in a one- or two-semester course. In addition to presenting those topics that are basic to an understanding of biology, we have added new material and revised extensively to reflect the comments of faculty and students who have used the earlier editions of this manual.

We do not believe that routine memorization of unrelated facts is a sound approach to biology, nor to any other science. The student will not be asked to perform such a task here. However, the student will be asked to master detailed information when that information is required to document, illustrate, or dramatize a basic biological principle. Descriptive material has been excluded except when such material is needed to illustrate concepts. The routine study of prepared slides and the creation of highly detailed drawings and dissections have not been emphasized in this manual.

While the basic sequence of topics reflects our own approach, the exercises are sufficiently comprehensive and independent to be adaptable to any laboratory program. Depending on course requirements, the exercises are well suited to two- or three-hour laboratory meetings or to any other variations. Every effort has been made to keep expenditures for supplies and equipment within the budgets of most colleges and universities.

To facilitate the use of this manual, the Instructor's Handbook has also been extensively revised and updated. This supplement, which contains lists of materials and equipment, sources of supply, instructions for the preparation of reagents and for the culture and maintenance of various organisms, is provided so that the laboratory studies can be effectively presented to the student.

. . .

We are grateful to the Literary Executor of the late Sir Ronald A. Fisher, F.R.S., to Dr. Frank Yates, F.R.S., and to Longman Group Ltd., London, for permission to reprint Table IV from their book *Statistical Tables for Biological Agricultural and Medical Research* (6th edition, 1974).

Peter Abramoff
September 1981 *Robert G. Thomson*

ix

LABORATORY OUTLINES
IN BIOLOGY-III

Use and Care
of the Microscope

The microscope is a major tool of biologists. Without the microscope, the cell theory would not have been developed, and we would lack most of our present knowledge of living things too small to be seen by the unaided eye. This exercise has been designed to familiarize you with the use and care of the microscope.

There are many kinds of microscopes in use today, with a wide range of magnifications from as low as 2 or 3 to more than 100,000. In your laboratory studies, you will be using mainly two kinds of microscopes: the compound microscope with magnifications ranging from 40 to 450, depending on the particular make, and the stereoscopic dissecting microscope with magnifications ranging from 4 to 60.

A. USE AND CARE
OF THE COMPOUND MICROSCOPE

A microscope is a precision instrument and should be treated accordingly. It may appear to be indestructible, but in reality the slightest jar may damage its working parts and optical system. Handle the microscope carefully at all times; repairs are costly and may require that the instrument be returned to the factory.

1. Parts of the Microscope

After removing the microscope from its cabinet, place it on the table in front of you so that you look at it from the side. As you examine the instrument, refer to Fig. 1-1 for help in locating the various parts described below.

The compound microscope is made up of a series of lenses that magnify objects lying outside the range of ordinary vision. These lenses are located in the **ocular**, or eyepiece, and in the **objectives**. A microscope may have one ocular—a **monocular** microscope—or it may have two oculars—a **binocular** microscope. Ocular and objective are kept a set distance apart by the **body tube**. Note that there are at least two objectives, attached to the body tube by means of a revolving **nosepiece**. Cautiously turn the nosepiece, taking care that the objectives do not

ARM

Supports body tube and coarse adjustment.

COARSE ADJUSTMENT

Moves stage or body tube up and down to approximately the correct distance.

FINE ADJUSTMENT

Permits exact focusing by moving stage or body tube up and down very slightly.

BASE

Firm support that bears weight of microscope.

OCULAR

Contains lenses to increase magnification. May be replaced with another of lower or higher magnification.

BODY TUBE

Holds lenses of ocular and objectives at the proper working distance from each other.

NOSEPIECE

Permits interchange of low- and high-power objectives.

OBJECTIVES

Contain lenses of different magnifications.

STAGE CLIPS

Hold slide firmly in place.

STAGE

Supports slide over opening that admits light from mirror or lamp.

IRIS DIAPHRAGM

Regulates amount of light passing through the specimen.

LIGHT SOURCE

Directs light upward through diaphragm and hole in stage.

FIG. 1-1
Parts of a compound microscope.

hit the **stage**. How can you tell when the objective is correctly lined up with the ocular?

_____

_____

_____

Note that the objectives differ in length. The smaller one is a **low-power objective**; the larger, a **high-power objective**.

Movement of either the body tube or the stage, up or down, enables you to focus the microscope. With the low-power objective in position, turn the coarse-adjust-

ment knob one full turn in a clockwise direction. Does this raise or lower the stage or the body tube?

_____

Approximately what distance can it be moved?

_____

In a similar manner, turn the fine-adjustment knob. In contrast to the distance the stage or body tube moved in the coarse adjustment, how far did it move this time?

_____

Proper use of the microscope dictates that the coarse adjustments not be used when the high-power objective is in position.

In the center of the stage, locate the opening through which light is reflected from a mirror or directed from a light source. Notice that one surface of the mirror is flat and the other surface is concave. These surfaces act as a lens to concentrate the light from the whole area of the mirror onto the microscope field. Daylight may be the source of light; however, it is of such variable intensity that artificial light is generally preferred. An **iris diaphragm**, located below the stage, may be opened or closed, thereby regulating the amount of light entering the microscope.

The arm of the microscope is attached to the base on which the microscope stands. When carrying the microscope, grasp the arm with one hand and support the base with the other so that you do not drop the instrument.

2. Using the Microscope

Clean lenses are essential to working with the microscope. If the lenses are dirty, wet, or scratched, the image will be obscured, and observation of the object under study will be difficult. *Develop the habit of cleaning the ocular and objective lenses each time you use the microscope. Use only lens paper—never filter paper, paper toweling, or any other substitute material that may scratch the lenses.*

Rotate the nosepiece until the low-power objective clicks into position. Obtain a slide of the letter *e* (or *a, k,* or *h*) from your laboratory instructor. Place the slide on the stage so that the cover slip or paper *e* is located *on top* of the slide as it is inserted over the center of the circular opening in the stage. Otherwise the subject will not come into focus on high power, and the objective may be rammed into the slide. Slowly lower the objective (or raise the stage) to a position about 0.5 centimeter (cm) from the slide.

Observation of any specimen is difficult unless proper light is reflected through the lens systems in the objectives and ocular. While looking through the ocular, "aim" the mirror (not the microscope) toward a light source and reflect the light up through the diaphragm and opening in the stage. If this is done properly, a bright, evenly distributed circle of light—the field—will be visible. If the field is too bright, close the diaphragm to reduce the amount of light reflected from the mirror.

When proper illumination of the field has been achieved, slowly raise the body tube (or lower the stage) by means of the coarse-adjustment knob until the letter comes into focus. It is helpful to move the slide slowly back and forth while doing this in order to help locate the material being studied. *In many microscopes, you may see a black line that cuts across the field. This is a pointer (usually made of hair or other fine material) that enables the student or the instructor to point out particular objects or regions of the material under observation.* After the letter has come into focus, a small adjustment with the fine-adjustment knob will bring it into clear, sharp focus.

When the letter is in sharp focus, move the slide to the left. In which direction does the letter image seem to move?

_____

Move the slide toward you. How does this affect the apparent direction of movement of the slide as you view it in the field?

_____

Closely observe the letter under low power. Is it in the same position it would be in if viewed with the naked eye, or is it inverted?

_____

Slowly swing the high-power objective into position, making sure that as the objective moves into position it does not hit the stage or the slide. Many modern microscopes are parfocal—that is, after the image has been brought into sharp focus under low power, it will remain in focus when the high-power objective is turned into position. If your instrument is not parfocal, a small adjustment of the fine-focus knob may be necessary. How does switching to high power affect the brightness of the field?

_____

A minor adjustment in the position of the mirror will generally correct any loss of light. Open and close the diaphragm several times until you have located the position in which light conditions are optimum for viewing under high power.

3. Precautions

In connection with the proper use of the compound microscope, there are several precautions that should be noted (Fig. 1-2).

Abuse   Use

1. When moved from one place to another, the microscope should always be held in an upright position.

2. Never touch the lens of the microscope with your hands. To clean the lenses in the ocular and objectives, use only the lens paper supplied for this purpose.

3. If you find that the microscope is out of order, do not attempt to make any repairs yourself. Notify your laboratory instructor.

4. Always locate the object to be studied with the low-power objective and then turn to the high-power objective if a more detailed study is desired.

5. Do not use the coarse adjustment when the high-power objective is in position. It is difficult to control the movement of this objective through small distances except by use of the fine-adjustment knob.

6. Never focus downward while looking through the ocular. Rather, look at the objective from the side to prevent moving the body tube too far and possibly damaging the objective lens—to say nothing of the possibility of breaking the slide that is being studied.

4. Measuring Microscopic Objects

Frequently, a professional biologist needs to know the dimensions of the object being examined under the microscope. Described below are two methods you can use to obtain estimates of the size of microscopic objects.

Method A enables you to obtain an approximate estimate of the size of an object by comparing it with the diameter of the field of view. To do this, it is first necessary to measure the size of the field. For this measurement, as well as others that you make in laboratory work, the metric system is used.

1. Place a short, transparent plastic ruler over the opening in the center of the stage so that the scale is visible through the microscope (Fig. 1-3A).

2. Line up one of the vertical lines so that it is just visible at the left side of the circular field of view (Fig. 1-3B).

3. The distance from the center of one line to the center of the next line is 1 millimeter (mm). Count the number of millimeters included from one side of the field to the opposite side. If the right side of the field does not coincide with one of the lines, estimate the fraction of a millimeter. What is the diameter (in millimeters) of the low-power field of view of your microscope?

For most microscopic measurements, a much smaller unit than the millimeter is required. Scientists use the micrometer (μm), which is one-thousandth of a millimeter

FIG. 1-2
Common abuse and correct use of the compound microscope.

(0.001 mm). What is the diameter of your low-power field in micrometers?

_____

4. Turn the high-power objective into place. Note that the field of view is *less* than 1 mm. Instead of measuring this field directly, it is more accurate to obtain the diameter by the following method: divide the magnifying power of the high-power objective by the magnifying power of the low-power objective; then divide this quotient into the diameter of the low-power objective field previously obtained. What is the diameter of the high-power field in millimeters?

_____

In micrometers?

_____

5. Your instructor will supply you with various prepared slides of cells or other objects for you to measure. In each case, find the length and width of the object in micrometers. For example, if the object's diameter is about one-third that of the low-power field, and you have calculated the diameter of the field as 1200 μm, then the diameter of the object is approximately 400 μm.

Method B is used for more accurate measurements and requires a microscope equipped with an **ocular micrometer**. This is a small glass disc on which uniformly spaced lines are etched. It is inserted into the eyepiece of the microscope (Fig. 1-4A). When an object is observed with a microscope having an ocular micrometer, the micrometer acts as a ruler that is superimposed on the object being measured. However, because microscopes vary in actual magnification, it is first necessary to calibrate the micrometer for your specific microscope.

1. Obtain a **stage micrometer** from your instructor; this is a glass slide that has uniform lines etched at standard known intervals. If you observe the stage micrometer with your microscope without the ocular micrometer in place, it will appear as shown in Fig. 1-4B. If you observe the stage micrometer with the ocular micrometer in place, it will appear as shown in Fig. 1-4C.

2. Turn the ocular in the tube until the lines of the ocular micrometer are parallel with those of the stage micrometer. Match the lines at the left edges of the two micrometers by moving the stage micrometer (Fig. 1-4D).

3. Calculate the actual distance in micrometers between the lines of the ocular micrometer by observing how many spaces of the stage micrometer are included within a

A. Place a transparent metric rule over hole in stage.

B. Line up one of the vertical lines so that it is just visible at left edge of field. Count number of millimeter divisions from one edge of field to the other. In this example, the field diameter is approximately 6 mm.

FIG. 1-3
Approximating the size of a microscope field (Method A).

given number of spaces on the ocular micrometer. Use the following formula: 10 spaces on the ocular micrometer = X spaces on the stage micrometer. Because the smallest spaces on the stage micrometer are known to be 0.01 mm apart,

$$1 \text{ ocular-micrometer space} = \frac{X \times 0.01 \text{ mm}}{10}$$

$$= \text{\_\_\_\_ mm} \quad \text{or}$$

$$= \text{\_\_\_\_ micrometers (μm)}$$

FIG. 1-4
Using an ocular micrometer to determine the size
of microscopic objects (Method B).

With this information, you now can use the ocular
micrometer in your microscope to measure various
microscopic objects available in your laboratory.

5. Using the Oil-Immersion Lens

Some microscopes have a 93 × or a 100 × objective lens.
Because the brightness and field of view are greatly
decreased at this magnification, oil must be placed
between the slide and the lens to maximize the amount
of light entering the lens system. This also increases the
resolving power of this lens.

Oil-immersion observation is carried out as follows:

1. Using the low- and high-power lenses, bring the
specimen into focus and position it in the center of the
field of view.

2. Rotate the nosepiece part way so that the high-
power objective is off to one side.

3. Apply a *small* drop of immersion oil to the cover
slip over the specimen being examined.

4. Carefully rotate the oil-immersion lens into position. The drop of oil should make contact with the lens
and form a continuous layer between the cover slip and
the lens.

5. Looking through the ocular, *carefully* adjust the
fine focus to bring the specimen into focus. You may have
to open the iris diaphragm to obtain more light.

6. Immediately after finishing the work, remove the
used oil from the lens by using a soft cotton cloth wetted
with xylol. (Never use alcohol for this purpose, and do
not immerse the top of the objective into xylol for cleaning.)

B. USE AND CARE OF THE STEREOSCOPIC DISSECTING MICROSCOPE

The stereoscopic dissecting microscope (Fig. 1-5) has
two distinct advantages over the compound microscope.
It (1) enables you to observe objects that are too large or
too thick to see with higher magnifications, but too small

FIG. 1-5
Parts of a stereoscopic microscope.

for the unaided eye, and (2) gives you an opportunity to observe objects in three dimensions. Magnifications obtained with the stereoscopic microscope commonly range between 4 and 60, depending on the lens combinations used.

Illuminate the stage of the microscope with a lamp or similar light source. What is the low-power magnification of your microscope?

_____

The high-power magnification?

_____

If there are any intermediate magnifications obtainable, what are they?

_____

Binocular microscopes are essentially two microscopes in one—a monocular microscope for each eye. The distance between the two oculars can be adjusted by moving the ocular tubes toward or away from each other. Looking through the microscope with the low-power objective in position, adjust the oculars to fit the distance between your eyes so that a single field of view is seen. Place a coin (or other object as directed by your instructor) on the center of the stage. Lower the objective as far as it will go. Looking through the oculars, raise the objective until the object comes into focus. If the object seems out of focus, it may be necessary to focus separately for each eye. If your microscope has separate focusing devices for each ocular, focus first with one ocular, and then the other. However, if your microscope has one ocular fixed in position, you will first need to look through the ocular that cannot be focused. Focus for this eye by turning the adjusting knob until the object is sharply outlined. Adjust the ocular for the other eye until the object is in focus for both eyes. If you have difficulty doing this, your instructor will help.

Move the object away from you. As you look through the microscope, which way does the image move?

_____

When the object is moved to the side, which way does the image move?

_____

How does the direction of movement compare with that of the compound microscope?

_____

Next observe the object at higher magnifications. As you increase the magnification, how does the area of the field of view change?

_____

To practice using the stereoscopic microscope, observe various objects supplied by your instructor. Try manipulating the objects with dissecting needles while observing them.

C. STUDY OF POND WATER

In your laboratory work, many of your observations with the microscope will be made on living organisms or on tissues or parts of organisms that you will want to keep alive. To allow them to dry out would greatly distort them, to say nothing of the effect death would have on a study of their movements. For observations of living material, you will be making **wet mounts.** To prepare a wet mount, first obtain a clean microscope slide and cover slip (Fig. 1-6). The cover slip is very thin so that the objective lens of the microscope can be brought as close as possible to the specimens.

Using an eyedropper, add a drop of pond water to the center of the slide. The cover slip should be placed on the drop of water in the following way:

Lower one end of the cover slip so that it touches one side of the drop of water at about a 45° angle.

After the water has spread across the edge of the cover slip, carefully lower it by supporting the free end with a dissecting needle or the tip of your pencil. If this is done carefully, it will prevent the accumulation of air bubbles under the cover slip. Air bubbles, which interfere with good observation, can be distinguished from other objects

A. Add drop of pond water to a clean microscope slide.

B. Add clean cover slip.

C. Gently lower cover slip into place with a dissecting needle.

D. Ready for observation

Air bubble

Microscope field

FIG. 1-6
Preparation of a wet mount.

by their even, round shape and their heavy, dark outline. Locate some air bubbles in your preparation, and point them out to your instructor before you proceed any further (Fig. 1-6D). If you do not have air bubbles on your slide, examine someone else's preparation where they are present so that you will be familiar with what these "structures" look like.

Excess water at the edges of the cover slip can be soaked up by carefully touching a piece of paper toweling to the edge of the cover slip. However, if your preparation begins to dry out while under observation, add 1 drop of water at the edge of the cover slip.

Under low power and with reduced light, make a survey of the drop of pond water. Identify as many of the organisms as you can. Carefully study their differences in structure and their method of movement. Figs. 1-7, 1-8, 1-9, and 1-10 should help you identify what you see.

Prepare additional wet mounts by taking samples from different parts of the jar of pond water. Do not be too hasty in discarding a slide as not containing any microorganisms; a systematic survey of the preparation is often necessary to locate the organisms. Why do the organisms often accumulate at the edge of the cover slip?

To identify the smaller organisms, it may be necessary to use the high-power objective. When your work is completed, clean and dry any slides and cover slips used. Wipe the lenses of the microscope with lens paper, clean the stage, and return the microscope to the cabinet.

REFERENCES

Eddy, S., and A. C. Hodson. 1961. *Taxonomic Keys to Common Animals*. 3rd ed. Burgess.

Needham, J., and P. Needham. 1962. *Guide to the Study of Fresh-Water Biology*. Comstock.

Taft, C. E. 1961. A Revised Key for the Field Identification of Some Genera of Algae. *Turtox News* 39(4):98–103.

Van Norman, R. W. 1971. *Experimental Biology*. 2nd ed. Prentice-Hall.

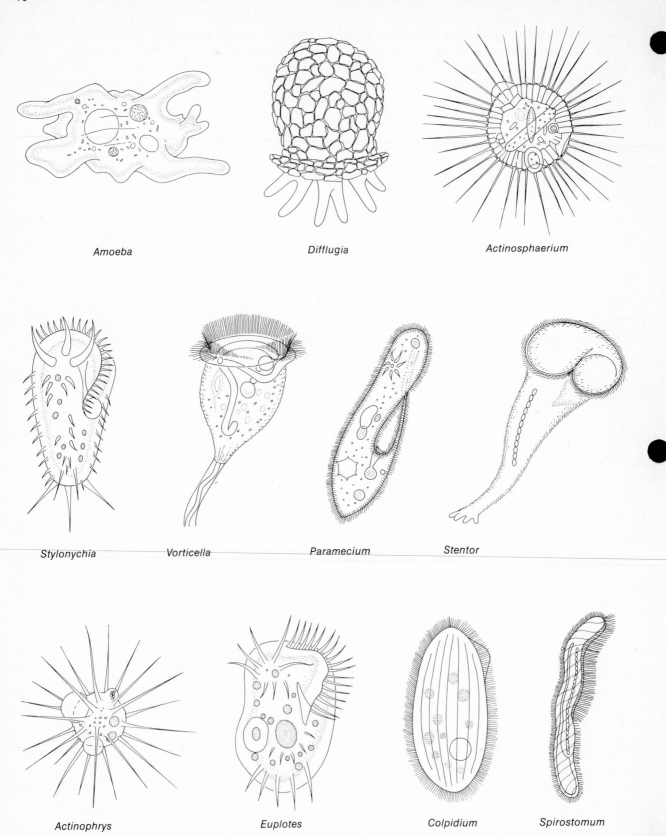

Amoeba

Difflugia

Actinosphaerium

Stylonychia

Vorticella

Paramecium

Stentor

Actinophrys

Euplotes

Colpidium

Spirostomum

FIG. 1-7
Protozoans commonly found in pond water.

FIG. 1-8
Unicellular algae commonly found in pond water.

Hydra

Daphnia

Rotifers

Daphnia

Macrothrix

Cladocerans

Cyclops   Diaptomus

Copepods

FIG. 1-9
Invertebrates commonly found in pond water.

Oscillatoria

Spirogyra

Zygnema

Pediastrum

Pandorina

Scenedesmus

Cladophora

Hydrodictyon

Anabaena

FIG. 1-10
Multicellular algae commonly found in pond water.

Cell Structure and Function

Just as there is diversity of form in life, so there is in the form and function of the cells that make up living organisms. Single cells, such as *Amoeba* and *Paramecium*, can be free-living organisms capable of carrying on an independent existence. Some cells live as part of a loosely organized colony of cells that move from place to place. Others are immovably fixed as part of the tissues of higher plants and animals and depend on the closely integrated activities of other cells for their existence.

Cells vary in size. For example, the length of many bacteria is roughly 1 micrometer (μm), which is equal to 10^{-6} meter. On the other hand, the yolk of an ostrich egg, also a single cell, is the size of a small orange. Some cells, such as red blood cells, transport oxygen and carbon dioxide. Other cells have different specialties. Whatever its form or function, the cell is now recognized as the basic unit of living matter, containing all those properties and processes that are collectively called *life*.

Although cells have diverse forms and functions, all cells are constructed according to a fundamental design and share certain common features. A basic knowledge of cell structure is indispensable to understanding the cell as an independent unit and its role in the life processes of plants and higher animals.

A. ORGANIZATION OF CELLS

In this study, you will examine several different types of cells. As you examine them, compare each with the structure of the "generalized" cell shown in Fig. 2-1A. Not all the structures shown in this drawing will be evident in the cells that you examine because it takes special staining procedures and high magnifications to bring out very small cellular components such as mitochondria and the Golgi apparatus.

1. Onion Cells

Following the procedure outlined in Fig. 2-2A–E, prepare a wet mount of onion epidermal tissue. Examine this tissue with the low-power objective ($10\times$). The "lines" forming the network between the individual cells are non-living cell walls composed chiefly of cellulose. The **cell wall** immediately surrounds the **cell membrane** (also called the **plasma membrane**), which encloses the **cytoplasm**. The central part of many plant cells (which is difficult to observe in living cells) is taken up by a fluid-filled **vacuole** containing mostly water and salts.

16

FIG. 2-1
Some of the intracellular components found in cells at the light (A) and electron microscopic (B) levels.

A. Cut an onion bulb into quarters.

B. Remove one of the fleshy "scale" leaves.

C. Snapping the "leaf" backward usually produces a ragged piece of epidermis.

D. Remove a small piece of epidermis and spread it evenly in a drop of water on a slide.

E. Gently lower a cover slip to prevent trapping air bubbles. Examine with your microscope. Add more water to the edge of the cover slip with an eye dropper if the slide begins to dry.

F. Add 1 or 2 drops of Janus Green solution to edge of cover slip.

G. Draw the stain under by touching lens paper to the opposite side of cover slip.

FIG. 2-2
Procedure for studying living onion cells.

Next examine the cells under high power. Locate the **nucleus**, which looks like a dense body in the translucent cytoplasm. In some cells, the nucleus seems to be lying in the central part of the cell and looks circular. In other cells, it seems to be compressed and pushed against the cell wall. Explain this apparent discrepancy in the shape and position of the nucleus.

_____

_____

The cytoplasm is separated from the central vacuole, nucleus, and cell wall by membranes, but the membranes are difficult to observe in this preparation.

In the onion cell, it is possible to observe **mitochondria**—those cellular organelles involved in cellular respiration. To do this, select another piece of onion epidermal tissue and cut it with a sharp razor so that it is approximately 1 × 3 mm in size. On a clean slide, mount the tissue in a drop of 5% sucrose solution to which you have added from three to five drops of the stain Janus Green B. Add a cover slip.

If your preparation is truly one cell in thickness, it will have the appearance of a nearly transparent brick wall when viewed under the low power of your microscope. Using the high-power objective, locate the mitochondria, which look like very small rods and spheres at the periphery of the cell. They should be blue in color when you first view your preparation. If they are not stained, place a strip of filter paper or other absorbent paper at the edge of the cover slip. Add a few drops of the Janus Green solution at the opposite edge of the cover glass, and draw it through your preparation by absorbing stain from the other side with the piece of absorbent paper as shown in Fig. 2-2F, G. Stained mitochondria will lose their color in about 5 minutes as a result of the action of the dehydrogenase enzymes located on their surface. How long did it require for the mitochondria in your preparation to lose their color?

_____

2. Elodea Cells

In this study, you will examine cells from the leaf of a water plant commonly called Elodea (Fig. 2-3). These cells are green because they contain a pigment called **chlorophyll**. In **photosynthesis**, this pigment absorbs light energy and converts it into chemical energy.

Remove a young leaf from the tip of the plant. Place the leaf in a drop of water on a slide, and add a cover

A. Elodea plant

B. Remove a young leaf, place it in a drop of water, add a cover slip, and examine the leaf with the low-power objective (10×).

C. Mount another leaf in water and examine with microscope.

D. Locate the "spine" cells along edges of the leaf.

FIG. 2-3
Preparation of Elodea cells for microscopic examination.

slip. Examine the preparation with the low-power objective in position. Locate the nucleus, cytoplasm, and cell wall.

Examine a group of cells near the center of the leaf. Carefully switch to high power. Bring the cells into focus by using the fine adjustment, and try to determine the number of cell layers.

_____

Note that the green pigment is located in small structures in the cytoplasm. These structures are called **chloroplasts**. As you examine the chloroplasts, you should see them moving in the cell.

The plant cell is enclosed by a nonliving cell wall and a cell membrane that is difficult to observe because it is pushed tightly against the inside of the cell wall. You can make this membrane easier to see, however, by placing the cell in a hypertonic solution (i.e., a saline solution that is more concentrated than the cytoplasm). The saline, being hypertonic to the cytoplasm, causes water to move out of the cell and the cell to shrink away from the wall, exposing the membrane.

Select another young Elodea leaf, mount it in a drop of water, and add a cover slip. Examine the preparation with the low-power objective. Along the edges of the leaf, locate "spine" cells (Fig. 2-3D). Switch to high power and study the cell. Note that the cell membrane cannot be distinguished from the cell wall.

Add one or two drops of a concentrated saline solution to one edge of the cover slip. Then touch the liquid on the opposite side of the cover slip with a piece of lens paper (or paper toweling) so that the paper draws up the liquid (Fig. 2-2F, G). Repeat this step two more times to be sure that the original water has been replaced by the saline. Examine the spine cell closely. Describe your observations, and account for the results you observed.

_____

_____

_____

3. Frog Epidermal Cells

On a clean glass slide, place a drop of water from a container in which frogs have been kept. This liquid will usually contain cells from the frog's skin, which is normally sloughed off.

Add a small drop of methylene blue stain and then examine microscopically. From what you see, in what way(s) are animal cells different from plant cells?

_____

_____

_____

4. Human Epidermal Cells

Following the directions outlined in Fig. 2-4, examine cells obtained from the inner epidermal lining of your cheek. Locate the cells under high power, and examine them carefully. What do these epidermal cells have in common with plant cells?

_____

_____

A. Gently scrape the inside of your cheek with the broad end of a toothpick.

B. Stir the scrapings into a drop of water on a slide.

FIG. 2-4
Procedure for studying human epidermal cells.

How are they different?

_____

_____

Some of the epidermal cells may have had their edges folded over. What does this indicate about the thickness of the cells?

_____

Add a drop of methylene blue to the edge of the cover slip, and draw it under as shown in Fig. 2-2F, G. What structure in the cell has been stained by this dye?

_____

5. Sperm Cells

On a clean glass slide, place a small drop of sperm suspension that has been prepared by removing the testes from a male frog and macerating (cutting) them into small pieces in water.

Add a cover slip, and examine microscopically. You may have to reduce the light intensity (close diaphragm) to obtain more contrast. From what you see, in what way are these cells more specialized than the cheek cells?

_____

_____

_____

B. CYTOPLASMIC STREAMING

In many cells, the cytoplasm can be seen flowing throughout the cell. This phenomenon is called **cytoplasmic streaming**, or **cyclosis**.

The phenomenon of cyclosis is perhaps best observed in the plasmodium of the slime mold *Physarum polycephalum*. The plasmodium, or plant body, is a multinucleate mass of protoplasm that lacks a cell wall. This organism is easily propagated during its dormant stage when it becomes a hard, crusty structure, called a **sclerotium**. To do this, pieces of sclerotia are placed on a moist substrate (e.g., agar) containing nutrients. In a short time, the organism begins to grow out over the surface. Channels of streaming cytoplasm become visible, usually after 72 hours of growth.

Examine a plasmodium of *Physarum* growing in a petri dish. Leaving the cover on, examine the organism carefully using a dissecting microscope. What seems to be unusual about cytoplasmic streaming in *Physarum?*

_____

_____

_____

_____

C. CELL ULTRASTRUCTURE

Progress in the life sciences has depended on the ability to develop ever more refined tools and techniques. This has been especially true for cytology—the study of cells—in which adequate magnification has been a major problem. The problem of magnification is one of increasing resolving power, which may be defined as the capacity of an optical system (the microscope in this case) to reveal details of structure.

The human eye has a resolving power of about 0.1 millimeter. Lines or objects that are closer together than this are seen as a single line. The resolving power of a microscope is limited by the kind of illumination used. Objects that are closer together than one-half of the wavelength of the light source will not be clearly distinguished in a light microscope. Therefore, if white light is used (average wavelength is 0.55 μm, or 550 nanometers [nm], or 5500 angstroms [Å]), a microscope using a 97 × oil-immersion objective cannot resolve two discrete points less than 0.27 μm apart. Because many structures in the cell have dimensions smaller than this, their presence had gone undetected until a means was found for increasing the resolving power of microscopes.

The electron microscope provides increased resolving power by using a different type of illumination. High-speed electrons, the negatively charged particles of an atom, are used instead of light. As the electrons pass through the specimen being viewed, parts of the cell differentially absorb or scatter the electrons, thus forming, by means of "lenses," an image of the specimen on an electron-sensitive fluorescent screen or photographic plate. The optical system is similar to that of a light microscope except that the "illumination" is focused by means of magnetic lenses instead of glass lenses (Fig. 2-5).

Under the high voltages used in an electron microscope (1,000,000 volts in the latest instruments), the electrons have a wavelength of about 0.05 Å. Thus an electron microscope could theoretically resolve objects of 0.025 Å. However, owing to the limitations imposed by the design of the instrument, the actual resolving power lies between 8 and 10 Å. In approximate figures, then, the human eye can resolve down to 100 μm, the light microscope to 0.2 μm, and the electron microscope to 0.0003 μm. The electron microscope, therefore, has enhanced our understanding of the structure and function of parts of the cell that previously had not been visible to the cytologist. In the following study, you will examine electron micrographs of cells and become familiar with the structure and function of several organelles that play vital roles in the life of the cell.

Figs. 2-6 and 2-7 illustrate the basic ultrastructure of plant and animal cells, respectively. Carefully examine each photograph. What are some obvious similarities and differences between plant and animal cells?

1. Cell Membranes

Whereas the light microscope shows that the typical cell has only two or three membranes (the cell, nuclear, and, in plants, vacuolar membranes), the electron microscope has revealed that membranes are found throughout the cell and are organized into several structures.

When viewed under electron-microscopic magnifications, the cell membrane, which appears as a fine line

OPTICAL MICROSCOPE

Eye

Glass lens

Glass lens

Specimen

Glass lens

Lamp (light source)

ELECTRON MICROSCOPE

Photographic plate or viewing screen

Projector coil (magnets)

Objective coil (magnets)

Specimen

Condenser coil (magnets)

Filament (electron source)

FIG. 2-5
Optical (light) microscope and electron microscope compared.

FIG. 2-6
Structure of a higher plant cell: N. nucleus; Nu. nucleolus, NE, nuclear envelope; Ch, chromatin; CW, cell wall; V, vacuole; P, plastids; M, mitochondrion; ER, endoplasmic reticulum. (Electron micrograph courtesy of Dr. Eugene L. Vigil, University of Maryland.)

FIG. 2-7
Fine structure of a typical animal cell: N, nucleus; NE, nuclear envelope;
CM, cell membrane; M, mitochondrion; ER, endoplasmic reticulum.

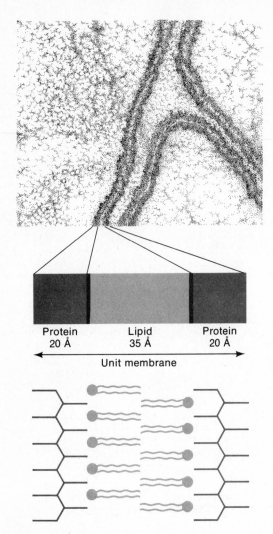

FIG. 2-8
The structure of a single-unit membrane: each outer protein layer is 20 Å thick, and the inner lipid layer is about 25 Å thick.

The membranes of the ER have the same three-layered structure as the cell membrane and frequently are in continuity with the cell or nuclear membranes.

The membranes that make up the ER are of two types: rough and smooth. The rough ER is located in cells engaged in protein synthesis, which involves structures called **ribosomes**—some of which are associated with the outer surfaces of the ER (Fig. 2-9). The large numbers of ribosomes, which are composed of protein and ribonucleic acid (RNA), give the rough appearance to the ER. Smooth ER lacks the extensive accumulations of ribosomes.

It has been suggested that the ER serves as a "canal system" through which materials, particularly proteins, can be transported to other parts of the cell or to the outside. The proteins synthesized by the ribosomes of the rough ER are released into the channels of the endoplasmic reticulum and stored there for eventual export.

3. Mitochondria

Mitochondria are subcellular structures that participate in cell respiration and contain enzymes that take part in the Krebs cycle. Fine-structure analysis of these organelles shows them to consist of two membranes: an **outer membrane** and an **inner membrane** that invaginates to the interior to form **cristae** (Fig. 2-10). The enzymes that take part in the Krebs cycle are located in the mitochondrial membranes, and it is believed that they are arranged in special configurations that favor the sequential reactions of the cycle. The energy that is released in the Krebs cycle is transferred to adenosine diphosphate (ADP) in a process called **oxidative phosphorylation**. The result is storage of energy in the form of adenosine triphosphate (ATP).

under the light microscope, is shown to consist of three distinct layers (Fig. 2-8). Sandwiched between the outer and inner dark layers is a light layer. The dark layers are composed of proteins, whereas the middle layer is composed of two lipid layers.

2. Endoplasmic Reticulum and Ribosomes

Internal to the cell membrane, the cell contains a complex, three-dimensional canalicular system that extends throughout most of the cytoplasm. This is the **endoplasmic reticulum**, or the **ER**, as it is frequently called (Fig. 2-9).

4. Golgi Apparatus

The Golgi apparatus (also called **dictyosomes**) is another system of membranes found in both plant and animal cells. As shown in Fig. 2-11, it consists of parallel flattened sacs. At the margins, the flattened sacs expand into vesicles. Although the function of the Golgi apparatus is not fully understood, it is thought that in secretory cells the products of secretion made in other parts of the cell are transported to the Golgi through the lumen (channels) of the ER. These products are then segregated in the vesicles at the margins of the Golgi apparatus, which are then pinched off to migrate elsewhere in the cytoplasm or to the cell surface.

A

B

FIG. 2-9
(A) Electron micrograph showing cytoplasmic organization of cells: N, nucleus; NP, nuclear pore; NE, nuclear envelope; ER, endoplasmic reticulum; M, mitochondrion; R, ribosome; CM, cell membrane. (B) The structural organization of the endoplasmic reticulum. (Electron micrograph courtesy of Dr. Eugene L. Vigil, University of Maryland.)

A

B

FIG. 2-10
(A) Fine structure of a mitochondrion: IM, inner membrane; OM, outer membrane.
(B) The structural organization of mitochondria.

A

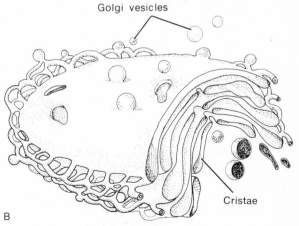

Golgi vesicles

Cristae

B

FIG. 2-11
(A) Electron micrograph of Golgi (dictyosomes) in the alga *Euglena:* G, Golgi apparatus; GV, Golgi vesicle; M, mitochondrion; C, chloroplast. (B) The structural organization of the Golgi apparatus.

REFERENCES

Avers, C. J. 1976. *Cell Biology*. D. Van Nostrand.

Capaldi, R. A. 1974. A Dynamic Model of Cell Membranes. *Scientific American,* 230(3):26–33. (Offprint 1292). *Scientific American* Offprints are available from W. H. Freeman and Company, 660 Market Street, San Francisco 94104, and 58 Kings Road, Reading RG1 3AA, England. Please order by number.

DeRobertis, E. D. P., and E. M. F. DeRobertis, Jr. 1980. *Cell and Molecular Biology*. 7th ed. Holt/Saunders.

DeWitt, W. 1977. *Biology of the Cell: An Evolutionary Approach*. Holt/Saunders.

Fawcett, D. W. 1981. *An Atlas of Fine Structure: The Cell*. 2nd ed. Saunders.

Fox, C. F. 1972. The Structure of Cell Membranes. *Scientific American* 226(2):30–38 (Offprint 1241).

Goodenough, U. W., and R. P. Levine. 1970. The Genetic Activity of Mitochondria and Chloroplasts. *Scientific American* 223(5):22–29 (Offprint 1203).

Green, D. E., and H. Baum. 1970. *Energy and the Mitochondrion*. Academic Press.

Karp, G. 1979. *Cell Biology*. McGraw-Hill.

Kennedy, D., ed. 1965. *The Living Cell: Readings from Scientific American*. W. H. Freeman and Company.

Kessel, R. G., and R. H. Kardon. 1979. *Tissues and Organs: A Text-Atlas of Scanning Electron Microscopy*. W. H. Freeman and Company.

Lazarides, E., and J. P. Revel. 1979. The Molecular Basis of Cell Movement. *Scientific American* 240(5):100–113 (Offprint 1247).

Lodish, H. F., and J. E. Rothman. 1979. The Assembly of Cell Membranes. *Scientific American* 249(1):48–63 (Offprint 1415).

McElroy, W. D., and C. P. Swanson. 1976. *Modern Cell Biology*. 2d ed. Prentice-Hall.

Neutra, M., and C. P. Leblond. 1969. The Golgi Apparatus. *Scientific American* 220(2):100–107 (Offprint 1134).

Nomura, M. 1969. Ribosomes. *Scientific American* 221(4):28–35 (Offprint 1157).

Racker, E. 1968. The Membrane of the Mitochondrion. *Scientific American* 218(2):32–39 (Offprint 1101).

Staehelin, L. A., and B. E. Hull. 1978. Junctions Between Living Cells. *Scientific American* 238(5):140–152 (Offprint 1388).

Swanson, C. P., and P. L. Webster. 1977. *The Cell*. 4th ed. Prentice-Hall.

Wolfe, S. L. 1981. *Biology of the Cell*. 2nd ed. Wadsworth.

Cellular Reproduction

A multicellular organism typically begins life as a **zygote**, which is formed from the union of a sperm and an egg (the **gametes**). The egg and sperm, although usually unequal in size, give an equal number of chromosomes to the newly developing organism: each contributes the **haploid** number (half complement) of chromosomes. The zygote, therefore, contains a **diploid** number of chromosomes—a haploid set from each parent. For example, the diploid complement of the human zygote (and subsequently all other body cells) is 46 chromosomes. The haploid complement for the egg and sperm is 23 chromosomes. The reduction from the diploid condition to the haploid condition is brought about by a type of cell division called **meiosis**, which occurs during the formation of the gametes. After fertilization, the zygote, through repeated cell division, called **mitosis,** gives rise to all the cells that make up the organism.

In this study, you will compare and contrast mitosis and meiosis.

A. MITOSIS

The tremendous diversity of form and function that cells assume is even more remarkable when you consider that multicellular organisms begin life as a single fertilized cell, the **zygote**. This cell, through repeated divisions, gives rise to all the cells that make up the organism. The complex series of events that encompasses the life span of an actively dividing cell is termed **mitosis**, or the **mitotic cell cycle** (Fig. 3-1). The actual replication of chromosomes including the synthesis of deoxyribonucleic acid (DNA), the main structural component of chromosomes, occurs during **interphase**. The role of DNA as the molecular basis of heredity will be examined in another exercise. The doubling of DNA during the synthesis, or S, period provides a full complement of DNA for the daughter cells that will result from the next active mitotic division. There are two nonmitotic and non-DNA-synthetic periods (gaps) during interphase: the one preceding DNA synthesis is G_1; the one following synthesis and just preceding mitotic division is G_2. During G_1 (prior to DNA synthesis), a cell may follow a pathway leading to differentiation, rather than continue in active division. This possibility is indicated in Fig. 3-1 by the arrow leading out of the cell cycle. The time required for one mitotic cycle varies from tissue to tissue and from organism to organism. The actual mitotic process usually occupies only 10% of the total time of the cell cycle. The rest of the time is spent in interphase. It is important to distinguish between several parts of mitosis. Thus, chromosomal duplication and separation (i.e., nuclear divi-

FIG. 3-1
Stages of the mitotic cycle.

Place the slide on the stage of your microscope, and locate one of the sections under low power. It is often possible, under low power, to determine whether a given section shows good mitotic stages. Because each section is very thin, not all will be equally good for study. After preliminary examination under low power, change to high power, being very careful not to break the slide. Keep in mind the sequence in which the different stages occur, but do not try to find them in sequence. Thus, if you happen to find an anaphase first, study it before proceeding to another stage. Chances are that most of the cells will be in interphase. The next largest number will be in prophase, and only a few will be seen in metaphase, anaphase, and telophase. The reason is that these cells remain in interphase and prophase longer than in the other stages.

a. Interphase

The nondividing cell is considered to be in interphase. Erroneously said to be "resting," the nondividing cell is actively respiring, undergoing protein synthesis, and replicating chromosomes (which includes the synthesis of deoxyribonucleic acid, DNA) in preparation for beginning mitosis (Fig. 3-1).

b. Prophase

During prophase, the chromosomes become distinguishable in the nucleus. The nuclear membrane breaks down, and the chromosomes become distributed throughout the cytoplasm (Fig. 3-2A, C). At this stage in the onion root tip, the chromosomes often appear as a coiled mass. These elongated chromosomes later become condensed into shorter chromosomes and the nuclear membrane disappears. Even at this early stage, each chromosome has probably doubled, although this will be difficult to see on the slides. Under very high magnifications, it is possible to see that each chromosome is composed of two separate strands, the sister **chromatids**. The chromatids, which are attached to each other in a region called the **centromere**, are identical copies made during DNA replication in prophase.

While the chromosomes are undergoing condensation, the apparatus that will sort them out and move them apart is being organized. This is the **spindle**; a system of fibers that runs from pole to pole of the nucleus. The composition of the spindle fibers is not known. It has been suggested that they form by the aggregation of protein molecules. Under the electron microscope, these fibers appear as fine, straight, hollow microtubules (Fig. 3-3). Although they lengthen and then shorten during mitosis, they do not appear to get thicker or thinner. This suggests that they do not stretch or contract but that new material is added to the fiber or removed from it as the spindle changes shape. In animal cells, the poles of the spindle

sion) is termed **karyokinesis**. Division of the cell body (i.e., cytoplasm and its organelles) is termed **cytokinesis**. Cytokinesis and karyokinesis need not occur together.

There are certain structural differences in plant and animal cells; the two vary to some extent also in the process of mitosis. However, in all organisms this process is essentially the same. It is the objective of this exercise to examine the essential steps in mitosis and to characterize the similarities and differences in this process in plant and animal cells.

1. Mitosis in Plant Cells

The onion root tip is one of the most widely used materials for the study of mitosis, because it is available in quantity, and preparations of the dividing cells are easily made, and the chromosomes are relatively large and few in number and hence easier to study than the cells of many other organisms. There are regions of rapid cell division in root tips; therefore, the chances are good that within such tissues one can identify every stage in mitosis. There are several reasonably distinct stages in cell division, although the process is continuous and there is some gradation among the various steps. These steps, in sequence, are interphase, prophase, metaphase, anaphase, and telophase (Fig. 3-2).

Obtain a slide of onion root tips, and note a series of dark streaks on the slide. Each streak is a very thin longitudinal section through an onion root tip.

A. Metabolic (interphase) nucleus

B. Early prophase

C. Late prophase

Nuclear envelope

Nucleolus

D. Metaphase

E. Anaphase

F. Early telophase

Spindle fibers

Cell plate

G. Late telophase

H. Daughter cells

FIG. 3-2
Diagrammatic representation of the mitotic stages in the onion root tip.

FIG. 3-3
Spindle fibers (SF) attached to a chromosome (Ch) at the centromere (Cm). Note the
tubular structure of the spindle fibers. (Electron micrograph courtesy of Dr. Eugene L.
Vigil, University of Maryland.)

are attached to organelles called **centrioles**. No centrioles
are found in onion cells or those of higher plants.

c. Metaphase

At metaphase, the short, thick, double-stranded chromosomes become arranged near the center of the cell in
a plane at right angles to the long axis of the spindle (Fig.
3-2D). Each chromosome becomes attached by its cen-

tromere to a spindle fiber. By the time the chromosomes
are organized along the **metaphase plate**, the nuclear
membrane has completely broken down.

d. Anaphase

At the beginning of anaphase, the two members of each
of the previously doubled chromosomes separate and
move toward opposite ends of the cell (Fig. 3-2E). This

stage can be recognized in the onion by the two groups of V-shaped chromosomes on opposite sides of the cell. The sharp end of the V is pointed toward the cell wall. The onion has 16 chromosomes; hence it is seldom possible to see all of them at one time. Reduce the light coming through the objective of your microscope, and see if you can find any spindle fibers near the center of the cell. They will appear as very fine lines between the two groups of chromosomes, but they are often not visible in a study of this kind. Anaphase ends when the two sets of single-stranded chromosomes have arrived at opposite ends of the cell.

e. Telophase

Cell division is completed during telophase, and reorganization of the cell contents of the two daughter cells begins. It is often difficult to distinguish between late anaphase and early telophase in the cells of the onion root tip. During telophase, however, a cell plate starts to form as a fine line across the center of the cell (Fig. 3-2F). When complete, the cell plate will divide the original cell into two daughter cells. In some cells, it will be indistinct. As telophase progresses, the nuclei begin to reorganize and the chromosomes uncoil, becoming longer and thinner, the nuclear membrane reforms, and the nucleoli reappear (Fig. 3-2G). Mitosis ends with the reassembly of two interphase nuclei, each with one complete set of single-strand chromosomes (Fig. 3-2H).

In both plant and animal cells, the daughter cells resulting from mitotic division have the same number and kinds of chromosomes as the original cell from which they came. Thus, in the onion each daughter cell has 16 chromosomes, just as the original cell had. This is not as evident in the slides you are studying, because specially prepared slides and considerable experience are necessary before this many chromosomes can be accurately counted.

One difference in mitosis between most plant and animal cells should be pointed out at this time. When plant cells divide, a cell plate forms, as we saw in the onion root tip. Animal cells do not have a cell wall but are surrounded only by the plasma membrane. When most animal cells divide, there is a constriction near the center of the original cell. This constriction, which goes completely around the cell, deepens until the cell cleaves into two daughter cells.

2. Mitosis in Animal Cells

Cell division is readily observed in animal cells by examining a prepared slide of a whitefish blastula—the early developmental stage formed by successive cell divisions after the egg has been fertilized by the sperm.

a. Interphase

Locate interphase cells, which are characterized by having a distinct nucleus bounded by a nuclear envelope (Fig. 3-4A). The nucleolus should be readily identifiable. Immediately adjacent to the nuclear envelope is a cytoplasmic organelle sometimes referred to as the **cell center**, or **centrosome**, which contains the centrioles.

b. Prophase

Karyokinesis begins with prophase. The chromosomes of early prophase, which have already doubled longitudinally, appear as thin, coiled filaments (Fig. 3-4B). As prophase progresses, the chromosomes shorten and thicken (Fig. 3-4C–E). Each doubled chromosome consists of two sister **chromatids**, which are joined together at a point called the centromere (**kinetochore**). During prophase, the nuclear envelope becomes indistinct and the nucleolus disappears. Electron-microscopic studies have shown that the nuclear envelope becomes part of the endoplasmic reticulum.

During prophase, two pairs of centrioles are organized within the centrosome. They begin to move apart, as if they repelled each other, migrating toward opposite poles of the cell (Fig. 3-4B, C). Fibers that radiate from each pair of centrioles like spokes on a wheel, then appear, forming a configuration known as an **aster**. The radiating fibers are called **astral rays**. Some of the fibers extend from one centriole to another, elongating as the centrioles separate. The centrioles continue to migrate until they lie at opposite sides of the cell. Their positions mark the **poles** toward which the chromosomes will move. When the nuclear envelope breaks down, the region between the centrioles becomes clearly visible as a relatively transparent region called the spindle. Electron microscopic studies have shown the spindle to consist of microtubules about 150 Å in diameter. These microtubules are so arranged as to form the spindle fibers. Some of these fibers extend from pole to pole; others attach to the centromeres of the chromosomes (Fig. 3-3). With the help of Fig. 3-4B–E, locate various stages of prophase on the slide.

c. Metaphase

During metaphase, the chromosomes move toward the central region of the spindle to form the metaphase, or **equatorial**, **plate** (Fig. 3-4F). Although not known with certainty, it is suggested that the chromosomes are maneuvered into position by the spindle fibers attached to the centromere of each chromosome. Locate this phase of mitosis on your slide. Look for two views of the chromosomes: a side view and a polar view (Fig. 3-4F, G).

34

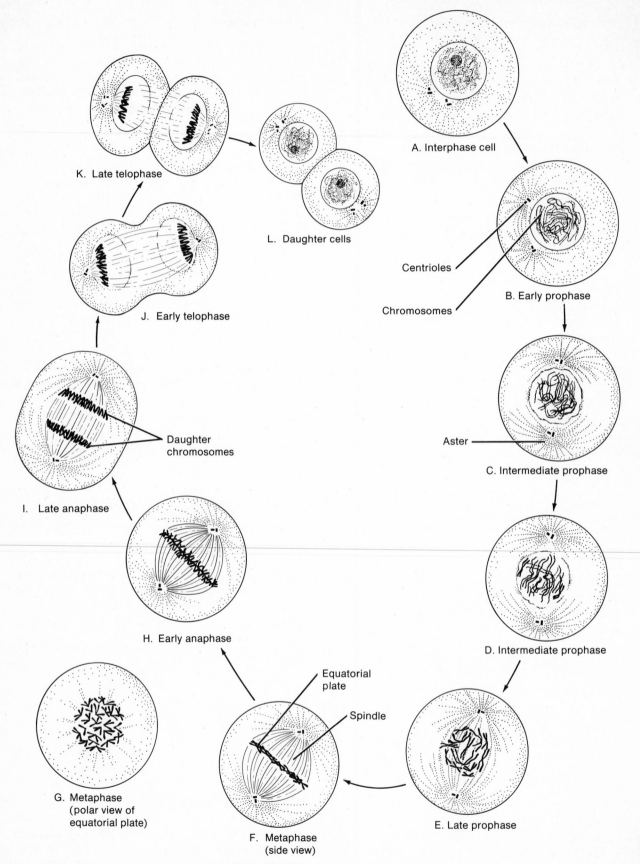

A. Interphase cell

Centrioles

Chromosomes

B. Early prophase

Aster

C. Intermediate prophase

D. Intermediate prophase

Equatorial plate

Spindle

E. Late prophase

K. Late telophase

L. Daughter cells

J. Early telophase

Daughter chromosomes

I. Late anaphase

H. Early anaphase

G. Metaphase (polar view of equatorial plate)

F. Metaphase (side view)

FIG. 3-4
Mitotic stages in the whitefish blastula.

d. Anaphase

Anaphase begins when the centromeres of the doubled chromosomes divide and the chromatids separate and become **daughter chromosomes**. Following this stage, the daughter chromosomes begin moving to the polar regions of the cell (Fig. 3-4H, I). The completion of the movement to the poles by the chromosomes marks the beginning of telophase.

e. Telophase

During telophase, the spindle disappears, two daughter nuclei are organized, the nucleoli reappear, and the nuclear envelopes are reformed by the fusion of parts of the endoplasmic reticulum (Fig. 3-4J, K).

In late telophase, after the cytoplasm has become deeply furrowed, or pinched in, cytokinesis takes place. This results in two daughter cells having equivalent nuclear contents and equal amounts of cytoplasm (Fig. 3-4L).

B. MEIOSIS

Meiosis is a singularly important biological event that not only maintains a constant chromosome number for most species of animals but also provides a means of genetic variability because of crossing over and the subsequent exchange of genetic material. In meiosis, immature or primordial germ cells undergo a "reduction" in the diploid number of chromosomes characteristic for the species and become mature gametes.

1. Meiosis in the Lily

Meiosis will be studied as it occurs in the development of mature pollen grains of the flowering plants. These pollen grains give rise to male gametes, which fuse with an egg to produce a zygote.

As you examine the series of slides in the meiotic sequence, refer to Fig. 3-5 to help locate the stages indicated in the following description.

The first meiotic division is **meiosis I**. Examine a lily flower, and locate the **anthers**, or pollen sacs, which contain numerous pollen mother cells (Fig. 3-5A, B). Each of these cells may undergo meiosis and produce mature pollen grains. Next examine slides of a cross section through a young lily anther, and locate the pollen mother cells (Fig. 3-5C, D). The nuclei of these cells contain the **diploid number** of chromosomes. Many of the pollen mother cells are in the prophase of the first meiotic division. During this phase, homologous chromosomes, each composed of two **chromatids**, lie adjacent to one another (**synapse**), form tetrads, and exchange

genetic components by a process called **crossing over**. What is the significance of this process?

_____

_____

This phenomenon is diagrammatically shown in Fig. 3-6.

Subsequent to synapsis the homologous chromosomes separate during anaphase, with one member moving to each pole of the division spindle. Because this is a separation of entire chromosomes, and not chromatids, the chromosome content of the cells at the end of meiosis I has been "reduced" from the diploid to the **haploid** condition. Examine slides of a lily anther showing separation of homologous chromosomes (Fig. 3-5D, E). The diploid number in lily is 24. What is the chromosome number following the first meiotic division?

_____

_____

The second meiotic division is **meiosis II**. Examine slides of anthers in which the cells resulting from the first meiotic division are in anaphase of meiosis II (Fig. 3-5F). In these cells, the chromatids that make up each chromosome now separate and migrate to the spindle poles (Fig. 3-7). As in mitosis, the chromatids when separated from each other are called **daughter chromosomes**. At the spindle poles, each group of daughter chromosomes becomes enclosed in a nuclear membrane.

Cell division follows the division of the nucleus. How many pollen grains are formed as a result of the two meiotic divisions of the pollen mother cells?

_____

What is the chromosome complement of each pollen grain?

_____

Examine lily anthers showing mature pollen grains (Fig. 3-5G).

2. Meiosis in *Ascaris*

The development of the gametes is called **gametogenesis** and requires two divisions, meiosis I and meiosis II. During meiosis I, the diploid number of chromosomes is reduced to the haploid number. In males, gametogenesis

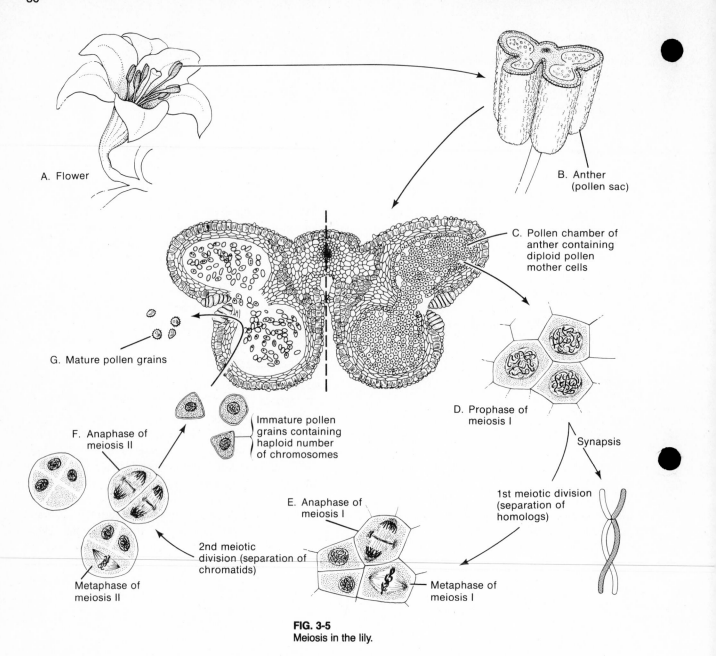

A. Flower

B. Anther (pollen sac)

C. Pollen chamber of anther containing diploid pollen mother cells

G. Mature pollen grains

D. Prophase of meiosis I

Synapsis

F. Anaphase of meiosis II

Immature pollen grains containing haploid number of chromosomes

1st meiotic division (separation of homologs)

E. Anaphase of meiosis I

2nd meiotic division (separation of chromatids)

Metaphase of meiosis II

Metaphase of meiosis I

FIG. 3-5
Meiosis in the lily.

occurs in the testis; in females, in the ovaries or oviducts. In this part of the exercise, the maturation of the egg (**oogenesis**) will be studied as it occurs in the parasitic roundworm *Ascaris*. Because this worm has a diploid number of chromosomes of only four, it is ideal for the study of this process.

The reproductive organ in *Ascaris* consists of a pair of long, highly coiled tubes that are regionally divided into the ovary, oviduct, and uterus (Fig. 3-8A). The "eggs," which are produced in the ovaries, pass into the oviducts, where they are fertilized by sperm.

Examine slides containing the oviduct and uterus of *Ascaris*. Locate the oviduct, which characteristically has

a large number of triangular sperm interspersed among numerous eggs (Fig. 3-8B). The eggs at this stage are still diploid, because in *Ascaris* the maturation process, or oogenesis, does not begin until after the egg has been penetrated by a sperm. Therefore, the term *egg* at this stage of development is not quite accurate. A more correct term would be **primary oocyte**, a cell that will undergo meiosis and produce the mature egg. On the slide, locate primary oocytes; some of them may have been penetrated by sperm. How many chromosomes are in the primary oocyte of *Ascaris*?

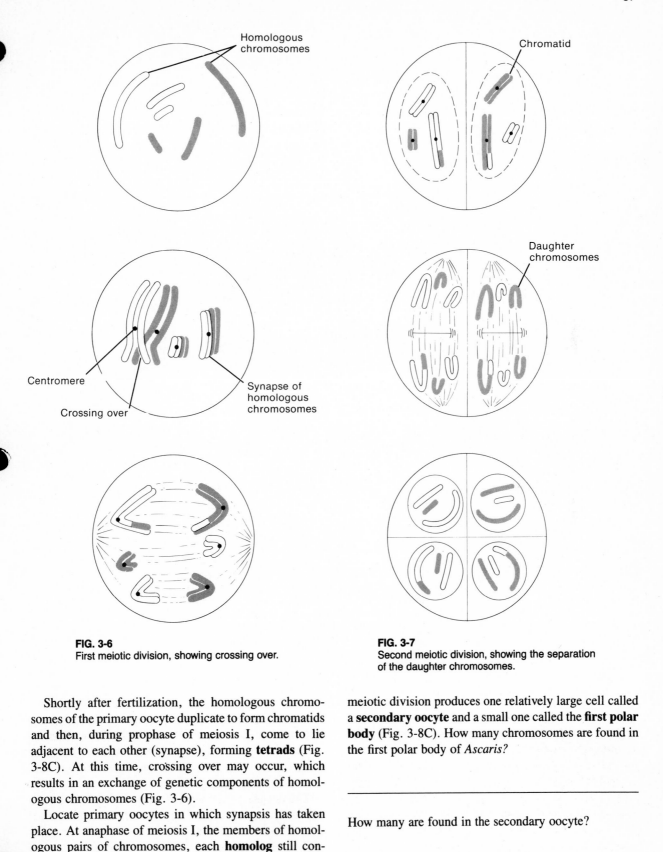

FIG. 3-6
First meiotic division, showing crossing over.

FIG. 3-7
Second meiotic division, showing the separation of the daughter chromosomes.

Shortly after fertilization, the homologous chromosomes of the primary oocyte duplicate to form chromatids and then, during prophase of meiosis I, come to lie adjacent to each other (synapse), forming **tetrads** (Fig. 3-8C). At this time, crossing over may occur, which results in an exchange of genetic components of homologous chromosomes (Fig. 3-6).

Locate primary oocytes in which synapsis has taken place. At anaphase of meiosis I, the members of homologous pairs of chromosomes, each **homolog** still consisting of a pair of chromatids, move to opposite poles (Fig. 3-8C). At telophase of meiosis I, an unequal division of the cytoplasm occurs (cytokinesis) so that the first

meiotic division produces one relatively large cell called a **secondary oocyte** and a small one called the **first polar body** (Fig. 3-8C). How many chromosomes are found in the first polar body of *Ascaris?*

_____

_____

How many are found in the secondary oocyte?

_____

_____

_____

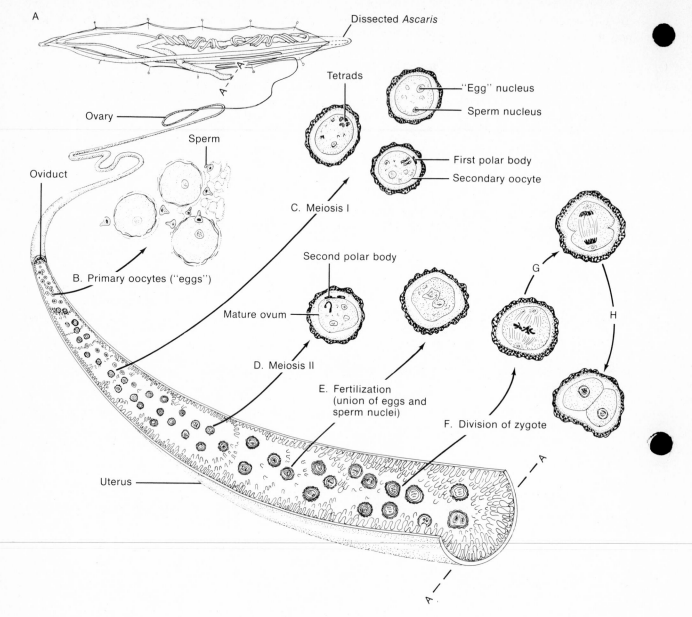

A

Dissected *Ascaris*

Ovary

Oviduct

Sperm

B. Primary oocytes ("eggs")

Tetrads

"Egg" nucleus

Sperm nucleus

First polar body

Secondary oocyte

C. Meiosis I

Second polar body

Mature ovum

D. Meiosis II

E. Fertilization
(union of eggs and
sperm nuclei)

F. Division of zygote

G

H

Uterus

A

A

FIG. 3-8
Meiosis in *Ascaris*.

Locate the first polar body on the slide.

After an interphase, the second division begins when the homologous chromosomes (homologs), which separated during meiosis I, line up on the equator of a division spindle in metaphase of meiosis II (Fig. 3-8D). Each homolog is composed of two chromatids, which, at anaphase of meiosis II, separate and migrate to the poles. The second meiotic division of the secondary oocyte produces a second polar body and a large cell, which differentiates into the egg cell, or ovum. The first polar body

produced in meiosis I may or may not go through a second meiotic division. Thus, when a diploid cell in the *Ascaris* ovary undergoes complete meiosis, only one mature ovum is produced; the polar bodies are essentially nonfunctional.

The unequal cytokinesis of oogenesis ensures that an unusually large supply of cytoplasm and stored food is allotted to the nonmotile ovum for use by the embryo that will develop from it. In fact, the ovum provides almost all the cytoplasm and initial food supply for the embryo.

The tiny, highly motile sperm cell contributes essentially only its genetic material.

During the maturation of the egg, the sperm nucleus has been lying inactive in the cytoplasm. Following the second meiotic division, the egg and sperm nuclei unite (**fertilization**) and form a single cell called a **zygote**. Locate eggs that show separate sperm and egg nuclei and eggs in which these two nuclei have fused (Fig. 3-8E). How many chromosomes does the zygote contain?

_____

If you did not know the actual number of chromosomes in the zygote, how would you describe the chromosome content of this cell?

_____

_____

In the uterus, the zygote nucleus and cell soon divide and form two cells, each of which divides again until a multicellular embryo is formed (Fig. 3-8F–H). What type of division is this?

_____

Locate as many of these later stages as are evident on your slide.

Obviously, all cells of the adult organism have their origin in the division of the zygote. It seems logical to assume that all cells of the adult have the same genes as the original zygote. Yet the diversity in the form and activity of the adult cells is readily apparent. Discuss how these changes in form and function may occur during the development of the organism.

_____

_____

_____

_____

_____

_____

C. SUMMARY

To help you compare and contrast mitosis and meiosis, fill in the following chart.

Characteristics	Type of Cell Division	
	Mitosis	Meiosis
1. Function (or role) in developing organism		
2. Differences between plant and animal		
3. Differences in stages		
4. Number of daughter cells formed following division		
5. Chromosome complement (i.e., N, haploid; $2N$, diploid)		
6. Where occurs in organism (plant and animal)		
7. When occurs in life cycle (plant and animal)		

REFERENCES

DeRobertis, E. D. P., and E. M. F. DeRobertis, Jr. 1980. *Cell and Molecular Biology*. 7th ed. Holt/Saunders.

DuPraw, E. J. 1970. *DNA and Chromosomes*. Holt, Rinehart and Winston.

Flagg, R. O., and W. R. West. 1969. Plant Mitosis and Cytokinesis. *Carolina Tips* 32:21–23.

Gillette, N. J. 1965. A Demonstration of Mitosis. *Turtox News* 43(3):90–91.

John B., and K. R. Lewis. 1972. *Somatic Cell Division*. Oxford Biology Reader (45-9626), Carolina Biological Supply Company.

Mazia, D. 1961. How Cells Divide. *Scientific American* 205(3):100–120 (Offprint No. 93). *Scientific American* Offprints are available from W. H. Freeman and Company, 660 Market Street, San Francisco 94140, and 58 Kings Road, Reading RG1 3AA, England. Please order by number.

Mazia, D. 1974. The Cell Cycle. *Scientific American* 230(1):54–64 (Offprint No. 1288).

McFall, F. D., and D. G. Keith. 1969. Animal Mitosis. *Carolina Tips* 32:1–3.

Taylor, J. H. 1958. The Duplication of Chromosomes. *Scientific American* 198(6):36–42 (Offprint No. 60).

Wilson, G. B. 1966. *Cell Division and the Mitotic Cycle*. Reinhold.

Plant Anatomy:
Roots and Stems

Growth and development are phenomena common to plants and animals. As you would expect, there are significant differences between plants and animals with respect to the changes that occur between the time of fertilization and the achievement of the characteristic form for any given plant or animal.

Development in plants differs from development in animals in that the former is **indeterminate**, while the latter is **determinate**. That is, in plants development continues throughout the life of the plant, with new organs, tissues, and cells being formed perpetually. Conversely, the animal becomes complete (i.e., determined) early in its life. For example, in a great redwood tree growing in California, some cells and tissues near the base of the tree may be more than 2,000 years old, while in the tips of its branches new cells, tissues, and organs continue to form and differentiate into their final structures. Theoretically, there is no limit to the growth of this tree. In a chicken, on the other hand, differentiation of cells and tissues occurs early in embryonic development. After the animal matures, no further differentiation occurs. An exception to this is the development of gametes and blood cells, which are formed throughout the life of the organism.

Another major distinction between plants and animals is that in plants cell division occurs in localized regions, whereas in animals it is general throughout the immature organism. The three principal growth regions of post-embryonic plants are (1) the **apical meristem**, which determines growth in the length of the stem and root and is instrumental in the production of leaves, flowers, and branches; (2) the **lateral meristem (cambium)**, which determines the growth in diameter of the stem and root; and (3) the **cork meristem (cork cambium)**, which determines the production of cork—the protective outer covering of the stem and root.

In order to understand the growth and development of plants and to comprehend their complex structure and the interrelationships between structure and function, it is necessary to study the anatomy of the organism under consideration.

A. ROOTS

Characteristically, the root is described as that part of the plant growing beneath the surface of the soil. The principal function of roots is the absorption of water and soluble minerals and the transport of these substances to the above-ground parts—the stem, leaves, and flowers. In addition, roots anchor the plant in the soil and serve as storage organs for the reserve food of the plant, as in

41

sweet potatoes, carrots, and turnips. Roots may function in food manufacture. For example, aerial roots of orchids contain chlorophyll, thereby supplementing the leaves in the photosynthetic process.

Roots may be broadly classified by form into two groups: **tap roots** and **fibrous roots**. In tap roots, the main root becomes many times larger than the branch roots (those that arise from the main root) and penetrates some distance into the soil. In some cases, the tap root may be greater in diameter than the stem. Examine the tap root of a carrot plant for the presence of branch roots. In fibrous root systems, the primary root and the branch roots are approximately the same length and diameter. Examine the fibrous root system of a bean plant. Do you think the fibrous root system would be more efficient in terms of absorption of water and minerals than the tap root? Explain.

_____

_____

_____

1. Root Apex

Just as the above-ground parts of the plant become extensive, so do roots grow and ramify throughout the soil. Obtain a germinating radish or grass seed from the instructor. Mount it in a drop of water on a slide and examine the young root with a dissecting microscope. Locate a cone-shaped mass of loosely arranged cells covering the root tip. This **root cap** covers the apical meristem and protects it from damage as the root passes through the soil. Locate the root apical meristem, which appears as a relatively dense, opaque region at the tip of the root. Somewhat behind the root tip, note the presence of root hairs—special absorbing cells on the root. These generally persist for a short time and then die. New root-hair cells formed near the root tip replace those that are lost. In what way do root hairs increase the efficiency of absorption of water and minerals by the root?

_____

_____

Examine a prepared slide of a longitudinal section through an onion root tip and locate the structures described above (Fig. 4-1A, B).

2. Primary Tissues of the Root

Using a compound microscope, examine a prepared slide of a cross section of the buttercup *(Ranunculus)* root, cut through a region in which the cells have differentiated (Fig. 4-1C, D). Three general regions are readily seen: the **epidermis**, the **cortex**, and the **vascular cylinder**. Starting from the outside, the primary tissues (those tissues having their origin from cells produced in the apical meristem) consist of an outer epidermis, which is a single layer of cells covering the outside of the root. In some instances, the epidermis dies and the outer cells of the cortex function as a special epidermal covering called the **hypodermis**. The cortex in most roots consists largely of parenchymatous cells (thin-walled, isodiametric cells). Note the presence of starch grains in many of the cortical cells, and the large intercellular spaces formed where the cells abut one another.

Limiting the cortex on the inside, and considered to be part of it, is the **endodermis**. It is represented by a single layer of cells separating the parenchyma of the cortex from the vascular cylinder. The endodermis, present in all roots, is believed to function in regulating the flow of water into the vascular cylinder from the cortex.

The vascular cylinder consists of several tissues lying internal to the cortex. The **pericycle**, a unicellular layer of cells adjacent to the endodermis, has the ability to become meristematic and to initiate the growth of lateral roots. The **xylem** is represented by three, four, or five radiating arms or plates. Alternating with the xylem arms are groups of **phloem** cells. This alternate arrangement is peculiar to roots and anatomically distinguishes roots from stems. Locate the region between the phloem and the xylem where the cambium will develop. The cambium is a lateral meristem responsible for growth in the diameter of a root. The tissues present in this cross section are all primary tissue; that is, they originate in the apical meristem of the root. When the cambium divides, it gives rise to cells that will differentiate as xylem and phloem, which are then called **secondary** xylem and phloem, because they originated in meristems other than an apical meristem.

Obtain a carrot root. Using a sharp razor, cut a thin cross section from the root and place it on a slide. Add 1 or 2 drops of iodine and a cover slip. Examine microscopically. Iodine reacts with starch to form a deep blue-black color. Where is the starch located in the root?

_____

Prepare a second cross section of carrot and stain with phloroglucinol-HC1. (CAUTION: This solution contains concentrated hydrochloric acid.) This chemical reacts

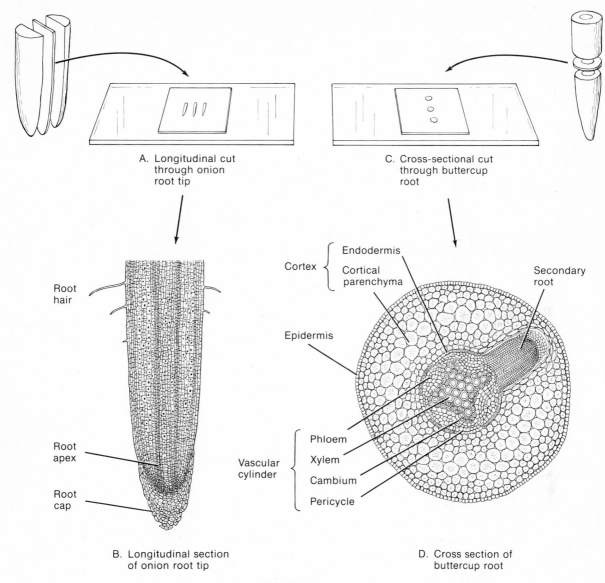

A. Longitudinal cut
through onion
root tip

C. Cross-sectional cut
through buttercup
root

Root
hair

Root
apex

Root
cap

B. Longitudinal section
of onion root tip

Cortex { Endodermis

Cortical
parenchyma

Epidermis

Secondary
root

Vascular
cylinder {

Phloem

Xylem

Cambium

Pericycle

D. Cross section of
buttercup root

FIG. 4-1
Study of root anatomy.

with a substance called **lignin** in the cells that make up the vascular tissue. How does the organization of vascular tissue of the carrot root differ from that of the *Ranunculus* root previously examined?

_____

_____

3. Branch Roots

As noted, the pericycle may give rise to branch or lateral roots. In lateral root formation, a new meristem is

formed, complete with root cap. Eventually, the young branch root grows, penetrates the cortex to the outside, and continues growing. Examine demonstration slides of developing branch roots (Fig. 4-1D). Remove young roots from water lettuce plants *(Pistia)*, if available, and examine developing branch (secondary) roots.

4. Adventitious Roots

Examine stem cuttings taken from various plants (i.e., *Coleus*, willow, geranium) that have been rooted in sand or vermiculite (Fig. 4-2A). The roots that arise from such stems are called **adventitious** roots and generally result

FIG. 4-2
Types of roots: (A) Adventitious roots on stem cutting and (B) Prop roots of corn.

from regenerative processes in stem cuttings, or in some cases, from the "dedifferentiation" of cells in detached leaves of such plants. What does the term *adventitious* mean?

_____

_____

Do you agree with the statement that adventitious roots are not part of the normal developmental morphology of the plant as a whole? Explain.

_____

_____

_____

5. Prop Roots

Examine the "**prop**" roots of a corn plant (Fig. 4-2B). Are these roots borne on the stem or root?

_____

How would you determine this?

_____

In contrast to adventitious roots, where do prop roots have their origin (i.e., cell layer, tissue)?

_____

What is (are) the function(s) of prop roots?

_____

If available, examine a microscopic section of a prop root. In what way(s) is it similar to the *Ranunculus* root previously examined?

_____

_____

_____

In what way(s) is it different?

_____

_____

_____

B. STEMS

The stem is the part of the plant that bears leaves and is commonly aerial and upright. Stems are like roots in general structure: they have an epidermis, cortex, and vascular cylinder, although there are variations within this overall structure. Stems differ from roots in the fundamental vascular structure and in having lateral appendages called *leaves*.

Several basic functions are filled by the stem. It is the framework supporting the leaves, flowers, and fruits. It provides for the transport of water and solutes absorbed by the roots and serves to transport and distribute the foods manufactured by the leaves to the places where it is used or stored. Some stems are green and carry on a limited amount of photosynthesis. Many stems function as food storage areas—sometimes to the extent of being economically important (e.g., Idaho or Wisconsin potatoes and sugar cane).

Growth and development in the stem occurs in the bud, a terminal or axillary structure consisting of a small mass of meristematic tissue, the **shoot apex**, or apical meristem of the shoot, covered wholly or in part by overlapping leaves.

1. The Bud and Other Structures Present on the Shoot

a. Classification of buds

Buds may be classified in a variety of ways.

Content:
    Foliage buds
    Floral buds
    Mixed buds (i.e., flower and foliage primordia)

Position
    Terminal buds
    Axillary buds
    Adventitious buds

Time of development
    Active buds
    Resting buds
    Latent buds

Protective covering
    Protected buds
    Naked buds

b. Examination of the Shoot of a Woody Perennial

Examine branches from the hickory tree. Locate and label the following structures on Fig. 4-3.

Terminal bud: A bud located at the tip of the branch and involving the entire stem tip.

Axillary bud: A bud developed from a branch primordium and located in the axil of a leaf (above the leaf scar if the leaf has fallen from the twig).

FIG. 4-3
External features of hickory branch.

Latent buds: Small axillary buds that normally do not develop into branches the spring following their formation; they may develop into branches if an accident destroys the terminal or other axillary buds.

Leaf scar: A scar on the stem formed when the petiole separated from the stem at the time of leaf fall.

Vascular bundle scars: Small spots located in the area of a leaf scar and indicating the number of vascular bundles that extended from the stem into the leaf. These vascular bundles were severed when the leaf fell.

Bud scales: Protective scalelike leaves covering all the buds.

Clusters of bud scale scars: Scars left at a point where there was formerly a bud. When a bud opens, the bud scales are shed, and each one leaves a scar. Because the bud scales are very close together, these scars will be found clustered together. The age of a twig can be determined by counting the sections of stem between successive clusters of bud scale scars. For example, from the tip back to the first cluster of bud scale scars is the growth of the past season. From the first cluster back to the second cluster will be the growth of the season before that, and so on.

Growth produced during the past growing season.

Growth produced during the growing season preceding the past growing season.

Lenticles: Small openings in the bark of the stem allowing for exchange of gases between the outside and inside of the stem. Loosely packed cells may protrude from these openings.

Floral branch scars: Small, round scars directly above some of the leaf scars. These scars were produced when the floral branches broke from the stem and fell off.

Node.

Internode.

c. Examination of the Shoot Apex

A brief study of the shoot apex shows how new stem tissue and the leaves it supports are formed and become differentiated.

1. Dissect one of the larger buds on the twigs that have been given you. Note the *bud scales* that enclose the bud. The bud scale represents a modification of what plant organ?

What makes up the bulk of the bud within the bud scales?

If possible, locate the extremely minute tip of the stem within the bud. What is the shape of the actual stem tip?

---

2. Examine a prepared slide of the *Coleus* stem tip showing a longitudinal section through the middle of a bud (Fig. 4-4). Locate the apical meristem, which is at the tip of the stem and enclosed by the embryonic leaves. Note the progressive increase in the size of the leaves as you move away from the stem tip. Can you find evidence of cell division in the apical meristem? If not, can you suggest a reason for absence of divisions?

Are the cells in the embryonic leaves all alike? If not, what evidence of differentiation do you find?

What do you find in the angle that each leaf makes with the stem?

A. Shoot apex has been removed from plant, cut into thin sections with special knives, stained, and mounted on a slide.

B. Examine the slide with your microscope.

FIG. 4-4
Study of the *Coleus* shoot tip.

As you move away from the tip, notice that not all the cells are alike. What differences do you observe among some of these cells?

_____

_____

_____

2. Primary Tissues of a Stem

Flowering plants are divided into two major groups called the **dicotyledons** (dicots) and **monocotyledons** (monocots). The differences in the number of cotyledons (food storage organs) in the embryo—one in the monocots and two in the dicots—provide the most familiar distinction between these groups. Other differences are based on (1) the leaf venation pattern (parallel in monocots; reticulate in dicots), (2) the vascular bundle arrangement in the stem (peripheral and arranged in a cylinder in dicots; scattered in monocots); (3) the presence (in dicots) or the absence (in monocots) of a vascular cambium; and (4) the numerical arrangement of floral parts (three in monocots; four or five, or multiples thereof, in dicots). Although you will examine plants that exhibit these classical distinctions in the studies that follow, be aware that there are always exceptions to the rule.

a. Primary Tissues of a Dicot Stem

Examine various representatives of dicots such as *Coleus,* geranium, bean plants *(Phaseolus),* tomato plants *(Lycopersicon),* and any other provided by your instructor. Identify the following:

Leaf: Composed of two parts called the **blade** (the expanded flat portion) and the **petiole** (the stalk that attaches the blade to the stem). In some cases, the blade may be subdivided into numerous smaller segments, called *leaflets.*

Stipules: Leaflike structures found near the base of the petiole. These are not always present.

Veins: The vascular network located in the leaf blade. In dicots, this pattern is described as *net* or *reticulate venation.*

Axil: The angle between the upper side of the petiole and the stem.

Lateral or axillary bud: A bud formed in the axil of the leaf. Develops into a leafy branch or flower, or sometimes both. You examined these in Part B-1 of this exercise.

Terminal or apical bud: A bud located at the tip of the main stem or at the end of a branch. To what does this structure give rise?

Node: That place on the stem where leaves arise.

Internode: The region between two nodes. Stem elongation is primarily the result of elongation of the internodes.

Obtain a portion of a geranium stem from the instructor. With a razor blade, make a fresh cut in a transverse plane to obtain the thinnest section possible. Prepare a fresh mount of this material, and examine it under the low power of the microscope. Locate the outer epidermal layer and the numerous hairs associated with it. Located beneath the epidermis is a layer of tissue composed of parenchymatous cells. This is the cortex. Note the presence of numerous chloroplasts in the cells. Describe a function for this tissue in the living plant.

_____

_____

The cortex is separated from the centrally located pith by a band of vascular tissue. Note that the vascular cylinder is not of uniform thickness but is composed of more or less separate vascular bundles (strands of vascular tissue). The vascular cylinder may be more readily observed if the tissue is stained with phloroglucinol-HC1. Mount the section in phloroglucinol solution. Wait about one minute and reexamine the section. How does the arrangement of the vascular tissue differ from that of the root?

_____

For a detailed examination of the primary tissues, obtain a prepared slide of a cross section of the alfalfa *(Medicago)* stem (Fig. 4-5). The cells in the central part of the stem differentiate into pith cells. Encircling the pith are vascular strands, which appear in cross section as separate vascular bundles. A mature vascular bundle consists of three main tissues—xylem, phloem, and cambium. The xylem is located on the inner side toward the pith. Adjacent to the xylem, appearing as small rectangular cells having the long axis at right angles to the radius of the stem, is the cambium. Division of cambial cells results in the formation of secondary tissues, which increase the diameter of the stem. How does the vascular arrangement in the stem contrast with that of the root?

_____

The phloem lies immediately external to the cambium.
Capping each vascular bundle is a group of thick-walled fibers. Morphologically, these fibers are part of

A. Alfalfa (*Medicago*)

B. Thin cross section of
stem removed, stained,
and mounted on slide

CROSS
SECTION
ALFALFA
STEM

Cambium — Pith

— Collenchyma

— Epidermis

— Fibers

— Parenchyma

— Xylem

— Phloem

C. Examine with
your microscope.

FIG. 4-5
Study of a dicot (alfalfa) stem anatomy.

the primary phloem tissue and are properly called **phloem fibers**. The parenchymatous cells lying between the vascular bundles are **pith rays**.

The cortex lies immediately outside the phloem fibers and consists of two distinguishable tissues—**cortical parenchyma** and **collenchyma** (mechanical tissue). The cortical parenchyma consists of loosely packed parenchymatous cells, many of which contain chloroplasts. In many stems, the collenchyma may be found exterior to the cortical parenchyma. In alfalfa, there is considerable development of the collenchyma at the corners.

The outermost layer of cells constitutes the epidermis. How many cell layers thick is the epidermis?

_____

The outer walls of epidermal cells usually have become thickened, and during their development a waxy substance (**cutin**) is secreted. Close the diaphragm on your microscope so that you can observe this layer of cutin. It will appear as a faint, pink, noncellular layer covering the epidermis. What effect does this waxy layer have on the loss of water from the stem?

_____

_____

What characteristics of dicots are exhibited by geranium and alfalfa?

_____

_____

_____

b. Primary Tissues of a Monocot Stem

Examine various representatives of monocots such as corn (*Zea mays*), wandering Jew (*Zebrina pendula*), dumbcane (*Dieffenbachia*), lawn grass, oats, and any others provided by your instructor. Identity the following:

Leaf blade: Generally narrow, parallel sided and flat. Which of the demonstration plants fit this description?

_____

Which do not?

_____

Sheath: The base of the leaf blade, which may partially or completely enclose the stem.

Node: As in dicots, the region of the stem at which the leaf arises. In monocots, the nodes frequently are swollen and look jointed.

Veins: The vascular tissue in monocots generally runs parallel to the leaf margins. Thus the network is usually called *parallel venation*.

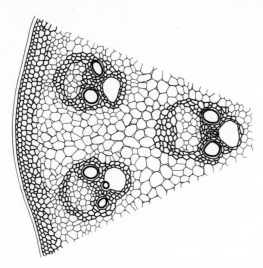

FIG. 4-6
Study of a monocot (corn) stem anatomy.

Examine a slide of a cross section of a young stem of corn *(Zea mays)* (Fig. 4-6). Answer the following questions:

	Yes	*No*
Are the vascular bundles located peripherally and in a ringlike pattern as they are in dicots?	——	——
Is there any kind of pattern evident with respect to the arrangement of vascular bundles?	——	——

If yes, describe the pattern. _____

_____

Are the vascular bundles all of the same size?	——	——

If not, are they larger in the center or at the periphery? _____

Is there any pith?	——	——
Is there any cortical tissue?	——	——

Using the high-power objective lens, study the details of an individual vascular bundle. Locate the following, and label them in Fig. 4-6.

1. *Xylem:* The xylem tissue consists of xylem **vessels** and xylem **parenchyma**. Two or three of the vessels frequently are arranged to give the appearance of the eyes and nose of a face. Indeed, the vascular bundle sometimes looks like a skull. Located between the larger vessels are smaller vessels and thinner-walled xylem parenchyma. A large hole (which looks like a "mouth" in the skull) is

created by cells that have been stretched during elongation of the stem and have collapsed.

2. *Phloem:* The phloem tissue, consisting of larger **sieve tubes** and small **companion cells**, is located in what could be described as the "forehead." In some sections, you may be able to see the perforated **sieve plate** of the sieve tube cell. What is the function of the sieve tubes and the companion cells?

_____

3. *Fibrous sheath:* Thick-walled fibers (**sclerenchyma cells**) surround each vascular bundle. Suggest a function for this tissue.

_____

3. Secondary Growth

In addition to the great diversity in structure of primary tissue systems in angiosperms, all dicots develop secondary tissues from a cambium and usually form an external tissue called **cork.** The extensive proliferation of secondary tissues results in the crushing and elimination of epidermal tissues, cortex, and primary xylem and phloem of the stem.

Because monocots typically lack cambial activity and the resulting secondary growth, this study will examine the secondary growth of a dicotyledenous plant.

Plants grow in diameter by the division and differentiation of cells produced in the lateral meristem or cambium. Tissues formed from cambial activity are designated as **secondary tissues.** Carefully examine cross sections of one-, two-, and three-year-old basswood stems. Label Fig. 4-7 as you locate each of the following:

a. Epidermis

The outermost portion of the cross section. There is a waxy layer, the cuticle, covering this outer layer of cells. In older stem sections, this cell layer may be disrupted and appear to be flaking away from the surface.

b. Periderm

This region is composed of

1. *Cork:* Cork cells are rectangular and are produced by the cork cambium. Walls of cork cells are impregnated with suberin, which makes the cells waterproof. Cork cells die soon after they are mature. How do you account for their early death?

FIG. 4-7
Cross section of a three-year-old basswood stem.

_____

_____

These cells are filled with tannin and are darkly stained.

2. _Cork cambium:_ The cells of the cork cambium are shaped like the cork cells produced by the cork cambium, but in the cork cambium cell nuclei are usually plainly visible.

3. _Cork parenchyma:_ In addition to producing cork, the cork cambium produces a small layer of parenchyma cells located just inside the cork cambium layer. The walls of these cells are flattened on the radial and outer tangential sides, with the inner side being rounded like the adjacent mechanical tissue cells.

c. Cortex

This zone is composed of several layers of thick-walled cells—mechanical tissue—and, just within the mechan-

ical tissue, an area of thin-walled parenchyma cells. Look for unique crystals in some of these cells.

d. Vascular Cylinder

1. _Phloem:_ Recall from lectures and previous laboratory work the physiological function of the phloem.

   a. _Primary phloem:_ The thick-walled phloem fibers are located as a cap over the remainder of the primary phloem. Examination of the thick-walled phloem with the high-power objective of your microscope will show the wall structure and reveal the very small "lumen" or cavity of the cell. Parenchyma cells are located at the outer end of the rays.

   b. _Secondary phloem:_ The secondary phloem in the basswood stem is conspicuously banded with alternating layers of thick-walled cells (**phloem fibers**) and layers of thin-walled cells (the other types of phloem cells such as **sieve tubes, companion cells,**

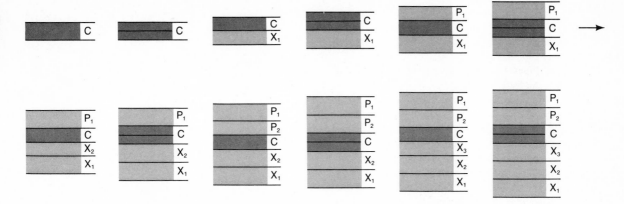

FIG. 4-8
Formation of secondary xylem and phloem by cambium. Cambium (C); P_1, (first-formed secondary phloem); X_1 (second-formed secondary phloem).

and **phloem parenchyma**). The thick-walled phloem fibers here are very similar in appearance to the thick-walled cells of the primary phloem.

2. *Cambium:* The cambium consists of a layer of thin-walled cells between the xylem and phloem. Cells of the cambium are rather uniform in size and appear rectangular in cross section. Epidermis, cortex, pith, xylem, phloem, and cambium are formed in the apical meristem of the herbaceous dicot stem as previously described. The cells of the cambium, however, differ from those of the other tissues in that they continue to divide. The planes of division are largely tangential. The cambium layer does not increase in thickness, because the cells produced mature into xylem and phloem cells (Fig. 4-8). In the vascular bundle, therefore, the cells that flank the cambium have been produced by it. Although primary and secondary xylem differ from each other in origin, they are similar in structure and function and, in the cross section of the stem, cannot be distinguished from each other except by position. The same is true of primary and secondary phloem.

3. *Xylem*
   a. *Secondary xylem:* The secondary xylem of woody plants normally shows a differentiation between the xylem elements formed early in the growing season (**spring wood**) and those xylem elements formed later in the growth period (**summer wood**). Those formed during the spring are larger and the amount of wall material is small in proportion to the total cell area. Those produced during the later part of the growing season are smaller and the walls are

relatively thick. The zone of spring wood and summer wood produced during one growing season constitutes an **annual ring**. The annual ring shows up conspicuously because of the size difference between the small cells produced at the end of one growing season and the large ones formed when growth is resumed in the next growing season.

   b. *Primary xylem:* The primary xylem is located in contact with the pith. Usually primary xylem cells are somewhat more irregularly arranged and are smaller in diameter than the secondary xylem cells. The primary xylem makes up only a small portion of the inner part of the first annual ring.

   e. Pith

The pith occupies the central area of the stem. In the pith of the basswood stem, there are numerous cells containing tannin and mucilage material, which strongly absorbs the stains used in preparation of the slides. Near the outer edge of the pith, there is a ring of such darkly stained cells.

   f. Rays

Some of the rays found in the stem extend from the pith outward to the cortex. As the stem grows in diameter, the cambium adds new parenchyma cells to these rays and also initiates new rays. These later-formed rays do not extend to the pith or outwardly to the cortex: they extend from the point in the xylem at which they originated outwardly through the secondary xylem and secondary phloem produced since the time of the origin. Sometimes the portions of rays found in the xylem, or wood, are called "**wood rays**."

REFERENCES

Cutter, E. 1978. *Plant Anatomy: Experiment and Interpretation*. Part 1. 2nd ed. Arnold.

Cutter, E. 1971. *Plant Anatomy: Experiment and Interpretation*. Part 2. Addison-Wesley.

Epstein, E. 1973. Roots. *Scientific American* 228:48–58 (Offprint 1271). *Scientific American* Offprints are available from W. H. Freeman and Company, 660 Market Street, San Francicso 94104, and 58 Kings Road, Reading RG1 3AA, England. Please order by number.

Esau, K. 1977. *Anatomy of Seed Plants*. 2nd ed. Wiley.

Foster, A. S., and E. M. Gifford, Jr. 1974. *Comparative Morphology of Vascular Plants*. 2nd ed. W. H. Freeman and Company.

Stevenson, F. F., and T. R. Mertens. 1976. *Plant Anatomy*. Wiley.

Weier, T. E., C. R. Stocking, and M. G. Barbour. 1974. *Botany: An Introduction to Plant Biology*. 5th ed. Wiley.

Plant Anatomy: Leaves and Flowers

We have already discussed two plant organs in Exercise 4: the root, which functions chiefly as an absorbing organ, and the stem, which serves to conduct water and soluble materials. A third organ, the leaf, is specialized to carry on photosynthesis; a physicochemical process that converts light energy to chemical energy. All forms of life, with the exception of some types of bacteria, depend on the process of photosynthesis at some point in their food chain.

Flowers are reproductive branches consisting of the stem axis and lateral appendages called *sepals, petals, stamens,* and *carpels.* The significance of the flower lies in its role in sexual reproduction.

A. LEAVES

Leaves consist basically of three parts: the blade, an expanded or flattened portion; the petiole, a thin, stemlike portion; and the stipules, small, paired, lobelike structures at the base of the petiole. The petiole and stipules may not be present in some plants.

Leaves may be classified according to the type of venation (arrangement of vascular tissue) or to the arrangement of the leaves on the stem. Thus leaves are parallel-veined when the larger vascular strands traverse the leaf without apparent branching, and net-veined (reticulate) when the main branches of the vascular system form a network. According to the position on the stem, leaves may be alternate or opposite, if they are borne singly or in pairs at each node. Examine the plants on demonstration, and become familiar with the parts of the leaf and the simple classification just given.

1. Epidermis

Obtain a leaf from a bean or geranium plant. Remove the lower epidermis by ripping the leaf as shown in Fig. 5-1A. Mount the thin, colorless piece of tissue in a drop of water on a slide, and then add a cover slip (Fig. 5-1B). Observe under low and high power. Note that many of the epidermal cells have an irregular shape. Scattered throughout the epidermis are openings called **stomata** (singular, **stoma**) (Fig. 5-1C). Each stoma is surrounded by two bean-shaped guard cells. Suggest a function for the stomata.

_____

_____

_____

_____

Which of the epidermal cells contain chloroplasts?

_____

What relationship there between the function of the chlorophyll-containing cells and the presence of chlorophyll?

_____

_____

_____

_____

2. Internal Anatomy

Obtain a prepared slide of a cross section of a lilac *(Syringa)* leaf for further examination of the internal tissues (Fig. 5-1F). Below the upper epidermis is a region of **palisade tissue**, consisting of one or more layers of elongated cells with the long axis of the cell perpendicular to the surface of the leaf. Palisade cells contain numerous chloroplasts. What function do you ascribe to this tissue?

_____

Beneath the palisade tissue, locate a region of rounded, parenchymatous cells, which constitute the **spongy** tissue. The palisade tissue and spongy parenchyma are collectively called **leaf mesophyll**. Note the presence of numerous intercellular spaces in the mesophyll. Locate the stomata. What is the relationship between the stomata and the intercellular spaces of the mesophyll tissue?

_____

_____

The veins of a leaf are vascular bundles (strands) that are continuous with the vascular tissues of the petiole and stem. A vein contains xylem and phloem and has the same cellular elements as the stem. What is the function of the thick-walled mechanical (supporting) tissue associated with the vascular bundles?

_____

_____

Examine demonstration slides of a corn leaf, a monocot leaf. Describe any differences in the arrangement of tissues between this leaf and the net-veined lilac leaf.

_____

_____

Examine demonstration slides of cross sections of a pine leaf (Fig. 5-2). Note the heavily cutinized epidermal cells. Locate a layer of sclerenchyma just beneath the epidermis. Find depressions, or pits, in the epidermis. Where are the stomata located in the pine leaf?

_____

How does the tree benefit by having the stomata located as they are?

_____

A. Remove a leaf from a plant. Make a ragged tear in the leaf to obtain a piece of the epidermis.

D

B. Place epidermis in drop of water on slide and place a cover slip over it.

E

CROSS SECTION OF LILAC LEAF

C

Stoma

Guard cell

Other epidermal cells

F

Upper epidermis

Palisade tissue

Stoma   Guard cell

Intercellular space

Spongy parenchyma

Phloem
Xylem

} Vascular tissue (vein)

FIG. 5-1
Study of leaf anatomy.

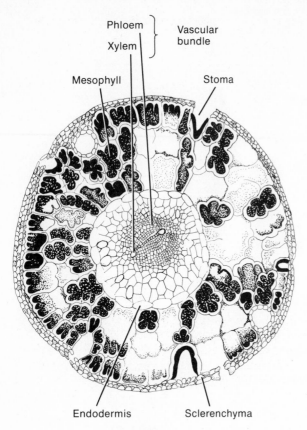

Phloem ⎫
         ⎬ Vascular bundle
Xylem ⎭

Mesophyll   Stoma

Endodermis   Sclerenchyma

FIG. 5-2
Pine needle leaf.

Locate the central vascular cylinder surrounded by an endodermis. How many vascular bundles are present?

_____

Examine cross sections of leaves of other species of pines. Describe any variation in structure among the various needles.

_____

_____

Examine the slides of the various leaves with a dissecting microscope. What correlation exists between the number of leaves in a cluster and the shape of an individual needle leaf?

_____

_____

_____

_____

3. Morphological Adaptations to the Environment

Water is one of the basic raw materials of photosynthesis. It is the major component of plant tissues, making up 90% of the plant body. Water is the substance in which most materials enter and leave the cells of plants, and it is the solvent for the various biochemical reactions that occur in living cells.

The amount of water used by plants is far greater than that used by animals of comparable weight. The reason for this is that a large amount of the water used by the animal is recirculated in the form of blood plasma or tissue fluid. In plants, over 90% of the water taken in by the root system is evaporated into the air as water vapor. This process, which largely occurs through the leaves, is called **transpiration**. Consequently, plants not only have developed extensive and efficient transport systems but also have evolved numerous morphological adaptations, many of which involve the leaves, to conserve water. In this study, you will examine some of the modifications of plants and plant parts to obtain and retain water.

There are many types of habitats found in nature with respect to water supply. These can be conveniently divided into **xeric, mesic**, and **hydric** habitats. The plants that are adapted for living in these habitats are called _xerophytes, mesophytes,_ and _hydrophytes,_ respectively.

Xerophytes include a number of species that live in habitats where the supply of water is physically or physiologically deficient (xeric habitat). **Mesophytes** inhabit regions of average or optimum water conditions (mesic habitat) and include the majority of wild and cultivated plants of the temperate regions. **Hydrophytes** form an extensive flora living on the surface of water or submerged at various depths (hydric habitat).

In this study, representative examples of hydrophytes and xerophytes will be studied, because the structural adaptations are more obvious in these groups. Following your examination of specimens characteristic of these groups, you will be asked to classify unknown specimens.

a. Hydrophytic Adaptations

The chief structural modifications exhibited by hydrophytes are an increase in leaf surface, the presence of air chambers, and a reduction in protective, supportive, and conductive tissues.

1. _Dissected leaves:_ Examine the hydric habitat at the demonstration table. Note that many of the plants have finely divided leaves. How may this condition be advantageous to the plant?

_____

_____

2. *Air chambers:* The leaves and stems of many submerged plants have chambers that are filled with gases. Examine prepared slides of cross sections of the leaf of *Potamogeton.* Locate these large air spaces, which are separated from each other by partitions of photosynthetic tissue. List several ways in which these air spaces may be of benefit in a hydric habitat.

_____

_____

3. *Supporting tissues:* Remove one of the hydrophytic plants from the water, and note how flaccid it becomes. This condition is due to the marked reduction of thick-walled supporting tissues or cells. Confirm this by examining prepared slides of *Potamogeton* stems and leaves. Why do submerged hydrophytes not need large amounts of supporting tissues?

_____

4. *Vascular tissues:* Because aquatic plants are submerged in, or floating on, a nutrient solution, the structures necessary for absorption and transport of mineral nutrients and water are greatly reduced and in some cases absent. The greatest reduction occurs in the xylem. The phloem, although reduced in amount, is fairly well developed. Examine prepared slides of *Potamogeton* stems and leaves. Locate the vascular tissue, and note the absence of xylem. By what process does water enter aquatic plants?

_____

5. *Protective tissues:* The epidermis of aerial plants has become modified to prevent or reduce desiccation. Under normal conditions, aquatic plants do not lose water through the epidermis, so the epidermis in hydrophytes is not a protective tissue. In these plants, nutrients and gases may be absorbed directly from the water. The cuticle overlying the epidermis is extremely thin and may be lacking. The epidermal cells usually contain chloroplasts and may form a considerable part of the photosynthetic tissue. Where would you expect to find guard cells in submerged hydrophytes?

_____

Where would they be located in floating hydrophytes?

_____

Examine slides of *Potamogeton* and locate the modifications just indicated.

b. Xerophytic Adaptations

The deficiency of water that characterizes xeric habitats may be the result of various environmental conditions—for example, intense light, heat, and high-velocity winds. Many of the adaptations of xerophytes that have evolved prevent desiccation of the plant when exposed to one, or any combination of these factors.

1. *Stomata:* The stomates function in the exchange of carbon dioxide and oxygen between the plant and the environment. When the stomates are open, however, water may also leave the plant, which harms the plant as a whole. Consequently, it is important to xerophytic plants to reduce the rate of transpiration. One way this is accomplished is by having the stomates situated below the level of the surrounding epidermal cells. Examine prepared slides of the cross section of a pine leaf and locate sunken stomates. How may this position of the stomates reduce the rate of transpiration?

_____

2. *Protective tissues:* In contrast to the hydrophytes, the epidermis of xerophytes commonly has a thick layer of cutin. In addition, the walls of the epidermal cells may be highly lignified. How does this serve to cut down on the amount of water lost from the plant?

_____

_____

Examine slides of pine leaf and locate the modifications mentioned here.

3. *Supporting tissues:* Xerophytes generally have a large proportion of supportive tissues that not only prevent water loss but also help support the stem or leaf. Examine a slide of pine leaf, and locate a layer of thick-walled tissue just below the epidermis. Why is it important that stems and leaves of aerial plants be supported in some manner?

_____

4. *Leaf rolling:* During drying conditions, the leaves of many xerophytes—notably the xerophytic grasses—roll up tightly. Because the stomates in these plants are more numerous on the upper surface, what effect does this have on the rate of transpiration? Explain.

_____

_____

_____

_____

_____

Examine a prepared slide of a corn leaf. In the upper epidermis, locate large, bulbous cells. These are **bulliform cells** (motor cells), which function in the rolling of the leaves in dry weather.

5. *Water storage:* Some xerophytes possess large amounts of water-storage tissue. These plants are called *fleshy xerophytes.* Examine specimens of this group. In some plants, the leaves may be fleshy (**leaf succulents**). In others, the stem is fleshy, and therefore the plants are called **stem succulents.** Note the absence, or greatly reduced number, of leaves on the stem succulents. What is the primary photosynthetic organ in these plants?

_____

Cut a thin cross section of a leaf succulent (for example, *Aloe*), and mount it in a drop of water on a slide. Examine microscopically. Note the large amount of water-storage tissue that makes up the bulk of the leaf. What other xerophytic characteristics are present that you are able to observe microscopically?

_____

_____

_____

_____

_____

c. Unknown Specimens

Examine slides of the species of plants listed in Table 5-1. Enter the information asked for in the table, and then decide in what habitat (xeric or hydric) each plant would be found. Your decision should be based on the information obtained from the examination of the various slides and characteristics cited in this study.

B. FLOWERS

Thus far, the plant has been studied as an organism composed of roots, stems, and leaves. These structures develop and function so as to ensure the successful existence of the plant. Ultimately, however, the plant dies. It is through a constant succession of new individuals that the species survives. This is accomplished by a process called *reproduction* in which the plant produces a group of offspring.

There are two main types of reproduction—**asexual** (or vegetative) and **sexual.** Flowering plants can reproduce asexually by numerous means. For example, in strawberry plants the tip of a branch may arch down, touch the soil, and develop leafy branches that root and form new plants. The most common method of reproduction, however, is by sexual means. To understand sexual reproduction in plants, it is necessary to study the anatomy of the flower.

Your instructor will provide you with two or three different flowers that you may use for this part of the exercise.

With the help of Fig. 5-3, locate the following parts of these flowers:

Sepals (which are modified leaves) are the outermost structures of the flower. They are typically green, although they may be other colors. In some cases, they may be absent.

Petals lie to the inside of the sepals and are often brightly colored. Both the sepals and petals are attached to the enlarged end of the branch—the receptable.

Carefully remove the sepals and petals. In the center of the flower, locate a stalklike structure (Fig. 5-3A, B). This is the female part of the flower—the **pistil.** Pistils are made up of one or more carpels—leaflike structures bearing ovules. It is thought that, during evolution, the carpels rolled inward, enclosing the ovules. The pistil is composed of a swollen base, the **ovary,** and an elongated **style** that is terminated by a **stigma.** There may be more than one pistil in a flower.

The ovary contains one or more **ovules.** These may be seen if the ovary is cut lengthwise and examined with a dissecting microscope. One of the cells in the young, developing ovule undergoes a special type of cell divi-

TABLE 5-1
Adaptations of vascular plants to the environment.

Species	Air chambers	Supporting tissues	Protective tissues	Leaf modifications (stomata, motor cells, other)	Vascular tissue	Water storage tissue	Habitat and reason for choice (xeric, hydric)
Potamogeton							
Yucca							
Myriophyllum							
Ammophila							
Acorus							
Typha							
Pinus							

60

Stamen { Anther, Filament }

Stigma, Style, Ovary } Pistil

A.

X — — X

F.

Y — — Y

Stamen

Petal
Sepal
Receptacle

B.

Carpel

Ovule

Cross section of ovary at X--X

G.

Cross section of anther at Y--Y

Anther contains cells that undergo meiosis, which then develop into pollen grains.

K.

J.

After fertlization, ovule develops into seed, which, when planted, grows into a new plant.

C.

MEIOSIS

H.

I.

Pollen grain carried to stigma where it germinates. Pollen tube grows through style. Gametes in pollen tube are released when tube reaches egg cell in ovule and fertilize egg.

D. Four daughter cells result, each having one-half the number of chromosomes of parent cells. One daughter cell undergoes mitosis to form a microscopic gamete-producing plant that gives rise to female egg.

Egg within ovule

E.

FIG. 5-3
Study of flower anatomy.

sion, called *meiosis,* where the daughter cells that are formed have one-half (haploid) the number of chromosomes possessed by the parent cell. One of these haploid daughter cells develops into a microscopic haploid plant that will produce a female gamete, the egg cell (Fig. 5-3C, D, E). Why is it necessary that meiosis occur during the formation of the gametes?

_____

_____

_____

Locate the stamens that surround the pistil (Fig. 5-3F). These are the male parts of the flower and consist of a terminal capsule—the **anther**—attached to a slender **filament**.

The anthers contain cells that also undergo meiosis to produce cells that eventually develop into microscopic gamete-producing plants, commonly called **pollen grains** (Fig. 5-3G, H). Crush one of the anthers in a drop of water on a slide, and add a cover slip. Examine it with your microscope, and locate the pollen grains. During **pollination**, the pollen grains are transferred to the stigma—the sticky surface of the pistil. The pollen grain germinates, and the pollen tube grows through the style to the ovary and enters the ovule (Fig. 5-3I). It is known that many organisms, or parts of organisms, grow toward or away from various stimuli such as light, chemicals, and gravity. Suggest a mechanism that could direct the growth of the pollen tube toward the ovules.

_____

_____

_____

During the growth of the pollen tube, two male gametes (sperm) are produced. These are released when the tube enters the ovule. One sperm fertilizes the egg cell and the other unites with the nucleus of another cell in the ovule. This second fertilization results in the formation of a special tissue—the **endosperm**—which functions as a nutrient tissue to the developing embryo.

Fertilization of the egg initiates extensive changes in the carpel. The ovary enlarges and develops into the fruit; in some cases, other floral parts also become part of the fruit. The ovules develop into seeds, which now contain the embryos of new plants (Fig. 5-3J, K). The development of the embryo and the regulation of plant growth are considered in other exercises.

REFERENCES

Arnett, R. H., and G. F. Bazinet. 1977. *Plant Biology.* 4th ed. Mosby.

Bold, H. C. 1978. *Morphology of Plants and Fungi.* 4th ed. Harper and Row.

Cutter, E. 1971. *Plant Anatomy: Organs.* Addison-Wesley.

Echlin, P. 1968. Pollen. *Scientific American* (Offprint 1105). *Scientific American* Offprints are available from W. H. Freeman and Company, 660 Market Street, San Francsco 94104, and 58 Kings Road, Reading RG1 3AA, England. Please order by number.

Esau, K. 1977. *Anatomy of Seed Plants.* 2nd ed. Wiley.

Foster, A. S., and E. Gifford. 1974. *Comparative Morphology of Vascular Plants.* 2nd ed. W. H. Freeman and Company.

Stebbins, H. L. 1974. *Flowering Plants. Evolution Above the Species Level.* Belknap Press of Harvard University Press.

Vertebrate Anatomy: External Anatomy, Skeleton, and Muscles

Frogs are probably the most commonly studied animals in general biology and zoology courses because they are easy to obtain and dissect, and their structure clearly shows the major features of the organ systems characteristic of the backboned animals, or vertebrates. Furthermore, the frog is one of the most widely used animals in vertebrate physiology and in other experimental work. Vertebrates are of particular interest to us because we, too, are members of the phylum Vertebrata. It is therefore an animal with which students should be familiar.

As members of the class Amphibia, frogs have characteristics that are between those of the lower vertebrates (fishes) and those of the advanced land vertebrates (reptiles, birds, and mammals).

Contemporary amphibians are grouped into three orders: frogs and toads, salamanders, and legless, worm-shaped caecilians of the tropics. All reproduce in the water or in very moist places on land. Most go through an aquatic larval stage, commonly called the *tadpole*. This period of development is followed by a metamorphosis to a terrestrial adult. Adult amphibians have only a rudimentary ability to conserve body water, so they must live in damp habitats on land and must often return to water. As a result of their phylogenetic position between fishes and reptiles and their double mode of life in water and on land, amphibians have a mixture of aquatic and terrestrial attributes.

The most widespread of our North American frogs is the leopard frog, also known as the grass or meadow frog. Its scientific name is *Rana pipiens*. Another frog, which is often studied because of its large size, is the bullfrog, *Rana catesbeiana*.

A. EXTERNAL ANATOMY OF THE FROG

The body of a frog can be divided into a **head**, which extends posteriorly to the shoulder region, and a **trunk** (Fig. 6-1). Fishes, which were ancestral to amphibians, have a powerful tail used in swimming. Aquatic tadpoles retain such a tail, but it is lost in the adult frog, which moves instead by means of its powerful hindlegs. The much smaller front legs are used primarily to keep the

63

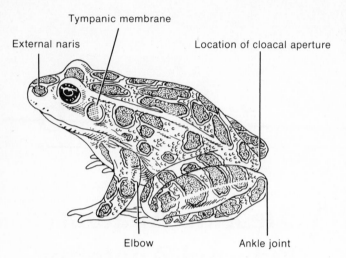

FIG. 6-1
Lateral view of a leopard frog, *Rana pipiens*. (From *Dissection of the Frog*, 2nd ed., by Warren Walker, Jr. W. H. Freeman and Company. Copyright © 1981.)

front of the body raised from the ground. Notice that a distinct neck is absent. This is due to the retention of a characteristic of fishes, for which an independent motion of the head and trunk would be disadvantageous during swimming.

The combined orifice of the digestive and urogenital tracts, the **cloacal aperture**, is at the posterior end of the trunk just dorsal to the junction of the hindlegs. Through this opening are discharged undigested food wastes (feces), the liquid excretory waste (urine) from the kidneys, and the sex cells (sperm or eggs) from the reproductive organs. The anus of human beings and other mammals, because it is the opening of just the digestive tract, is only partly comparable to the cloacal aperture.

A large **mouth**, a pair of nostrils, or **external nares** (singular **naris**), and the **eyes** will be recognized on the head. The upper **eyelid** is a simple fold of skin. The lower lid is a transparent **nictitating membrane** that can be drawn across the surface of the eyeball. The disc-shaped area posterior to each eye is a flat eardrum, or **tympanic membrane**. Although it is the same size in male and female leopard frogs, it is considerably larger in male bullfrogs than in females. This is one example of **sexual dimorphism** (structural differences between the sexes). Look carefully at the top of the head between the eyes, and you may see a small, light **brow spot**, which is about the diameter of a pin. This is a remnant of a light-sensitive eye that characterized primitive groups of fishes and amphibians.

The appendages of a frog have the same parts as our own. In the front leg, or **pectoral appendage**, notice the

upper arm, the elbow, the forearm, the wrist joint, and the hand. There are only four fingers. Although the finger closest to the body is comparable to our second digit, it is often called the *thumb* because it is stouter than the others. During the breeding season, the thumb in the male is particularly stout and darkly pigmented—another example of sexual dimorphism. In the hind limb, or **pelvic appendage**, observe the thigh, the knee, the shank, the ankle joint, and the very long foot. Two elongated ankle bones lie within the proximal part of the foot, and the distal part bears five toes with a conspicuous web between them. The first toe is the smallest and the one closest to the body, and is comparable to our great toe. Technically it is called the **hallux**, and the small spur at its base is the **prehallux**. The prehallux is much larger in toads, which use their hind feet in burrowing.

B. VERTEBRATE SKIN

All organisms are covered by some sort of external covering. In one-celled organisms, this may be only a thin cell membrane; in higher organisms, the coverings are complex structures consisting of several layers of cells. The skin of vertebrates is a highly functional organ that provides physical protection, excludes disease organisms, acts as a means of water absorption, and in some forms serves an essential role in respiration. In frogs, both the adult and tadpole stages absorb oxygen and eliminate carbon dioxide through the skin (**cutaneous respiration**). It functions as a respiratory organ both in water and in air. During the winter, when the frog lies buried in the mud, the skin becomes the only respiratory organ. Shortly after hatching, the tadpole develops gills, which also function in the absorption of oxygen. This **branchial respiration** lasts until the tadpole begins to change into a frog. Adult frogs absorb oxygen and give off carbon dioxide through the lining of the mouth (**buccal respiration**) and through the lungs (**pulmonary respiration**). Even in full-grown frogs, however, three or four times as much oxygen can be absorbed through the skin as through the lungs. In warm-blooded mammals, the skin helps to regulate the temperature of the body. The skin of some vertebrates has been modified into hair (mammals), feathers (birds), scales (fish), and teeth (sharks).

1. Amphibian Skin

Microscopically examine a stained slide of a cross section of frog skin (Fig. 6-2). The stains used in preparing the slide are hematoxylin, which stains nuclei blue or purple, and eosin, which stains most cytoplasmic structures pink or shades of red.

FIG. 6-2
Vertical section through frog's skin.

The skin consists of two distinct regions. The outer layer, or **epidermis**, is an epithelial layer that is predominantly stained purple because it contains large numbers of cell nuclei. The inner layer, or **dermis**, is predominantly pink and contains only a few nuclei. Rounded structures in the dermis are sections through glands. The dark layer between the epidermis and the dermis contains **chromatophores**, which contain pigment granules that regulate the protective coloration of the frog.

Note that the cells of the outermost layer of the epidermis are thin and lie parallel to the surface; the deeper epithelial cells are more cuboidal in shape, and the cells in the basal (bottom) layer are usually columnar in shape—that is, they are longer in the direction perpendicular to the skin surface. The cell membranes are often not clearly visible, but the shapes of the nuclei give an idea of the shapes of the cells. If the nucleus is long in one direction, the cell is ordinarily long in the same direction. The epidermis, with its gradation from squamous to columnar cells in successive layers, is an example of **stratified squamous epithelium**. The basal layer is often called the **germinative layer**, because it continually produces new cells that are pushed out toward the surface, becoming steadily flatter and harder (more **cor-**

nified) as new cells are formed. Every month or so during the summer, a new layer forms beneath, and the old skin covering is molted, or sloughed off.

In the dermis, there are two types of glands: **mucous (slime) glands** and **poison glands**. These glands produce useful fluids or secretions that move to the surface of the epidermis through fine ducts. Both types of glands are surrounded by a layer of cuboidal secretory cells. The poison gland can be identified by its larger size and the presence of granular material in the cavity of the gland. If a frog is roughly handled, the poison glands discharge a thick, whitish secretion that burns to the taste, protecting the animal, to a degree, from enemies. The smaller, mucous glands secrete a colorless, watery fluid that keeps the skin moist, glistening, and sticky. Locate a mucous gland that shows its duct opening to the surface. The surface opening of these ducts can be widened or narrowed by the contraction of a cell (a stoma), which regulates the amount of mucus discharged. Examine a slide of frog squamous epithelium, find a stoma cell, and note its star-shaped opening.

Just beneath the epidermis is a prominent layer of pigment cells, or **chromatophores**. Grass frogs, usually protectively colored to resemble their surroundings, are green on the dorsal and lateral surfaces and pale green to whitish on the ventral surface. The patterns of most amphibians are stable, but the colors of some undergo marked changes. The skin darkens when the pigment granules in the chromatophores spread out and cover other elements in the skin, and it lightens when they are concentrated. Changes in color result from both external conditions and internal states; a low temperature produces darkening, whereas a high temperature, drying of the skin, or increased light intensity causes the color to lighten.

The dermis contains a large number of small blood vessels that transport food and carbon dioxide to the skin and take back oxygen absorbed through surface layers from the air. Nerve fibers and muscle fibers are also present in the dermis but will not be readily seen in your slides.

2. Mammalian Skin

Examine a slide of mammalian skin taken from the scalp, and compare and contrast it with the skin of the frog. The **epidermis** consists of stratified squamous epithelium, usually composed of several more layers of cells than is that of the frog and having more flattened horny (keratinized) layers at the surface (Fig. 6-3A). Keratin is a tough, proteinaceous material that serves several functions. It is a relatively waterproof substance and therefore prevents water from entering the body through the skin, but, more importantly, it prevents water loss. Because it is a tough material, it protects the underlying epithelial layers from being damaged through ordinary wear. It is particularly protective on the palms of the hands and soles of the feet.

The **dermis** is composed mainly of densely interwoven connective tissue. Note the abundance of small blood vessels whose contractions and dilations play an important role in the control of body temperature in mammals. Suggest a mechanism of temperature regulation by blood vessels.

_____

_____

Chromatophores, when present, are usually confined to the basal layer of the epithelium. At various levels in the dermis are **hair follicles, sweat** and **sebaceous (oil) glands**, and nerves. Locate a hair follicle, and notice that each hair arises in a tubular invagination of the epithelium. The root of the hair develops into the hair shaft, the free end of which protrudes beyond the surface of the

skin. One or more sebaceous glands (Fig. 6-3B) are associated with each hair follicle. These branched glands are located in the dermis and open into the hair follicle. They secrete an oily substance, called **sebum**, onto the hair or on the surface of the epidermis. The sebum's function is to oil the hair and lubricate the surface of the skin. It may also prevent evaporation during cold weather and thus aid in conserving body heat.

Distributed along the surface of the skin are the openings of the sweat glands (Fig. 6-3C). The long, tubular, and highly convoluted ducts of the glands penetrate deeply into the underlying dermis and connect with the secretory parts of the gland. What type of epithelial cell (cuboidal or columnar) lines the secretory and duct parts of these sweat glands?

_____

Because of the highly coiled structure of a sweat gland, it is difficult to see an entire duct or gland in one section. Rather, you will see cross or oblique sections of the various parts (Fig. 6-3C).

The secretions produced by the sweat glands flow onto the surface of the skin, where, by the process of evaporation, the surface is cooled. The activity of these glands is another body temperature regulating mechanism that is under the control of the nervous system.

The subcutaneous (below skin) layer is composed of fat cells (**adipose tissue**), the number of such cells present depending on the part of the body and the nutrition of the organism. The fat cells in your slide will look empty, because the method of preparing the slide caused the fat droplet that occupied the greater part of each cell to dissolve, leaving only a thin film of cytoplasm with its compressed nucleus. The fat cells are held together by fine, fibrous connective tissue. In the areas between the adipose tissue, heavy strands of connective tissue traverse the subcutaneous layer and bind it to the dermis and to the underlying organs. The subcutaneous layer is especially important in heat conservation by acting as an insulating layer.

C. VERTEBRATE SKELETON

One of the more significant evolutionary advances of the vertebrates over the invertebrates is the possession of an internal skeleton (**endoskeleton**). The external skeleton (**exoskeleton**) of the invertebrates has the disadvantage of limiting the ultimate size of an organism and in several cases is so heavy as to restrict the movements of some animals. The endoskeleton of vertebrates, on the other hand, permits relatively unrestricted development in size,

A

Epithelium

Sebaceous glands

Duct of sweat gland

Hair

Blood vessel

Secretory parts
of sweat gland

Adipose (fat) tissue

C

Duct

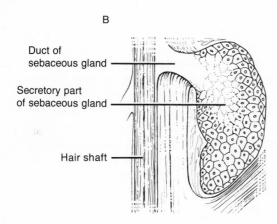

B

Duct of
sebaceous gland

Secretory part
of sebaceous gland

Hair shaft

1

2

3

FIG. 6-3
(A) Vertical section of human scalp. (B) Sebaceous gland and
adjacent hair follicle. (C) Sweat gland. Sections 1, 2, and 3 indicate the appearance, in cross and oblique section, of various
parts of the gland as it would be seen on a tissue section. (After
Atlas of Human Histology, 3rd ed., by M. DiFiore. El Ateneo,
1967.)

as evidenced by such vertebrates as the whale and elephant.

The vertebrate skeleton, in addition to protecting and supporting the internal organs of the body, is a highly efficient supporting structure for the attachment of muscles. Furthermore, the flexibility due to the large number of separate bones, coupled with the strength and relative lightness of vertebrate skeletons, enables even the largest animals to have a great deal of mobility.

The skeletal systems of all animals having an endoskeleton have a basic pattern consisting of two major parts: the **somatic skeleton**, located in the body and appendages, and a less conspicuous **visceral skeleton**, located chiefly in the wall of the upper parts of the digestive tract. The somatic skeleton is subdivided into the **axial skeleton**, which consists of the skull, the vertebral column, and the sternum (breastbone), and the **appendicular skeleton**, which consists of the pelvic (hip) and pectoral (shoulder) girdles and the limbs.

As you study the parts of the vertebrate skeleton, examine a mounted specimen of a frog skeleton and, if possible, a human skeleton to see both the similarities and differences (Fig. 6-4).

1. Axial Skeleton

a. Skull

The **cranium** is the part of the **skull** that contains the brain and the olfactory, optic, and auditory capsules for the organs of smell, sight, and hearing. In sharks and rays, the skull is cartilaginous, but in higher vertebrates most of the cartilage has been replaced by bone. Primitive vertebrates tend to have a larger number of skull bones than do higher forms. Some fish have 180 skull bones; amphibians and reptiles, from 50 to 95; and mammals, 35 or less. Human beings have 29.

Examine the dorsal surface of a frog skull, and refer to Fig. 6-5. The skull is attached to the anterior end of the vertebral column. Note the large jaws and the very small brain case, or **cranium**, which is roofed mainly by the **frontoparietals**, the **nasal** bones (which cover the nasal capsules), the **prootics** (which house the inner ears), and the **exoccipital** bones (each of which has a rounded **occipital condyle**). The two condyles fit depressions in the first vertebra, permitting slight movements of the head on the spinal column. Between the condyles is a large opening, the **foramen magnum**, through which the spinal cord passes. Between the prootics and the maxilla are the **squamosal** and **pterygoid** bones, which form the lateral borders of the cranium. The upper jaw consists of the small **premaxillary** bones in front and the larger

maxillary bones extending posteriorly to join with the pterygoid.

Now examine the ventral surface of the skull, and note the **maxillary teeth** on the margin of the upper jaw and the **vomerine teeth** on roof of the mouth (Fig. 6-6A). The **sphenethmoid**, which connects with the frontoparietal bone dorsally and the **parasphenoid** ventrally, surrounds the anterior part of the brain.

The lower jaw (mandible) consists of a rodlike **Meckel's cartilage** encased by the dentary and **angulare** bones, which are united with the **quadrate cartilage** on the cranium by means of joints (Fig. 6-6B). Notice that the bones of the lower jaw do not have teeth.

b. Vertebral Column

The vertebrae vary greatly with different animals and with different regions of the vertebral column in the same animal. The vertebral column in fish is differentiated into trunk vertebrae and caudal vertebrae; in many of the other vertebrates, it is differentiated into neck (or **cervical** vertebrae), chest (**thoracic**), back (**lumbar**), pelvic (**sacral**), and tail (**caudal**). In birds, as well as in human beings, the caudal vertebrae are reduced in number and size, and the sacral vertebrae are fused. The number of vertebrae varies for different animals. The python has the largest number—435. Human beings have 7 cervical, 12 thoracic, and 5 lumbar vertebrae, plus 5 that have fused to form the **sacrum** and **coccyx**. How many vertebrae does the frog have? _____ The first cervical vertebra, the **atlas**, is modified for articulation with the skull. The vertebral column terminates in a long bone, the **urostyle**.

Note that the vertebrae are much alike. The lateral projections are called **transverse processes**. The ribs of higher vertebrates are attached to these processes. There are many variations in the ribs of the vertebrates. The basic plan seems to have been a pair of ribs for each vertebra from head to tail, but the tendency has been to reduce the number from the lower to the higher forms. Ribs, however, are not universal among vertebrates; many, including the frog, do not have them at all. Human beings have 12 pairs of ribs.

2. Visceral Skeleton

The visceral skeleton of very primitive fishes is a series of arches, of either cartilage or bone, embedded in the lateral wall and the floor of the pharynx, one of which is at the base of each gill. Because terrestrial vertebrates do not have gills, they also have very little visceral skeletal tissue. Of what remains in terrestrial vertebrates, some

69

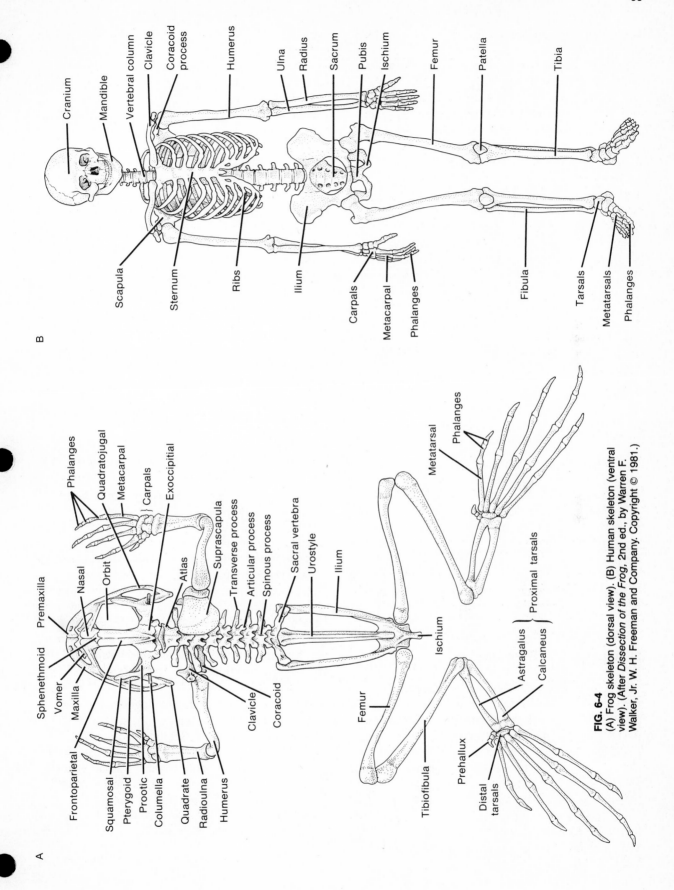

FIG. 6-4
(A) Frog skeleton (dorsal view). (B) Human skeleton (ventral view). (After *Dissection of the Frog*, 2nd ed., by Warren F. Walker, Jr. W. H. Freeman and Company. Copyright © 1981.)

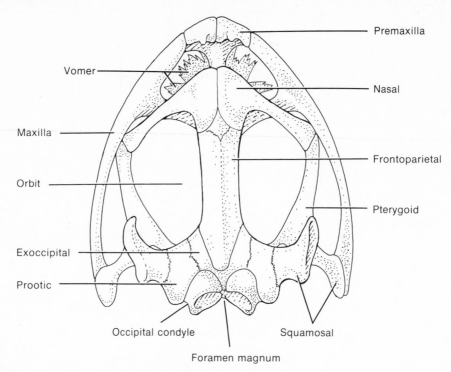

FIG. 6-5
Frog skull (dorsal view).

has become a part of the skull (the quadrate cartilage, Meckel's cartilage, and, in some vertebrates, the columella are of visceral origin), but most of it forms the **hyoid apparatus**, a plate of cartilage on the floor of the pharynx at the base of the tongue forming a sling that supports the tongue. Arches of cartilage and bone around the pharynx extend from the hyoid apparatus toward the skull. Some of the visceral skeleton is found in the walls of the glottis, the entrance to the larynx, but the amount is very small and difficult to observe.

3. Appendicular Skeleton

Most vertebrate animals have some form of paired appendages, which are supported by **pectoral** (shoulder) and **pelvic** (hip) **girdles**. Among vertebrates, there are many modifications in the girdles, limbs, and digits, which enable the animals to meet the requirements of their special modes of life. Whatever the modification, in forms higher than the fish, the girdles and appendages are built according to the same plan. Both the cartilaginous and bony fishes have pectoral and pelvic fins, which are supported by the pectoral and pelvic girdles, respectively. The single strong bones closest to the body in the legs of

a frog are the **humerus** in the anterior limb (Fig. 6-7) and the **femur** in the posterior (Fig. 6-8). Distal (away from the body) to these are two roughly parallel bones—the **radioulna** (a fusion of the **radius** and **ulna**) in the forelimb and the **tibiofibula** (a fusion of the **tibia** and **fibula**) in the hindlimb. The humerus is attached to the pectoral girdle at the **glenoid fossa** by means of ligaments. The bone passing dorsally, the **scapula,** has a broader extension folded toward the midline called the **suprascapula**. Ventrally, the posterior larger bone is the **coracoid**. The anterior smaller one is the **clavicle**. At the point of junction of the two clavicles is the sternum, which continues anteriorly as the **omosternum** and **episternum** and posteriorly as the **mesosternum** and **xiphisternum**.

The femur attaches to the pelvic girdle (Fig. 6-8) in a socket, the **acetabulum**, which is formed by the fusion of three bones, the **ilium**, **ischium**, and **pubis**. The feet and hands are built according to a common pattern, with a number of wrist (**carpal**) or ankle (**tarsal**) bones followed by a group of elongated hand (**metacarpal**) and foot (**metatarsal**) bones, and then the bones of the fingers or toes (**phalanges**). The two large tarsal bones joining the **tibiofibula** of the frog are called the **astragalus** (inside the foot).

A

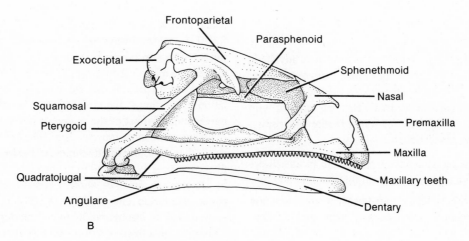

B

FIG. 6-6
Frog skull: (A) ventral view and (B) lateral view.

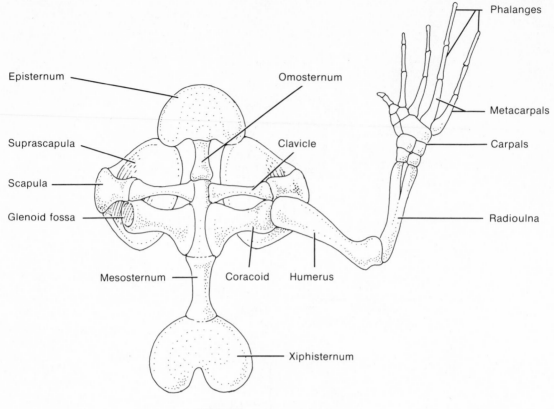

FIG. 6-7
Frog pectoral girdle (ventral view).

D. VERTEBRATE MUSCULATURE

1. Joints

Before studying the muscles of the frog, it is advisable to learn something about the joints between bones, because these joints allow the muscles to bend, twist, and turn the various parts of the body. Become familiar with the following classification of joints before proceeding with the muscle dissection.

Ball-and-socket joints allow movement in any direction, including rotation, as in the shoulder and hip.

Condyloid joints allow movement in any direction except rotation, as between metacarpals and phalanges.

Hinge joints allow bones to bend in only one direction, as in the knee, and between flat surfaces of bones, as between the vertebrae.

Plane joints allow sliding movements between flat surfaces of bones, as between the vertebrae.

Radial joints permit rotation of one bone on another, as between the proximal ends (ends nearest the humerus) of the radius and ulna.

2. Muscle Terminology

Much of a vertebrate's body consists of muscles, which function in several ways. They support the body by holding the bones in proper relationship to each other. They are responsible for the movement of the body as a whole, the passage of food down the digestive tract, the ventilation of the lungs, the circulation of the blood, and the movements of most of the materials in the body.

Each end of most muscles is attached to either a bone or another muscle. An attachment is **fleshy** if the muscle fibers are directly attached to the bone. Muscle fibers can be attached to bone or another muscle by a cordlike, connective-tissue **tendon** or by a broad, connective-tissue sheet called an **aponeurosis**. In contracting, one end of a muscle is in a fixed position, and the contraction causes the other end to move, pulling a bone or other structure toward the fixed end. The fixed end is the **origin** of the muscle, the other end is its **insertion**, and the part that lies between the two ends is its **belly**.

The action of a muscle is to cause a contraction, or shortening in length, so that the structures to which it is attached are brought together. Muscles are commonly arranged in opposing groups, with one muscle moving in one direction and an opposing muscle moving in the

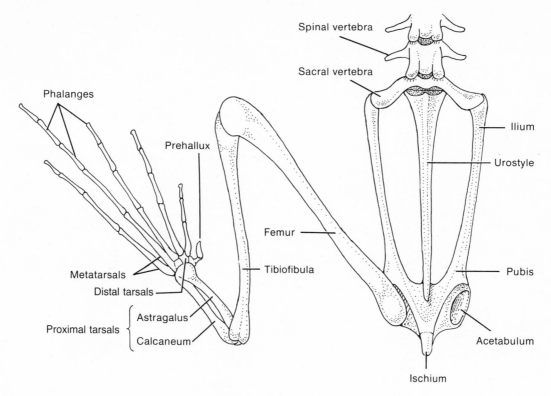

FIG. 6-8
Frog pelvic girdle (dorsal view).

opposite direction. The following list includes some of the common types of opposing muscles:

Flexors cause bending, or decrease in the angle, between two structures (e.g., the biceps muscle bends the forearm toward the upper arm).

Extensors straighten or extend a part of the body (e.g., the triceps muscle extends the forearm on the upper arm).

Adductors move a part towards the axis of the body (e.g., the latissimus dorsi muscle draws the arm back against the body).

Abductors move a part away from the axis of the body (e.g., the deltoid muscle draws the arm forward).

Depressors lower a part (e.g., the depressor mandibulae muscle moves the jaw down to open the mouth).

Levators elevate or raise a part (e.g., the masseter muscle raises the jaw to close the mouth).

Begin your dissection by cutting through the skin around the abdomen of the frog. Grasp the skin firmly, and pull it posteriorly over the legs, turning it inside out, until the abdomen and legs are completely free of skin.

As noted earlier, the skin of the frog is an important site for the exchange of gases between the blood and the environment; it therefore contains an intricate vascular system. It will be necessary to remove sheets of tough connective tissue, called **fascia**, from some parts of the body; this tissue binds certain groups of muscles together. Separate the muscles of a given part of the frog by carefully dissecting away connective tissue from between them. Do not try to cut muscles apart. Observe the direction of the groups of muscle fibers, and then separate the muscle from the adjacent muscles by using probing needles with blunt ends. The fibers of a given muscle, or major part of it, run in the same direction; those of an adjacent muscle run in a different direction.

3. Muscles of the Shoulder

The major muscles of the shoulder and forelimb can be identified by referring to Figs. 6-9 and 6-10. The **cucullaris**, the **dorsalis scapulae**, and the **latissimus dorsi** extend from the scapula, across the shoulder to the proximal end of the humerus (Fig. 6-9). All these muscles move the forelimb toward the body. On the ventral surface of the body, identify the **deltoid**, the **pectoralis**, and the

74

FIG. 6-9
Muscles of the frog as seen in a dorsal view: superficial mus-
cles (right side of drawing), deeper muscles (left side). (After
Dissection of the Frog, 2nd ed., by Warren F. Walker, Jr. W. H.
Freeman and Company. Copyright © 1981.)

FIG. 6-10
Ventral view of the muscles: (left side of drawing) superficial
muscles; (right side) deeper muscles. (After *Dissection of the
Frog,* 2nd ed., by Warren F. Walker, Jr. W. H. Freeman and
Company. Copyright © 1981.)

coracobrachialis muscles, which extend from the pectoral girdle to the humerus (Fig. 6-10). These three muscles move the forelimb away from the body. The **coracoradialis**, another ventral shoulder muscle, extends from the girdle to the radioulna and is the major flexor of the forearm. The **anconeus**, situated on the dorsal surface of the humerus, is the major extensor of the forearm.

4. Muscles of the Forearm

Using Fig. 6-9, locate the major group of muscles that extends the hand and digits. The muscles in this group are the **extensor carpi radialis**, the **abductor indicis longus**, the **extensor digitorum communis longus**, and the **extensor carpi ulnaris** (Fig. 6-9). The flexor muscles that bend the forearm toward the body are the **flexor carpi radialis**, the **flexor carpi ulnaris**, and the **palmaris longus** (Fig. 6-10).

5. Muscles of the Trunk

The **cutaneous abdominis** on the dorsal surface of the trunk and the **cutaneous pectoris** on the ventral surface extend from the abdominal wall to the skin. It is believed that the contraction of these two muscles compresses certain lymph sacs and thus helps to circulate lymph fluid.

The **longissimus dorsi** and **iliolumbaris**, located on the dorsal side of the trunk (Fig. 6-9) serve to flex and extend the vertebral column. Located behind these two muscles is the **coccygeoiliacus** muscle, which is attached at one end to the urostyle and at the other to the ilium bones. These three muscles are thought to extend the urostyle and pelvic girdle when the frog is making strong leaps.

The ventral body wall of the frog is largely supported by the **rectus abdominis** (Fig. 6-10). The rest of the abdominal wall is covered on the outside by an **external oblique muscle** and an inner **transverse muscle**, whose fibers run nearly perpendicular to each other. These muscles support and tense the abdomen.

6. Muscles of the Head

The **temporalis, pterygoideus,** and **masseter** muscles, located on the dorsal surface of the head (Fig. 6-9) elevate the mandible. The **depressor mandibulae** lowers the mandible, thereby opening the mouth. Extending transversely on the ventral surface of the head are the **mylohyoid** and **subhyoid** muscles, forming the ventral surface of the lower jaw. These muscles raise the floor of the

mouth and are therefore important in the swallowing and breathing movements of the mouth.

7. Muscles of the Thigh

Located on the anterior part of the thigh is the **triceps femoris** (Fig. 6-9), which extends the shank during jumping and swimming. The rest of the dorsal surface of the thigh is composed of the large **semimembranosus**, the **gracilis minor**, and a slender **iliofibularis** muscle (Fig. 6-9). The origins of all three of these muscles are on the bones of the pelvic girdle; their insertions are on the tibiofibula.

On the ventral surface of the thigh is the **sartorius** (Fig. 6-10); its origin is on the pubis and its insertion on the tibiofibula. This muscle flexes the thigh at the hip. The **adductor longus** and **adductor magnus** muscles lie on either side and partly beneath the sartorius. Their main function is to move the thigh toward the body. Lying posterior to the adductor magnus is the **gracilis major**, which flexes the knee and extends the thigh.

In order to observe the short muscles that extend from the pelvic girdle to the femur, it is first necessary to cut through some of the superficial thigh muscles as shown in Fig. 6-9. When this is done, you can identify the **gluteus** and **iliacus internus** (Fig. 6-9), which extend from the ilium bone of the pelvic girdle to the proximal end of the femur. These two muscles flex and rotate the thigh.

In order to observe the deep muscles on the ventral side of the thigh, cut the gracilis major, gracilis minor, and sartorius muscles as shown in Fig. 6-10. Locate the **pectineus** muscle between the adductor longus and adductor magnus. This muscle helps to move the thigh toward the body. Posterior to the adductor magnus is the **semitendinosus**, which acts both to reflect the shank and to extend the thigh.

8. Muscles of the Shank of the Hindlimb

The largest muscle of the shank is the **gastrocnemius**. This muscle arises by means of two large tendons from the distal end of the femur and ends in the Achilles tendon, which passes around the ankle and spreads into a sheet of connective tissue called the **plantar aponeurosis**. Its function is to flex the knee and toes. Anterior to the gastrocnemius, as viewed from the dorsal surface, are the **peroneus** and **tibialis anticus longus** muscles, both of which assist in foot extension.

From the ventral view of the shank, identify the **extensor cruris brevis** (Fig. 6-10), which inserts on the tibiofibula and is an extensor of the flank. The **tibialis pos-**

ticus, which arises from the shaft of the tibia and inserts on the astragalus bone of the foot, assists in foot extension. The **tibialis anticus brevis**, which arises from the distal part of the tibiofibula and inserts on the tarsal bones, is a flexor of the foot.

REFERENCES

Gilbert, S. G. 1965. *Pictorial Anatomy of the Frog*. University of Washington Press.

Romer, A. A. 1977. *The Vertebrate Body*. 5th ed. Holt/Saunders.

Underhill, R. A. 1980. *Laboratory Anatomy of the Frog*. 4th ed. Brown.

Young, J. A. 1962. *The Life of Vertebrates*. 2nd ed. Oxford University Press.

Vertebrate Anatomy:
Digestive, Respiratory, Circulatory, and Urogenital Systems

In this exercise, you will study the digestive, respiratory, circulatory, and urogenital systems of the frog as a representative vertebrate.

A. DIGESTIVE SYSTEM

1. Oral Cavity

Place a frog on its back, and with scissors make a small cut at the angle of the jaw on each side so that the jaws can be opened widely (Fig. 7-1). Rinse the oral cavity with cold water to remove any accumulation of mucus. The **oral (buccal) cavity** narrows into the **pharynx**, which connects to the **esophagus** (or gullet). Just anterior to the opening to the esophagus is the **glottis**, a short longitudinal slit in the floor of the pharynx (Fig. 7-2). The glottis opens for breathing but closes when food is being swallowed. Behind each eyeball and near the corners of the mouth are small openings to the **eustachian tubes**, which connect to the chamber of the middle ear

beneath the eardrum. In many frog species, the males have openings into two **vocal sacs** located at the posterior corners of the oral cavity. The vocal sacs are inflated to amplify the croaking of the male frog, especially during the breeding season.

Note the **maxillary teeth** on the margin of the upper jaw and the two patches of **vomerine teeth** on the roof of the mouth. Because the frog swallows its food whole, these teeth are not used for chewing but primarily to hold the food.

Lying on the floor of the oral cavity and attached to the mouth anteriorly is a large **tongue**. The forked posterior end of the tongue can be quickly thrust out of the mouth to capture food, scraping off a sticky substance secreted by glands in the roof of the mouth. This substance makes the prey adhere to the tongue when it is retracted into the mouth.

Near the vomerine teeth are two small openings, the **internal nares**, that lead to the **external nares** (nostrils) through which air passes to and from the oral cavity during respiration.

FIG. 7-1
Procedure for dissection of the frog mouth.

2. Body Cavity

Make a longitudinal incision (X–Y) just left of the mid-ventral line, and extend it from the pectoral to the pelvic girdle (Fig. 7-3). Cut through the layers of muscle forming the abdominal wall, and lift the wall up to expose the **ventral abdominal vein**. Carefully pull this blood vessel away from the midventral line, and cut it so that it can be pushed aside. Now make transverse incisions (A–B and A′–B′) through the skin and muscle just anterior to each hindleg and posterior to each foreleg. Continue the cuts to the back, turning the flaps of the body wall back and pinning them to a dissecting pan. Lift the pectoral girdle and cut through the bone to expose the cardiac cavity.

The body cavity, or **coelom**, in which the visceral organs are located, is completely lined by a shiny layer of epithelium, called **parietal peritoneum**. The epithelium covering the viscera is called **visceral peritoneum**. Membranes of this epithelium, the **mesenteries**, extend

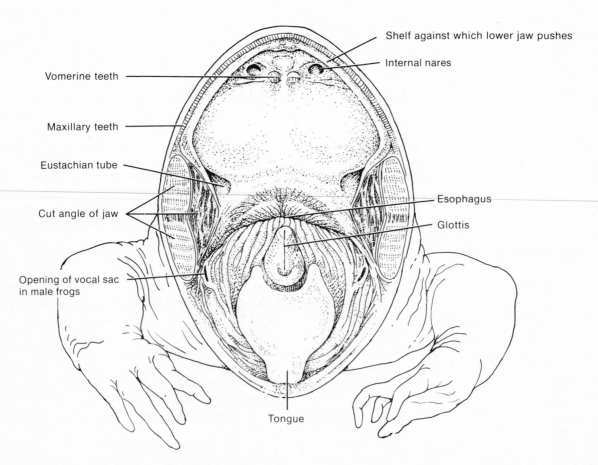

FIG. 7-2
Interior view of the buccopharyngeal cavity of a male frog. The angles of the jaw have been cut so that the mouth can be opened widely. (After *Dissection of the Frog,* 2nd ed., by Warren F. Walker, Jr. W. H. Freeman and Company. Copyright © 1981.)

from the dorsal body wall to the organs as well as between many of the organs. The coelom is a space that facilitates the expansion, contraction, and other functional movements of the internal organs, but these movements are limited by the mesenteries, which also provide pathways for blood vessels and nerves.

The coelom of the frog consists of two cavities: the **pleuroperitoneal cavity**, containing the lungs and most of the other viscera, and the **pericardial cavity**, containing the heart. The epithelial lining of the pericardial cavity is called the **pericardium**.

3. Visceral Organs

The **liver** is a large, trilobed organ occupying much of the anterior part of the body cavity (Fig. 7-4). Attached to its dorsal surface is a small, dark sac—the **gall bladder**. The **stomach** lies dorsal to the liver and to your right as you view the body cavity. The **lungs** also lie in the anterior part of the body cavity. Lift up the stomach and locate a small, dense, round structure—the **spleen**—on the left side of the mesentery supporting the intestine. The spleen is intimately related to the circulatory system, because in adult frogs it is the most important site for the production of both red and white blood cells. In the spleen, some blood cells are stored and senescent (aging) red cells are destroyed. It is also a major site for the production of antibodies (protein molecules produced in response to foreign organisms as a defense mechanism). The coiling **small intestine** leads from the posterior end of the stomach to the large intestine, or **colon**. The colon has a large anterior diameter but tapers posteriorly as it passes through the pelvis to enter the **cloaca**. The cloaca is the terminal part of the digestive tract; it also receives the urinary and genital ducts. The small, oval bodies in the male, one on each side of the mesentery supporting the intestine, are the **testes**. The fingerlike lobes attached to the testes or kidney are **fat bodies**. The **ovaries**, which are located in the same places in the female as the testes are in the male, vary greatly in size, depending on the female's reproductive state. Just before ovulation, they are filled with ripe eggs, taking up all the available space in the pleuroperitoneal cavity. Dorsal to each **gonad** (testis or ovary) is an elongated **kidney**. A long, coiled white tube—the **oviduct**—is lateral to each kidney in the female. Males may have a small vestigial oviduct. The bilobed sac lying ventral to the large intestine is the urinary **bladder**.

Connecting the pharynx to the stomach is a short **esophagus**. The stomach is a large, saclike organ in which food is stored and digested. Use a scalpel to cut it open longitudinally, and observe that its inner walls form longitudinal folds that help to grind the food. At the

FIG. 7-3
Procedure for dissection of the abdominal body wall.

posterior end of the stomach is the **pyloric sphincter**, which is able to contract to hold food in the stomach until it is partly digested.

The stomach connects to the slender, coiled small intestine where digested food is absorbed. Note that the intestine is held in place by a dorsal fold of the peritoneum. The intestine is divided into a short **duodenum**, curving upward to the liver, and a much-coiled **ileum**, leading into the **colon**, where water and ions are absorbed and undigested waste products (feces) are stored before elimination through the **cloacal opening**. Also emptying into the cloaca are the products of the kidneys and the reproductive organs.

Digestion is aided by secretions from the two largest digestive glands, the **liver** and **pancreas**. One of the functions of the liver is the production of bile, an alkaline secretion that aids in the digestion of fatty materials. Bile is stored in the gall bladder until food enters the intestine, at which time the bile is released through a **common bile duct** into the duodenum. Lying between the duodenum and the stomach is the other major digestive gland, the slender, irregular, and whitish pancreas. This gland secretes an alkaline digestive fluid that also empties into the common bile duct. The pancreas has microscopic clumps of endocrine tissue, the **islets of Langerhans**, which produce the hormones insulin and glucagon, which are essential for normal carbohydrate metabolism.

82

FIG. 7-4
Ventral view of the digestive tract and associated organs. The liver has been pulled forward and the pelvic region cut open. (After *Dissection of the Frog,* 2nd ed., by Warren F. Walker, Jr. W. H. Freeman and Company. Copyright © 1981.)

B. RESPIRATORY SYSTEM

The primary functions of the respiratory system are to supply the tissues with oxygen and to eliminate excess carbon dioxide. In the frog, such gas exchanges take place not only in the lungs (**pulmonary respiration**), but also through the skin (**cutaneous respiration**) and the epithelial lining of the mouth and pharynx (**buccopharyngeal respiration**).

In pulmonary respiration, air passes through the nostrils (external nares) into the nasal cavity and then through the internal nares into the oral cavity (Fig. 7-5). The external nares are then closed, the floor of the mouth is raised, and air is forced through the glottis into a short

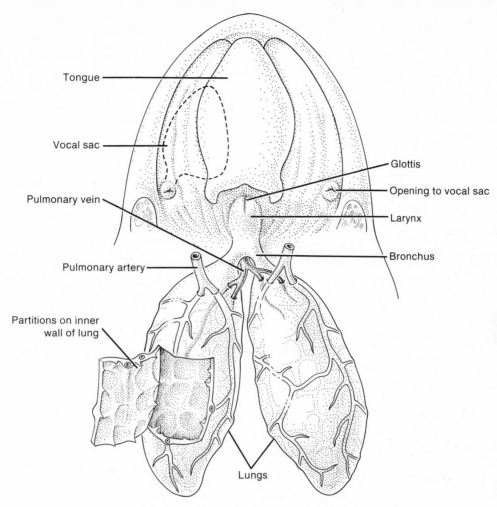

Tongue

Vocal sac

Pulmonary vein

Pulmonary artery

Partitions on inner
wall of lung

Glottis

Opening to vocal sac

Larynx

Bronchus

Lungs

FIG. 7-5
Dorsal view of floor of mouth and respiratory system.

tube, the **larynx**. The larynx is reinforced by cartilage and contains two elastic bands, the vocal cords, that vibrate and produce croaking sounds when air is forced vigorously from the lungs. The larynx is connected to the lungs by a very short tube, the **bronchus**. In most preserved specimens, the lungs tend to be contracted by the preservative. An idea of the true size of the lungs can be gained by inserting a small glass tube into the glottis of a recently killed frog and then blowing them up. Remove part of the lung, and slit it open to observe the network of partitions that divides the lung into many minute chambers called **alveoli**. These alveoli, with their blood capillaries, supply the extensive surface area necessary for gas exchange.

C. CIRCULATORY SYSTEM

The chief functions of the circulatory system are to transport (1) body fluids and nutrients to all of the cells and tissues; (2) oxygen and carbon dioxide between the respiratory organs and body tissues; (3) stored materials from place to place as needed; (4) organic wastes, water, and excess minerals to the excretory organs; (5) hormones from endocrine glands to the target organs; and (6) molecules (antibodies) and cells (leukocytes) of defense to areas in which they are needed.

The circulatory system of vertebrates includes a main pumping organ (the heart) and a system of vessels (arteries, veins, and capillaries) to conduct blood and lymph throughout the body.

1. Frog Heart

In order to study the structure of the frog heart, you will first have to cut away the enveloping **pericardium**. Using Fig. 7-6, identify the thin-walled left and right **auricles** and the thick-walled **ventricle**.

The frog heart is different from that of most other vertebrates because it has only one ventricle instead of two.

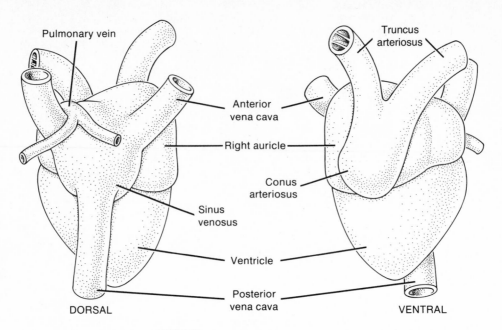

FIG. 7-6
Dorsal and ventral views of frog heart.

Because the walls of the auricles are thinner than that of the ventricle, the blood within them makes them look darker. Arising from the base of the ventricle on its ventral side is a stout, cylindrical vessel, the **conus arteriosus**. This vessel receives blood from the ventricle and carries it anteriorly to a pair of large arteries (**trunci arteriosi**), which distribute the blood to the lungs and body. Lift up the heart and locate a triangular **sinus venosus**, a thin-walled sac lying in the dorsal region of the heart. It is formed by three large veins. At its posterior apex, the sinus venosus receives the **posterior vena cava** and, at the two anterior apices, the left and right **anterior venae cavae**. Locate the **pulmonary veins**, which drain the lungs and enter the left atrium directly.

The action of the heart can be studied by examining a pithed frog that has been dissected to expose the beating heart. As you observe the heart, note that the sinus venosus contracts first and sends the nonoxygenated venous blood into the right auricle. Oxygenated blood from the lungs passes into the left auricle via the pulmonary veins. Then both auricles contract and pump their contents into the ventricle. Contraction of the ventricle and conus arteriosus next drives the blood to the lungs and the rest of the body. The blood is prevented from flowing back into the heart by means of the valves shown in Fig. 7-7. Because these valves are difficult to find in a dissection of the frog heart, you will next study the sheep heart, which is approximately the size of a human heart.

2. Sheep Heart

The sheep heart lies in a tough, double-walled membranous sac, the **pericardium**. The inner surface of the pericardium is a membrane that faces the outer surface, or **epicardium**, of the heart. The pericardial space between these facing membranes contains a serous pericardial fluid. In removing the pericardium, observe that it is attached only around the base of the heart, where the large vessels emerge. The cavities of the heart are lined with **endocardium**, which is the same type of tissue as the endothelium lining all of the blood vessels. Between the epicardium and endocardium is the bulk of the heart tissue—the **myocardium**, or heart musculature.

The right and left sides of the heart can be identified in two ways: (1) the pointed end, or **apex**, is entirely a part of the left ventricle, and the right and left divisions are indicated superficially by a diagonal furrow containing the coronary vessels; (2) the left ventricle is firm and muscular to the touch, whereas the right ventricle feels soft and flabby. The auricles look like ears projecting from the base of the heart. The cavity within each auricle is referred to as an **atrium**, a reception chamber for incoming blood.

1. Make a long incision through the **right auricle** in line with the superior vena cava. Lift the edges of the flaps, and observe the wide mouths of the great veins

Septum separating carotid and
systemic channels in truncus arteriosus

Carotid arch

Right auricle

Opening to left systemic arch

Systemic arch

Opening to right
systemic arch

Openings to
carotid arches

Left auricle

Entrance of pulmonary veins

Anterior vena cava

Pulmocutaneous
arch

Truncus arteriosus

Entrance to both pulmo-
cutaneous arches

Pulmonary vein

Interatrial septum

Spiral valve in conus arteriosus

Entrance from sinus venosus

Semilunar valves

Dorsal atrioventricular valve

Ventricle

Posterior vena cava

FIG. 7-7
Longitudinal section of a frog heart. The position of the sinus
venosus on the dorsal surface of the heart is shown by broken
lines. (After *Dissection of the Frog*, 2nd ed., by Warren F.
Walker, Jr. W. H. Freeman and Company. Copyright © 1981.)

(**superior** and **inferior venae cavae**) as they enter the atrium (Fig. 7-8). Using scissors, carry the incision downward toward the ventricle, and determine the relationship between the two cavities. Note the irregular bands of muscle lining the interior of the auricular wall, the **pectinate muscles**. Find the **coronary sinus**, which receives venous blood directly from the heart musculature and enters the auricle. Note that the partition separating the auricles is membranous rather than muscular. Locate the thinnest part of the wall between the two auricles.

This area is the **fossa ovalis**, an oval depression marking the place in fetal circulation through which blood was carried directly to the left side of the heart and thus bypassed the pulmonary circuit.

2. Carry the incision from the right auricle in a straight line through the lateral wall of the **right ventricle**. Note the three rounded flaps of membranous tissue suspended into the ventricle and held in place by tendinous cords. These flaps constitute the **tricuspid valve**. Study in detail its position, structural character, and attachments. If nec-

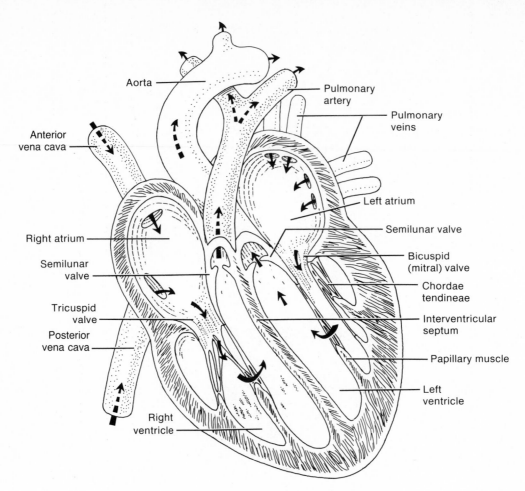

FIG. 7-8
Schematic longitudinal section of the mammalian heart.

essary, wash out both cavities. Note that pointed columns of ventricular muscle (**papillary muscles**) are continuous with the wall of the ventricle and with the strong fibrous cords (**chordae tendineae**) that extend to the edges of the cusps, or flaps, of the valve. Observe the heavy muscular ridges within the ventricle, the **columnae carneae**. Find the exit of blood from the right ventricle, considering the tricuspid valve to be closed between auricle and ventricle. Carry an incision upward through the wall of this exit (**pulmonary artery**), and note that the mouth of the artery is surrounded by three membranous pockets (the pulmonary **semilunar valves**).

3. Open the **left auricle** in the same manner as the right one. Before cutting down through the ventricle, push your finger from the auricle into the ventricles and distend the auriculoventricular opening. Determine the number of openings draining into the auricle from the lungs. These openings are the mouths of **pulmonary veins**.

4. On the **left ventricle**, make an incision to expose the cavity. Study the details of the **mitral**, or **bicuspid** (two-part), **valve** between this auricle and ventricle. Explore the thickness of the septum between the two ventricles. Probe with your finger to find the outlet of the ventricle into the aorta. Open the aorta to expose its semilunar valve. Find the openings of the two coronary arteries just above the valve—that is, within the pockets. Trace these to the walls of the heart. Observe the tough ligamentous connection, which is usually covered with a conspicuous pad of fat, between the pulmonary artery and aorta. This is a remnant of the vessel that connected the pulmonary artery and aorta in the embryo. If this vessel remains open in human beings after birth, oxygenated and unoxygenated blood mix, leading to a condition commonly referred to as "blue baby."

In studying the dissected heart, emphasis should be placed on the structural arrangement of the parts and their

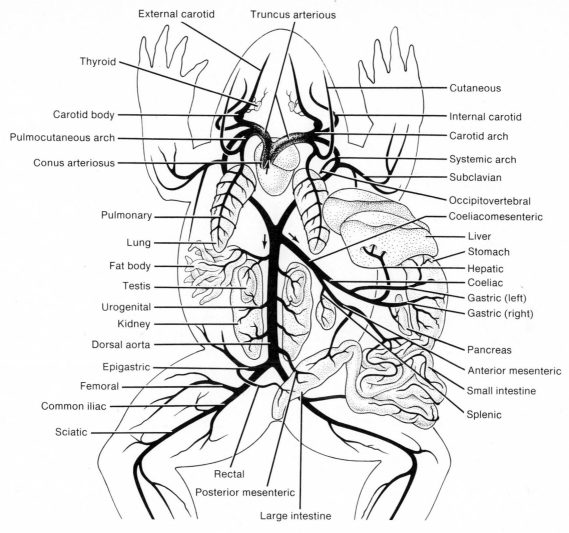

FIG. 7-9
Arterial system of the frog.

functional continuity. The mammalian heart is essentially a double pump equipped with specially designed valves. It is the propelling force for two circuits of blood that do not mix in the heart. The circuit from the heart to the lungs and back is the **pulmonary circuit**, and the circuit from the heart to all the body tissues and back is the **systemic circuit**. These circuits act concurrently and interdependently in that no more blood can be sent through the pulmonary circuit than is delivered to it by the systemic circuit.

3. Frog Arterial System

The arterial system consists of vessels that carry blood away from the heart to the capillaries and tissues. These vessels have firm, elastic walls that do not collapse when empty.

The conus arteriosus of the heart divides into two branches; each branch is a **truncus arteriosus** and gives rise to three arteries (Fig. 7-9). The first of the three arteries is the **pulmocutaneous arch**, which divides into the **pulmonary artery** going to the lung and the **cutaneous artery** to the skin. Note that this artery and its branches carry nonoxygenated blood.

The next artery to come off each truncus arteriosus is the **carotid arch**, which divides into the **external carotid**, leading to the ventral part of the head and the tongue, and the **internal carotid**, leading to the dorsal part of the head. The most highly oxygenated blood coming from the heart goes to the carotid arches. Note the

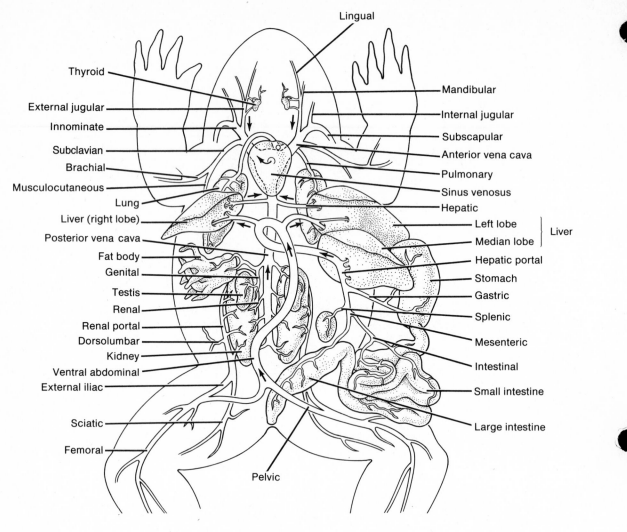

FIG. 7-10
Venous system of the frog.

small oval swellings, the **carotid bodies**, at the junctions of the two carotids. It is believed that these glands help to regulate blood pressure and blood flow.

The final blood vessel to come off each truncus arteriosus is the **systemic (aortic) arch**. The two systemic arches bend dorsally around the esophagus and unite to form the large **dorsal aorta**. Before this union, several blood vessels are given off. The anterior one is the **occipitovertebral**, which divides into the **occipital**, leading to the skull, and the **vertebral**, leading to the vertebral column. The next blood vessel coming off the systemic arch is the **subclavian artery**, which gives off branches to the shoulder region and the forelimbs.

The first vessel arising from the aorta, near the junction of the systemic arches, is the **coeliacomesenteric artery**. This vessel divides into two branches, the **coeliac** and **anterior mesenteric arteries**. The coeliac further divides into the **hepatic artery**, going to the liver, and the **gastric**

arteries, supplying the stomach. The mesenteric supplies branches to the spleen (**splenic**) and the large and small intestines. The dorsal aorta next gives off from four to six **urogenital** arteries to the kidneys, gonads, and fat bodies. The **posterior mesenteric artery** arises from the dorsal aorta to supply the colon. Next, the aorta divides into two **common iliac arteries**, which supply the hindlimbs. As you trace these vessels down the legs, you can observe the **epigastric arteries**, which extend to the urinary bladder, large intestine, and body wall; the **femorals**, which supply the hip and outer part of the thigh; and the **sciatics**, which serve the thigh, shank, and foot.

4. Frog Venous System

The vertebrate venous system, which consists of the vessels that carry blood back toward the heart, is somewhat

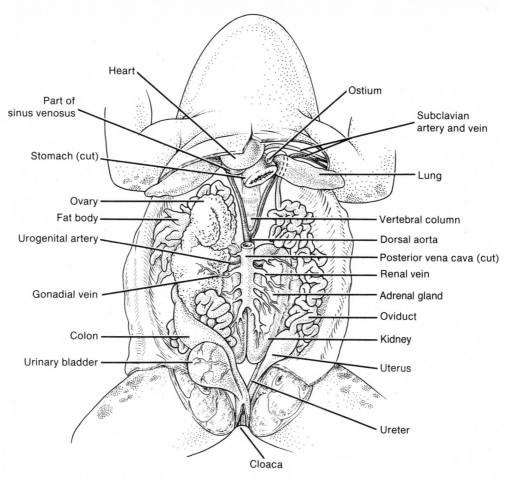

FIG. 7-11
Ventral view of the female urogenital system. One ovary and one fat body have been removed. Because this drawing is based on a specimen taken in midsummer, the ovaries and fat bodies have not reached their full size. (After *Dissection of the Frog*, 2nd ed., by Warren F. Walker, Jr. W. H. Freeman and Company. Copyright © 1981.)

more complex than the arterial system. Anteriorly, the head, forelimbs, and skin are drained by a pair of **anterior venae cavae**, which enter the heart by way of the sinus venosus (Fig. 7-10). Each anterior vena cava receives blood from three veins. The first of these is the **external jugular**, which collects blood from the tongue and floor of the mouth (**lingual**) and from the lower jaw (**mandibular**). The next veins draining into the anterior venae cavae are the **innominates**, which collect blood from the head by means of the **internal jugulars** and from the shoulder and back of the forelimb by means of the **subscapular veins**. The third and largest veins draining into the anterior venae cavae are the **subclavians**, which collect blood from the forelimbs by means of the **brachial veins** and from the muscles and skin on the lateral and dorsal part of the head and trunk by means of the **musculocutaneous veins**.

The single **posterior vena cava** enters the sinus venosus posteriorly and collects blood from the testes or ovaries through the **genital vein**, from the kidneys through from four to six pairs of **renal veins**, and from the liver by means of a pair of **hepatic veins**.

Veins that do not pass from organs or tissues directly to the heart but instead enter another organ and subdivide within it to join its capillary system, are termed **portal veins**. A system of double capillary veins is called a **portal system**. In the frog, there are two such portal systems, the **renal** and the **hepatic portal systems**. The renal portal system is found only among lower vertebrates.

The renal portal system consists of a **renal portal vein**, which receives blood from the hindlimbs by means of the **sciatic** and **femoral veins** and from the body wall by means of the **dorsolumbar**. The renal portal vein carries blood to the dorsal border of the kidney.

The hepatic portal system consists of a large number of veins that carry blood into the liver from the stomach, intestine, spleen, and pancreas. Such blood is heavily laden with recently digested food products absorbed by these organs. As this blood passes through the liver before entering the main circulation, food products (glycogen

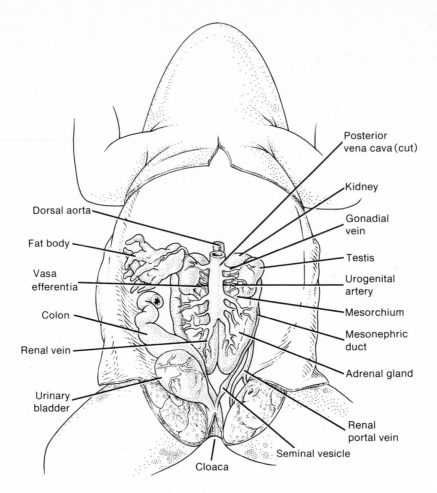

FIG. 7-12
Ventral view of the urogenital system of a male frog. One fat body has been removed. (After *Dissection of the Frog,* 2nd ed., by Warren F. Walker, Jr. W. H. Freeman and Company. Copyright © 1981.)

and glucose) are removed and stored and other substances are added to the blood. The main vein draining into the kidney is the **hepatic portal vein**, which collects blood from the spleen via the **splenic vein**, from the stomach via the **gastric vein**, and from the intestine via the **intestinal vein**.

D. UROGENITAL SYSTEM

Because the urinary and reproductive system of the frog are closely connected, they are termed the *urogenital system*.

1. Urinary System

The main organs of the urinary system are two elongate, reddish brown **kidneys** that lie close together on the dorsal wall at the posterior end of the body cavity. The urine from each kidney is drained by a **ureter**, which can be seen along the kidney's lateral edge. The ureters empty into the dorsal surface of the cloaca, and the urine must flow across the cloaca to enter the bilobed **urinary bladder**, which is attached to its ventral surface. The yellow or orange stripe running along the ventral side of each kidney is an adrenal gland, which secretes adrenalin into the blood. This hormone increases the heart rate, raises blood sugar levels, and helps the body react to stress conditions.

2. Female Reproductive System

The **ovaries** in most frogs are very conspicuous, occupying much of the body cavity. However, they vary greatly in size according to the season of the year. They are largest during the fall and winter, when they are filled with thousands of ripe eggs and smallest after ovulation in the spring.

In order to identify the rest of the female reproductive system, dissect out one of the ovaries. Using Fig. 7-11, locate the **oviduct**, a highly looped duct extending forward to the anterior end of the body cavity. At the end of the oviduct is a funnel-shaped **ostium**. In the spring, eggs are released from the ovary into the body cavity and are carried to the ostium by currents created by movement of the cilia of the coelomic epithelium. The posterior ends of the oviducts are enlarged to form the **uteri**, whose entrance to the cloaca is on its dorsal surface next to that of the ureters.

3. Male Reproductive System

Using a male specimen, locate the two oval, yellowish **testes**, each suspended from the dorsal abdominal wall by a mesentery (Fig. 7-12). Nearby are the bright yellow, finger-shaped masses of the **fat bodies**. These fat bodies are largest during the fall of the year. Some of the food stored in them is used during hibernation, and the rest is absorbed during the highly active spring breeding season.

Lift up one of the testes, and locate the **vasa efferentia**, the fine, threadlike tubes that connect the testes to the kidneys. Sperm produced by the testes are carried to the kidneys via the vasa efferentia and from the kidneys to the cloaca via the ureters, which also serve as the urinary ducts. It is not uncommon to find vestigial oviducts (**mesonephric ducts**) alongside the kidneys in male leopard frogs; these ducts should not be mistaken for the ureters.

REFERENCES

Gilbert, S. G. 1965. *Pictorial Anatomy of the Frog*. University of Washington Press.

Griffin, D. R. 1970. *Animal Structure and Function*. 2nd ed. Holt, Rinehart and Winston.

Romer, A. A. 1977. *The Vertebrate Body*. 5th ed. Holt/Saunders.

Underhill, R. A. 1980. *Laboratory Anatomy of the Frog*. 4th ed. Brown.

Walker, W. F., Jr. 1981. *Dissection of the Frog*. 2nd ed. W. H. Freeman and Company.

Wiggers, C. J. 1957. The Heart. *Scientific American* 196(5): 74–87 (Offprint 62). *Scientific American* Offprints are available from W. H. Freeman and Company, 660 Market Street, San Francisco 94104, and 58 Kings Road, Reading RG1 3AA, England. Please order by number.

Young, J. A. 1962. *The Life of Vertebrates*. 2nd ed. Oxford University Press.

Movement of Materials Through Cell Membranes

To perform their functions, cells must maintain a steady state in the midst of an ever-changing environment. This constancy is maintained by the regulation of the movement of materials into and out of the cell. To achieve this control, cells are bounded by a delicate membrane that can distinguish between different substances, slowing down the movement of some while allowing others to pass through. Because not all substances penetrate the membrane equally well, the membrane is said to be **differentially permeable**.

The external and internal environment of cells is an aqueous solution of dissolved inorganic and organic molecules. Movement of these molecules, both in the solution and through the cell membrane, is by a physical process called **diffusion**—a spontaneous process by which molecules move from a region in which they are highly concentrated to a region in which their concentration is lower.

As an example of diffusion, consider a colored dye dissolved in water. If a drop of the dye solution is placed in the water, it will soon become dispersed throughout the water. Ultimately, the dye molecules become equally distributed as a result of the random movements and kinetic energy of the solute and solvent molecules. This type of diffusion is called **passive diffusion** because movement is caused by the kinetic energy of the diffusing molecules. No outside energy is required for passive diffusion to occur.

In contrast, **active transport** is a type of diffusion in which solute molecules may move *against a concentration gradient*. For example, it has been shown that human erythrocytes have almost 30 times more potassium than the surrounding blood plasma. These cells accumulate potassium by an active process that requires energy.

Another kind of diffusion that occurs in biological systems is **osmosis**. Simply defined, osmosis is the diffusion of water through a differentially permeable membrane from a region in which it is highly concentrated to a region in which its concentration is lower. This phenomenon is diagrammatically shown below:

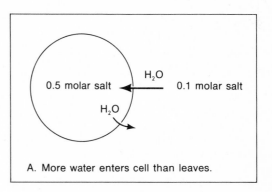

A. More water enters cell than leaves.

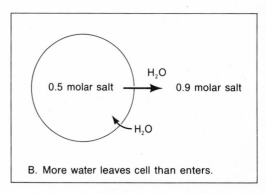

B. More water leaves cell than enters.

94

Observations
Conclusions

FIG. 8-1
Apparatus for studying gas diffusion.

Diffusion and osmosis, although basically phenomena resulting from the kinetic activity of molecules, are affected by a number of other factors such as temperature, the physical nature of the medium in which diffusion is occurring, the molecular weight of the diffusing substance, the lipoid solubility of the solute, and so forth. In this study, you will become familiar with diffusion and osmosis and examine some of the factors regulating these processes.

A. DIFFUSION

The kinetic energy of molecules causes them to move from regions in which their concentration is high to regions in which it is lower until they become uniformly distributed throughout the space available to them. Thus, a gas set free in a room is in time equally distributed throughout the room. A crystal of salt put into a glass of water dissolves, and the molecules of which it is composed become uniformly distributed throughout the water. This movement of gases and dissolved substances from a region of high concentration to one of low concentration is termed *diffusion*. Diffusion can thus be defined as *the net movement of the molecules of a substance, under their own kinetic energy, from a region of greater to one of lesser molecular activity of that particular substance*. The rate at which particles will diffuse

depends on several factors, such as their size, their concentration, and the permeability of the dispersion medium.

1. Diffusion of a Gas in a Gas

A striking demonstration of diffusion is the movement of gases through air. An apparatus to demonstrate gas diffusion is shown in Fig. 8-1.

Saturate a piece of cotton on one side with ammonium hydroxide (NH_4OH). Saturate another piece of cotton with hydrochloric acid (HCl). (CAUTION: *Handle chemicals carefully*. Open only *one* reagent bottle at a time.) Place the pieces of cotton *simultaneously* in opposite ends of the glass tubing as shown in Fig. 8-1. Why simultaneously?

_____

_____

Ammonium hydroxide and hydrochloric acid react to form ammonium chloride (NH_4Cl, a cloudy, white precipitate) and water. The equation for this reaction is as follows:

$$NH_4OH + HCl \rightarrow NH_4Cl + H_2O$$

What do you expect will happen when these two gases meet in the tube?

_____

_____

_____

The molecular weights of the ammonium (NH_4^+) and chlorine (Cl^-) ions are 18 and 35.5, respectively. At which end of the tube does the reaction occur?

_____

What, if any, relationship is there between the molecular weights of these gases and their rates of diffusion?

_____

_____

_____

_____

2. Diffusion of a Liquid in a Solid

The procedure used in this study is a modification of a rather simple but most useful and informative technique used to characterize the complex relationships between antigens and antibodies. This technique has widespread clinical application, although it is being replaced by more sensitive procedures.

Basically, the procedure consists of pouring agar, a gellike material obtained from certain seaweeds, into a petri dish and then punching circular wells close to one another in the gel. The liquid substances that are to be characterized are poured into the wells and then allowed to diffuse radially until they meet and react to form a line of precipitate. In this study, you will use this procedure, called the **Ouchterlony test**, to study the effect of molecular weight on diffusion.

Your instructor will give you a disposable petri dish containing agar (Fig. 8-2A). Using a No. 5 cork borer, punch four holes in the agar as shown in Fig. 8-2B and C. Fill each of the holes uniformly with a small amount of 1 N solutions of sodium chloride (NaCl), potassium bromide (KBr), potassium ferricyanide ($K_3Fe[Cn]_6$), or silver nitrate ($AgNo_3$). Periodically examine the petri dishes, and record your observations in Fig. 8-3. The approximate molecular weights of each of the migrating groups formed when these substances are placed in solu-

tion are: chloride anion (Cl), 35; bromide anion (Br), 80; ferricyanide anion ($Fe[CN]_6$), 212; nitrate anion (NO_3), 124.

From this study, what can you conclude about the relationship between the rate of diffusion of a molecule and its molecular weight?

_____

_____

_____

B. MEASURING THE RATE OF OSMOSIS

Each group of students will be given five dialysis bags, which will function as artificial, differentially permeable membranes. Each bag should be tied at one end by folding the end over and tying with a thread (Fig. 8-4). Fill these bags as follows:

Bag 1. 15 ml of tap water

Bag 2. 15 ml of 20% sucrose solution

Bag 3. 15 ml of 40% sucrose solution

Bag 4. 15 ml of 60% sucrose solution

Bag 5. 15 ml of tap water

As each bag is filled, remove the air by gently squeezing the bottom end of the bag to bring the liquid to the top of it. Press the sides of the bag together so that air does not reenter. Fold the end of the bag over about 2 inches (5 cm), and tie securely with a thread. Weigh each bag separately to the nearest 0.5 g, and record the weights in Table 8-1, at zero time.

Place Bags 1, 2, 3, and 4 in separate beakers of water, and place Bag 5 in a beaker of 60% sucrose solution.

TABLE 8-1
Osmosis data.

Time (minutes)	Weight of bags (grams)				
	1	2	3	4	5
0					
15					
30					
45					
60					
75					

96

A. Agar is poured into disposable Petri dish to a depth of 6 mm. Cover and allow agar to cool and solidify.

B. Punch four holes in agar by using a No. 5 cork borer. Remove each agar plug from borer before making another hole.

C.

AgNO$_3$

15 mm

15 mm

NaCl

15 mm

K$_3$Fe(CN)$_6$

KBr

D. Obtain bottles of the following solutions.

AgNO$_3$

NaCl

KBr

K$_3$Fe(CN)$_6$

Silver nitrate

Sodium chloride

Potassium bromide

Potassium ferricyanide

E. Add several drops of each solution to separate holes. Do not allow them to overflow.

AgNO$_3$

NaCl

K$_3$Fe(CN)$_6$

KBr

FIG. 8-2
Procedure for determining the effect of molecular weight on diffusion.

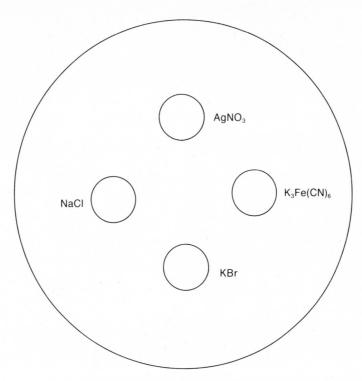

FIG. 8-3
Effects of molecular weight on diffusion.

At 15-minute intervals (i.e., after 15, 30, 45, 60, and 75 minutes) remove the bags from the beakers, carefully wipe off all excess water, and again weigh each bag separately. Record the data in Table 8-1. Plot the changes in weight of each bag against time in Fig. 8-5. What relationship (if any) is there between the concentration of sucrose and the rate of osmosis? How do you account for any differences observed?

_____

_____

_____

_____

_____

_____

C. OTHER FACTORS AFFECTING THE MOVEMENT OF MATERIALS THROUGH CELL MEMBRANES

In Parts A and B of this exercise, you examined the effects of molecular weight and concentration of diffusing molecules on diffusion and osmosis. In this study, you will determine whether the movement through cell membranes of substances that ionize (**electrolytes**) or of substances that are soluble in lipids is enhanced by these properties.

Red blood cells can be conveniently used to illustrate some of the factors that affect the osmotic relations of the living cell. The membrane of a red blood cell is freely permeable to water but differentially permeable to most other substances. A red blood cell increases in volume as substances such as water and dissolved solutes enter it, but it does not increase indefinitely. Instead, when it reaches a limited size, it ruptures and its hemoglobin diffuses out of the cell, leaving only the membrane (**ghost**) behind. This phenomenon is called **hemolysis**.

Dilute suspensions of red blood cells transmit very little light, but, if the cells are hemolyzed, the solution becomes transparent. The rate at which a dilute red blood cell suspension becomes transparent in solutions contain-

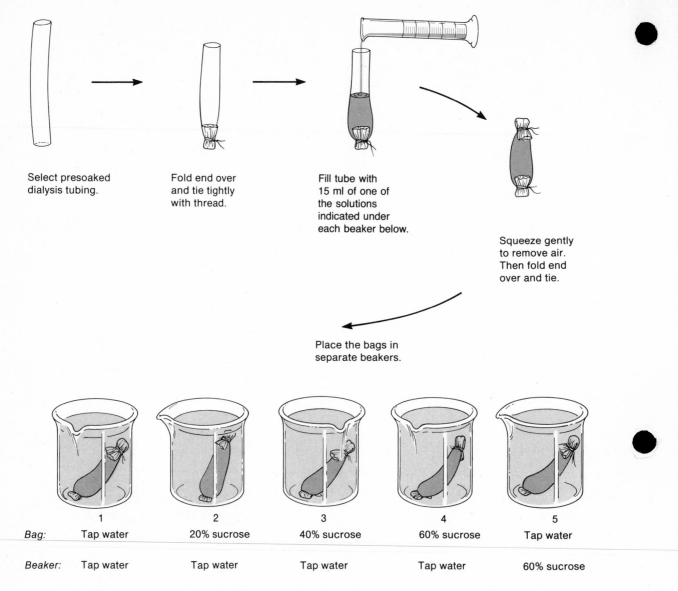

Select presoaked
dialysis tubing.

Fold end over
and tie tightly
with thread.

Fill tube with
15 ml of one of
the solutions
indicated under
each beaker below.

Squeeze gently
to remove air.
Then fold end
over and tie.

Place the bags in
separate beakers.

	1	2	3	4	5
Bag:	Tap water	20% sucrose	40% sucrose	60% sucrose	Tap water
Beaker:	Tap water	Tap water	Tap water	Tap water	60% sucrose

FIG. 8-4
Procedure for measuring rate of osmosis.

ing different kinds of molecules can be used as a measure of the rate at which such molecules enter the cell.

1. Effect of Concentration of Electrolytes and Nonelectrolytes on the Permeability of Cell Membranes

In this experiment, you will determine the effect of electrolytes and nonelectrolytes on the permeability of red blood cells.

Set up two rows of seven test tubes each, one row for glucose solutions and the other for sodium chloride (NaCl) solutions. To each tube, add 2 ml of the molar solution of glucose or of NaCl given in Table 8-2. To each tube, add two drops of a red blood cell suspension and mix immediately (Fig. 8-6). Set the tubes aside for 15 or 20 minutes, and then indicate in Table 8-2 the tubes in which hemolysis has occurred. (*Note:* Assume that the solution in the test tube *immediately preceding* the tube in which hemolysis has occurred is isotonic to the red blood cells.) Which concentrations of NaCl and glucose are *closest* to being isotonic with the red blood cells?

_____

_____

FIG. 8-5
Osmosis data.

A. Add blood cell suspension
to test tubes containing
substances being tested.

B. Mix by holding your thumb
over the opening and inverting the tube once or twice.

C. Hold each tube flat against a
sheet of printed paper. The time
it takes for the print to become
plainly readable is the time it
takes for hemolysis to occur.

FIG. 8-6
Procedure for determining hemolysis time.

Although the percentage concentration of the solutions of nonelectrolytes (i.e., substances that do not ionize) that fail to hemolyze may be quite different, they are
found to have approximately the same molar concentration (i.e., they have the same number of molecules per
liter). Thus solutions having the same number of molecules per liter show, by hemolysis, the same osmotic pressure. If, however, NaCl or any other electrolyte to which
the cell membrane is comparatively impermeable is used,
hemolysis occurs at much lower concentrations because
it has been shown that every ion in a solution exerts the
same osmotic pressure that would be produced by a molecule. For example, if an $M/5.5$ (i.e., $1/5.5 \ M$) sugar
solution is isotonic with an $M/10.3$ potassium chloride
(KCl) solution, we find that the sugar is 1.87 times as
concentrated as the KCl ($M/5.5 \div M/10.3 = 1.87$). In
other words, 100 molecules of KCl exert as much osmotic
pressure as 187 molecules of sugar. The ratio of the concentration of a nonelectrolyte to that of an electrolyte
having the same osmotic pressure is called the **isotonic
coefficient**. Thus, if the isotonic coefficient of a KCl
solution is 1.87, it behaves as if 87% of its molecules
were dissociated. In other words, out of every 100 molecules, 87 seem to have separated into two ions, so that
there is a total of 187 particles capable of exerting osmotic
pressure; this is equal to 187 sugar molecules in an
$M/5.5$ sugar solution.

The isotonic coefficient (i) of NaCl is given by the
formula

$$i = \frac{\text{isotonic molar concentration of glucose}}{\text{isotonic molar concentration of NaCl}}$$

Using your hemolysis data, calculate i and account for
the difference in isotonic concentrations of glucose and
NaCl.

_____

_____

With the same data, it is possible to calculate the proportion of molecules of NaCl that are dissociated, using
the following formula:

$$i = 1 + (k - 1)a$$

in which i is the isotonic coefficient of NaCl, k is the
number of ions from each molecule of the salt, and a is
the degree of dissociation. Calculate the degree of dissociation (a) for NaCl in your experiment.

TABLE 8-2
Determination of isotonic molar concentrations of glucose and sodium chloride.

Hemolysis solutions	Tube number and molarity						
	1 $M/6 = \frac{1}{6}M$	2 $M/8$	3 $M/10$	4 $M/12$	5 $M/14$	6 $M/16$	7 $M/18$
	(Indicate the occurrence of hemolysis by X)						
Glucose							
Sodium chloride							

TABLE 8-3
Effect of partition coefficient on the ability of materials to enter cells.

Compound	Formula	Partition coefficient	Hemolysis time (seconds)
3 M methyl alcohol	CH_3OH	0.010	
3 M ethyl alcohol	C_2H_5OH	0.036	
3 M propyl alcohol	C_3H_7OH	0.156	

2. Effect of Lipoid Solubility on the Permeability of Cell Membranes

Nonpolar compounds are those in which electrons are equally shared by the two atoms forming a bond, as in the paraffins, olefins, and cyclic compounds. These types of compounds are readily soluble in fats or fat solvents but have little solubility in water. The ratio of the solubility of such a compound in fat solvents in relation to its solubility in water is called the **partition (or distribution) coefficient**.

Add two drops of a suspension of red blood cells to each of three test tubes containing 2 ml of methyl, ethyl, and propyl alcohol, respectively (refer to Fig. 8-6). Mix the contents of each of the tubes, and then determine the hemolysis time for each solution.

Record your data in Table 8-3. Using the left ordinate, plot hemolysis time against length of carbon chain (1 for methyl alcohol, 2 for ethyl alcohol, 3 for propyl alcohol) in Fig. 8-7. Using the right ordinate, plot hemolysis time against the partition coefficient for these alcohols.

From these data, what can you conclude about the effect of the length of the carbon chain on the permeability of red blood cell membranes?

What is there about the chemical makeup of the cell membrane that supports the data you obtained?

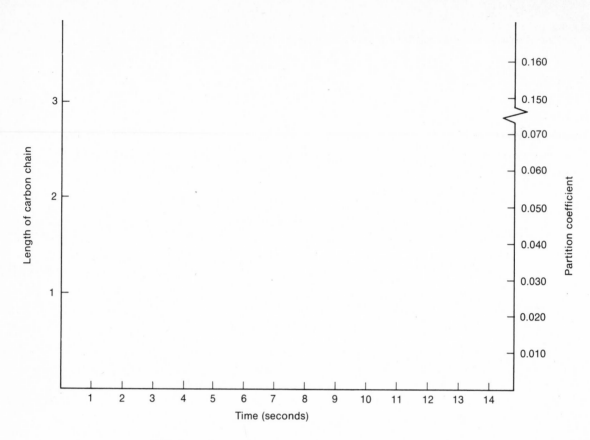

FIG. 8-7
Effect of lipoid solubility on the permeability of cell membranes.

REFERENCES

Capaldi, R. A. 1974. A Dynamic Model of Cell Membranes. *Scientific American* 230(3):26–33 (Offprint 1292). *Scientific American* Offprints are available from W. H. Freeman and Company, 660 Market Street, San Francisco 94104, and 58 Kings Road, Reading RG1 3AA, England. Please order by number.

DeRobertis, E. D. P., F. A. Saez, and E. M. F. DeRobertis. 1980. *Cell Biology*. 7th ed. Holt.

Giese, A. C. 1979. *Cell Physiology*. 5th ed. Holt/Saunders.

Holter, H. 1961. How Things Get into Cells. *Scientific American* 205(3):167–180 (Offprint 96).

Loewy, A. G., and P. Siekevitz. 1969. *Cell Structure and Function*. 2nd ed. Holt, Rinehart and Winston.

McElroy, W. D. 1971. *Cellular Physiology and Biochemistry*. 3rd ed. Prentice-Hall.

Novikoff, A. B., and E. Holtzman. 1976. *Cells and Organelles*. 2nd ed. Holt, Rinehart and Winston.

Robertson, J. D. 1962. The Membrane of the Living Cell. *Scientific American* 206(4):64–72 (Offprint 151).

Rosenberg, E. 1971. *Cell and Molecular Biology*. Holt, Rinehart and Winston.

Rustad, R. C. 1961. Pinocytosis. *Scientific American* 204(4):120–130.

Solomon, A. K. 1960. Pores in the Cell Membrane. *Scientific American* 203(6):146–156 (Offprint 76).

Solomon, A. K. 1962. Pumps in the Living Cell. *Scientific American* 207(2):100–108.

Swanson, C. P. 1977. *The Cell*. 4th ed. Prentice-Hall.

Young, J. H., and L. Brubaker. 1963. A Technique for Demonstrating Diffusion in a Gel. *Turtox News* 41:274–276.

Biologically Important Molecules: Proteins

The bulk of the dry matter of cells consists of carbon, oxygen, nitrogen, and hydrogen organized into large molecules of four main types: proteins, carbohydrates, lipids (fats), and nucleic acids. These molecules often combine to make even larger molecules of importance to the cell.

Proteins are large molecules that range in molecular weight from about 5,000 (insulin) to 40 million (tobacco mosaic virus protein). They are constructed of long chains of nitrogen-containing molecules known as **amino acids**, which are linked by **peptide bonds** and often conjugate with carbohydrates, lipids, nucleic acids, and heme groups. Protein molecules exhibit an unlimited variety of sizes, configurations, and kinds of physical properties because of

The large number of amino acids that enter into making a single protein molecule (thousands in many cases)

The almost infinite number of combinations of different amino acids that can be formed

The reactivity of side groups of the individual amino acids

For example, a single complex organism, such as a human being, is composed of thousands, possibly hundreds of thousands, of different proteins. Each protein has a special function, and by its unique chemical nature each is specifically suited to that function.

Proteins have no competitors in the diversity of roles they play in biological systems. They make up a significant portion of the structure of cells and form a large part of most cellular membranes and organelles (for example, mitochondria, ribosomes, spindle fibers, and chromosomes). In addition to their structural role, proteins act as biological catalysts (enzymes), regulate cellular and tissue functions (hormones), and fight disease (antibodies).

Because of their biological significance, it becomes important to know something about the chemistry of proteins. In this exercise, you will become familiar with

TABLE 9-1
Qualitative chemical reactions of amino acids and proteins.

Reagents tested	Test	Observations
Distilled H_2O	Ninhydrin	
0.1% egg albumin		
Distilled H_2O	Sakaguchi	
1.0% egg albumin		
0.1% arginine		
10 mg/ml histidine	Pauly	
10 mg/ml tyrosine		
10 mg/ml glycine		
Distilled H_2O		

several tests used to identify the presence of protein molecules and to determine the amino acid composition of casein, a milk protein.

A. QUALITATIVE TESTS TO DETECT PROTEINS

The free terminal amino ($-NH_2$) and carboxyl ($-COOH$) groups of proteins undergo the same kinds of chemical reactions as those of the amino and carboxyl groups of free amino acids. This reaction is widely used for the detection and quantitative estimation of proteins in electrophoretic and chromatographic procedures used to separate complex mixtures of molecules.

1. Ninhydrin Reaction

The reaction of ninhydrin with amino acids is of particular importance for the detection and quantitative estimation of amino acids. Ninhydrin is a powerful oxidizing agent that removes the amino groups of amino acids, liberating ammonia, carbon dioxide, the corresponding aldehyde, and a reduced form of ninhydrin. The ammonia then reacts with an additional mole of ninhydrin and the reduced ninhydrin to form a purple substance.

Add 3.0 ml of distilled water to one test tube and 3.0 ml of 0.1% egg albumin solution to a second tube. Add solid sodium acetate to each test tube (scoop-type spatula loaded to a depth of 1 inch). Add 8 drops of ninhydrin to each tube. Heat for 3 minutes in a boiling water bath, and cool. Record your observations in Table 9-1.

2. Sakaguchi Test

Alkaline solutions of proteins that contain the amino acid arginine react with α-naphthol and sodium hypobromite to produce an intense red color. This color disappears rapidly unless stabilized by the addition of urea. Thus the Sakaguchi test is a useful tool for the detection of proteins containing arginine.

Pipet 3.0 ml of distilled water into Test Tube 1; 3.0 ml of a 1% albumin solution into Test Tube 2; and 3.0 ml of a 0.1% arginine solution into Test Tube 3. Add 1.0 ml of 10 N sodium hydroxide to each tube, followed by 1.0 ml of a 0.02% α-naphthol solution. Add 2 drops of sodium hypobromite to Tube 1, followed immediately (within 10 seconds) by 1.0 ml of a 40% urea solution. Repeat this procedure on Tubes 2 and 3. Record your observations in Table 9-1.

3. Pauly Test

When the amino acids tyrosine and/or histidine are present in a protein hydrolysate (product of enzymatic hydrolysis of protein), they react in alkaline solution with sulfanilic acid to give an intense red color. No other amino acids react. Thus, this test is useful as a confirmation of the presence of histidine and/or tyrosine.

Pipet 2.0 ml of histidine (10 mg/ml) into Tube 1; 2.0 ml of tyrosine (10 mg/ml) into Tube 2; 2.0 ml of glycine (10 mg/ml) into Tube 3; and 2.0 ml of distilled water into Tube 4. Add 1.0 ml of sulfanilic acid reagent and 1 ml of 5% sodium nitrite to each tube. Mix and let stand for 30 minutes. Add 3.0 ml of 20% sodium carbonate to each tube, and mix. Record your observations in Table 9-1.

TABLE 9-2
Protocol for quantitative determination of protein.

Tube number	Bovine serum albumin 2.5 mg/ml (ml)	Total protein content (mg)	0.5 M KCl (ml)	Biuret reagent (ml)	% T	A_{540}
1 (Control	0.0	0	5.0	3.0	100	0.0
2	1.0	2.5	4.0	3.0		
3	2.0	5.0	3.0	3.0		
4	3.0	7.5	2.0	3.0		
5	4.0	10.0	1.0	3.0		
6	5.0	12.5	0.0	3.0		
7	Unknown No. 1 5.0		0.0	3.0		
8	Unknown No. 2 5.0		0.0	3.0		

B. QUANTITATIVE CHEMICAL DETERMINATION OF PROTEIN

In protein molecules, the successive amino acid molecules are bonded together between the carboxyl and amino groups of adjacent amino acids to form long, unbranched molecules. Such bonds are commonly called **peptide bonds**. The structures resulting from the formation of peptide bonds are called dipeptides, tripeptides, or polypeptides, depending on the number of amino acids involved. The individual amino acids are called **residues**.

Biuret, a simple molecule prepared from urea, contains what may be regarded as two peptide bonds and thus is structurally similar to simple peptides. This molecule when treated with copper sulfate in alkaline solution (the biuret reaction) gives an intense purple color. The reaction is based on the formation of a purple-colored complex between copper ions and two or more peptide bonds. Proteins give a particularly strong biuret reaction because they contain a large number of peptide bonds. The biuret reaction may be used to quantitate the concentration of proteins because peptide bonds occur with approximately the same frequency per gram of material for most proteins.

In this experiment, you will determine the concentration of unknown protein solutions by measuring colorimetrically the intensity of their color production in the biuret reaction as compared with the color produced by a known concentration of the protein bovine serum albumin (BSA).

1. Prepare a set of six test tubes, containing increasing amounts of a standard solution of bovine serum albumin and 0.5 M KCl, as shown in Table 9-2. Also prepare two test tubes containing 5 ml each of two unknown concentrations of protein solutions.

2. Add 3 ml of biuret reagent to each of the tubes, and mix thoroughly by rotating the tubes between the palms. The color is fully developed in 20 minutes and is stable for at least an hour. While waiting for the color to develop, standardize the colorimeter, using Tube 1, which is a blank containing all reagents except protein. Set the colorimeter at a wavelength of 540 nm (see Appendix A for instructions on the use of the Bausch & Lomb Spectronic 20 Colorimeter). After zeroing the instrument, set Tube 1 at 0.00 absorbance (100% transmittance) and read Tubes 2 through 6 against it (see Appendix B for a discussion of spectrophotometry). Record your readings in Table 9-2. Convert the % T into absorbance (A) for Tubes 1 through 6 using Table 9-3, and then plot your data in Fig. 9-1 to obtain a standard curve for BSA. Using this curve, determine the concentrations of your unknown protein solutions.

C. CHROMATOGRAPHIC SEPARATION OF AMINO ACIDS

A variety of physical procedures are available for the isolation and purification of proteins and amino acids. One of the simplest and most elegant techniques available

TABLE 9-3
Conversion of percent transmittance (% T) into absorbance.

%T		Absorbance (A)			%T		Absorbance (A)		
		1 (.25)	2 (.50)	3 (.75)			1 (.25)	2 (.50)	3 (.75)
1	2.000	1.903	1.824	1.757	51	.2924	.2903	.2882	.2861
2	1.699	1.648	1.602	1.561	52	.2840	.2819	.2798	.2777
3	1.523	1.488	1.456	1.426	53	.2756	.2736	.2716	.2696
4	1.398	1.372	1.347	1.323	54	.2676	.2656	.2636	.2616
5	1.301	1.280	1.260	1.240	55	.2596	.2577	.2557	.2537
6	1.222	1.204	1.187	1.171	56	.2518	.2499	.2480	.2460
7	1.155	1.140	1.126	1.112	57	.2441	.2422	.2403	.2384
8	1.097	1.083	1.071	1.059	58	.2366	.2347	.2328	.2310
9	1.046	1.034	1.022	1.011	59	.2291	.2273	.2255	.2236
10	1.000	.989	.979	.969	60	.2218	.2200	.2182	.2164
11	.959	.949	.939	.930	61	.2147	.2129	.2111	.2093
12	.921	.912	.903	.894	62	.2076	.2059	.2041	.2024
13	.886	.878	.870	.862	63	.2007	.1990	.1973	.1956
14	.854	.846	.838	.831	64	.1939	.1922	.1905	.1888
15	.824	.817	.810	.803	65	.1871	.1855	.1838	.1821
16	.796	.789	.782	.776	66	.1805	.1788	.1772	.1756
17	.770	.763	.757	.751	67	.1739	.1723	.1707	.1691
18	.745	.739	.733	.727	68	.1675	.1659	.1643	.1627
19	.721	.716	.710	.704	69	.1612	.1596	.1580	.1565
20	.699	.694	.688	.683	70	.1549	.1534	.1518	.1503
21	.678	.673	.668	.663	71	.1487	.1472	.1457	.1442
22	.658	.653	.648	.643	72	.1427	.1412	.1397	.1382
23	.638	.634	.629	.624	73	.1367	.1352	.1337	.1322
24	.620	.615	.611	.606	74	.1308	.1293	.1278	.1264
25	.602	.598	.594	.589	75	.1249	.1235	.1221	.1206
26	.585	.581	.577	.573	76	.1192	.1177	.1163	.1149
27	.569	.565	.561	.557	77	.1135	.1121	.1107	.1093
28	.553	.549	.545	.542	78	.1079	.1065	.1051	.1037
29	.538	.534	.530	.527	79	.1024	.1010	.0996	.0982
30	.532	.520	.516	.512	80	.0969	.0955	.0942	.0928
31	.509	.505	.502	.498	81	.0915	.0901	.0888	.0875
32	.495	.491	.488	.485	82	.0862	.0848	.0835	.0822
33	.482	.478	.475	.472	83	.0809	.0796	.0783	.0770
34	.469	.465	.462	.459	84	.0757	.0744	.0731	.0718
35	.456	.453	.450	.447	85	.0706	.0693	.0680	.0667
36	.444	.441	.438	.435	86	.0655	.0642	.0630	.0617
37	.432	.429	.426	.423	87	.0605	.0593	.0580	.0568
38	.420	.417	.414	.412	88	.0555	.0543	.0531	.0518
39	.409	.406	.403	.401	89	.0505	.0494	.0482	.0470
40	.398	.395	.392	.390	90	.0458	.0446	.0434	.0422
41	.387	.385	.382	.380	91	.0410	.0398	.0386	.0374
42	.377	.374	.372	.369	92	.0362	.0351	.0339	.0327
43	.367	.364	.362	.359	93	.0315	.0304	.0292	.0281
44	.357	.354	.352	.349	94	.0269	.0257	.0246	.0235
45	.347	.344	.342	.340	95	.0223	.0212	.0200	.0188
46	.337	.335	.332	.330	96	.0177	.0166	.0155	.0144
47	.328	.325	.323	.321	97	.0132	.0121	.0110	.0099
48	.319	.317	.314	.312	98	.0088	.0077	.0066	.0055
49	.310	.308	.305	.303	99	.0044	.0033	.0022	.0011
50	.301	.299	.297	.295	100	.0000	.0000	.0000	.0000

Note: Intermediate values may be arrived at by using the .25, .50, and .75 columns. For example, if %T equals 85, the absorbance equals .0706; if %T equals 85.75, the absorbance equals .0667.

FIG. 9-1
Bovine serum albumin (BSA) standard curve.

to the biologist for the separation of the components of a mixture of molecules is **chromatography**. This technique permits the resolution of mixtures of substances by separation of the components between two phases. In **column chromatography**, these phases are a solid or **stationary phase**, such as calcium carbonate or sephadex, and a **mobile phase**, a liquid solvent. In paper chromatography, the paper acts as the stationary phase and the solvent as the mobile phase. **Thin-layer chromatography** (TLC) is a recent adaptation of chromatographic methods that is designed to increase the resolution of component separations. The name of the process is derived from the thin, uniform layer of an adsorbent, such as silica gel or alumina, spread on a flat glass plate and treated in a similar manner to a paper strip. The thinness of the adsorbent layer requires less material and results in a very rapid migration of the components in a mixture. (See Appendix B for a more detailed discussion of chromatography.)

In this study, you will use thin-layer chromatography to separate and identify the amino acid residues of a hydrolysate of casein, a milk protein.

If possible, precoated silica gel chromatographic plates should be purchased for this exercise. Otherwise, the following procedure can be used to prepare your own slides coated with silica gel.

1. Obtain a *clean* glass slide. Holding the slide by the sides, immerse it as far as possible into a jar containing silica gel. Swish the slide back and forth several times. Stop, and then carefully lift the slide *straight up* (Fig. 9-2).

2. Allow the slide to air-dry for several minutes. (*Note:* The white, silica gel coat is very fragile. Do not damage the surface.)

3. Select the side of the slide with the smoothest surface. Then, by wiping with a paper towel, remove the silica gel from the other side. (*Note:* Avoid excessive handling of the slide, because your hands may contaminate it with amino acids. Touch it only at the edges.)

4. Lay the slide down with the coated side upward. "Spot" the coated surface at two points approximately 12 mm apart and 6 mm from the bottom. To Spot 1, add a very small drop of casein hydrolysate, a milk protein solution. To Spot 2, add a known amino acid supplied by your instructor. Other students in the class will be given other known amino acids to test.

5. Allow the spots to dry. Then carefully place the slide in a chromatographic developing jar and cover. When the **solvent front** (i.e., the leading edge of the solvent) has moved to about 6 or 12 mm from the top of the slide (30–45 minutes), remove the slide from the jar. Allow the slide to dry for 4–5 minutes.

6. In a hood or other well-ventilated area designated by your instructor, cautiously spray the surface of the slide with ninhydrin. *Do not inhale the fumes.* Allow the slide to dry for 2–3 minutes, and then heat the slide as directed by your instructor for 2–3 minutes.

The amino acids in the hydrolysate will react with the ninhydrin and will show up as colored spots on the slide. The ninhydrin test yields purple colors with most amino acids and a yellow spot with the amino acid proline. Record the color of the spots on your chromatogram in Table 9-4.

Roughly estimate the center of each amino acid spot and measure the distance it has traveled up the slide from its point of application. This distance, divided by the total distance traveled by the solvent from the origin line, is known as the **R_f value**. Two substances having the same R_f are probably identical and thus this value can be used to identify specific amino acids separated from a mixture.

Record your observations, as well as those of other students who were given known amino acids other than your own, in Table 9-4.

A. Clean glass slide

B. Dip into silica-gel solution.

C. Swirl four or five times. Then lift straight up.

Coated surface

12 mm

6 mm

D. Dry 1 or 2 minutes. Remove roughest surface by wiping with paper towel. Spot with lipid extract.

FIG. 9-2
Preparation of plate for thin-layer chromatography.

REFERENCES

Bailey, J. L. 1967. *Techniques of Protein Chemistry*. 2nd ed. Elsevier.

Baker, J. J. W., and G. E. Allen. 1974. *Matter, Energy, and Life*. 3rd ed. Addison-Wesley.

Barry, J. M., and E. M. Barry. 1969. *An Introduction to the Structure of Biological Molecules*. Prentice-Hall.

Dickerson, R. E., and I. Geis. 1969. *The Structure and Action of Proteins*. Harper & Row.

Koshland, D. E. 1973. Protein Shape and Biological Control. *Scientific American* 229(4):52–64 (Offprint 1280). *Scientific American* Offprints are available from W. H. Freeman and Company, 660 Market Street, San Francisco 94104, and 58 Kings Road, Reading RG1 3AA, England. Please order by number.

Lehninger, A. L. 1975. *Biochemistry*. 2nd ed. Worth.

Stryer, L. 1980. *Biochemistry*. 2nd ed. W. H. Freeman and Company.

White, A., P. Handler, and E. L. Smith. 1978. *Principles of Biochemistry*. 6th ed. McGraw-Hill.

TABLE 9-4
Chromatography of amino acids.

Reagents	Distance spot moved (mm)	Color of spot	R_f value
Aspartic acid			
Glutamic acid			
Methionine			
Proline			
Tyrosine			
Histidine			
Alanine			
Lysine			
Slide No.			
Slide No.			
Slide No.			
Slide No.			
Slide No.			
Slide No.			
Slide No.			
Slide No.			

Carbohydrates and Lipids

A. CARBOHYDRATES

Carbohydrates, formed when a green plant captures light energy in the process of photosynthesis, play a key role in making this captured energy available to the cell. They also supply important carbon "skeletons" (carbon atoms linked together) for the synthesis of other biologically important molecules.

The term *carbohydrate* means "hydrate of carbon." This name is used because it includes many compounds that contain atoms of hydrogen and oxygen in the same proportion occurring in water—two hydrogens to one oxygen. Thus, a carbohydrate can be described by the general formula $C(H_2O)n;$ n represents the number of $C(H_2O)$ units that make up carbohydrates ranging from relatively simple molecules, called *sugars,* to the complex molecules of starch and cellulose.

Most carbohydrates have a basic unit of six carbon atoms (sugars), which are linked together in various ways. On the basis of the number of these six-carbon compounds that are linked together to make longer units, the carbohydrates are divided into three classes: **monosaccharides**, which consist of a single six-carbon molecule (e.g., glucose); **disaccharides**, which consist of two single sugar molecules linked together (sucrose is made up of glucose linked to fructose); and **polysaccharides**, which consist of three or more sugar molecules linked together (starch and glycogen are long chains of glucose molecules). Starch and glycogen are storage forms of carbohydrates; starch is usually produced in plants, and glycogen in animals.

Carbohydrates may be identified by color reactions with specific reagents. These tests can be used to determine the amount as well as the kind of carbohydrate by measuring the variations in color obtained with different concentrations of reagent. Most of the procedures require heating the carbohydrate and reagent together in a hot water bath. It is usually best to carry out a procedure on all the carbohydrates in the same water bath at the same time so that a direct comparison can be made of the relative behavior of all of the carbohydrates in a given test.

In this study, you will become familiar with some of the more common tests for detecting the presence of specific types of carbohydrates. You will be asked to identify the carbohydrate composition of an "unknown" solution containing one or more carbohydrates. Each carbohydrate in the solution will be at a concentration of 6%. Only the carbohydrates you test will be found in the unknown. About one-half of each unknown solution should be diluted to give a 1% solution, which will be used in most of the tests. *The unknowns should always be run simultaneously with the known carbohydrates.*

1. Tests for Reducing Sugars

A carbohydrate with a free or a potentially free

aldehyde ($-C \overset{\displaystyle O}{\underset{\displaystyle H}{\Big\langle}}$) or ketone ($\diagup C = O$) group

is a reducing sugar and, in a solution of sufficiently high pH, can reduce weak oxidizing agents such as cupric, silver, or ferricyanide ions. For example, Cu^{2+} ions react with glucose to form a colored precipitate of cuprous oxide. The color of the precipitate will range from green to reddish brown, depending on the quantity of the reducing sugar present.

$$Glucose + Cu(OH)_2 \xrightarrow{\text{Heat}}$$
$$\underset{\text{Colored}}{CU_2O} + H_2O + \text{Oxidized glucose}$$

a. Benedict's Test

Benedict's solution contains sodium bicarbonate, sodium citrate, and copper sulfate. If combined with a reducing sugar (such as glucose or fructose) and heated, the divalent copper ion (Cu^{2+}) of copper sulfate ($CuSO_4$) is reduced to the monovalent copper ion (Cu^+) of cuprous oxide (Cu_2O), which forms a precipitate.

Place 5.0 ml of Benedict's reagent in a test tube, and add 8 drops of a 1% solution of the carbohydrate to be tested. Heat the contents for 2 minutes over a Bunsen burner, and allow to cool to room temperature. Or place the test tube in a boiling water bath for 3 minutes, and

TABLE 10-1
Qualitative carbohydrate tests.

Carbo-hydrates	Tests		
	Benedict's	Barfoed's	Phenylhydrazine
Glucose			
Fructose			
Galactose			
Mannose			
Xylose			
Lactose			
Maltose			
Sucrose			
Starch			
Unknown			

allow to cool to room temperature. When several sugars are tested at one time, the latter method is preferred.

Record the color and amount of precipitate formed for each of the carbohydrates tested in Table 10-1. Use a plus sign (+) to indicate a small amount of precipitate, a double plus (+ +) for a moderate amount, and a triple plus (+ + +) for a large amount.

b. Barfoed's Test

Barfoed's test is used to distinguish between monosaccharides and disaccharides. The reagent is similar to Benedict's reagent except that it is slightly acidic, having a pH of about 4.5. At this pH, disaccharides *will not* reduce Cu^{2+} to Cu_2O, whereas monosaccharides *will* reduce the Cu^{2+} when heated for 2 minutes. Longer heating of disaccharides may lead to some reduction because of the formation of monosaccharides by hydrolysis, and so it is essential that all the sugars be treated in exactly the same way and that the time of appearance of a precipitate be noted.

For each carbohydrate to be tested, put 5 ml of Barfoed's reagent in a test tube and add 0.5 ml (10 drops) of a 1% solution of the carbohydrate. Mix the solutions well. Place the test tubes in a boiling water bath, and heat for 2 minutes. A positive test for monosaccharides is the appearance of a red precipitate of Cu_2O within 1 or 2 minutes. Record the results in Table 10-1, noting the time of appearance of the precipitate.

FIG. 10-1
Reaction of phenylhydrazine with mannose.

c. Reactions with Phenylhydrazine

Reducing sugars react with phenylhydrazine to form phenylhydrazones. This reaction takes place at room temperature. All of the common reducing sugars, except mannose, form phenylhydrazones that are soluble in H_2O. Mannose forms an insoluble phenylhydrazone (Fig. 10-1). Thus, this test is specific for the detection of mannose.

For each carbohydrate, put about 6 mm of solid phenylhydrazine reagent into a test tube. (CAUTION: *Phenylhydrazine is poisonous. Do not spill or get on skin.*) To each test tube, add 2 ml of a 1% solution of one of the carbohydrates to be tested. Mix until the solid has dissolved, and allow to stand at room temperature from 10 to 15 minutes. The formation of a white, crystalline precipitate indicates mannose. Record your results in Table 10-1.

d. Unknown Carbohydrates

Using the tests in Part A, determine the carbohydrate content of the "unknown" that you have been given to analyze. Confirm your results with your instructor.

B. LIPIDS

Lipids are a group of diverse fatty or oily substances that are classified together because they are insoluble in water and soluble in the so-called fat solvents (for example, ether, acetone, and carbon tetrachloride). The simplest lipids (butter, coconut oil, and animal and plant fats) are composed of carbon, hydrogen, and oxygen atoms, and on hydrolysis yield glycerol and fatty acids (Fig. 10-2). They have a higher proportion of carbon-hydrogen bonds than carbohydrates and consequently release a larger amount of energy on oxidation than do other organic substances. Fats, for example, release about twice the calories released by an equal amount of carbohydrates. These molecules also form a large part of most cellular membranes, in which they control the movements of other lipids or lipid-soluble materials in and out of cells.

In this study, you will attempt to separate a lipid extract into its component fatty acids using thin-layer chromatography (see Appendix C for a discussion of the principles of chromatography).

If possible, precoated silica gel chromatographic plates should be purchased for this exercise. Otherwise, the following procedure can be used to prepare your own slides coated with silica gel.

1. Obtain a *clean* glass slide. Holding the slide by its sides, immerse it as far as possible into a jar containing silica gel. Swish the slide back and forth several times. Stop, and then carefully lift the slide *straight up* (Fig. 10-3).

2. Allow the slide to air-dry for several minutes. (*Note:* The white, silica gel coat is very fragile. Do not damage the surface.)

3. Select the side of the slide with the smoothest surface. Then, by wiping with a paper towel, remove the silica gel from the other side. (*Note:* Avoid excessive handling of the slide; your hands may contaminate it with lipids. Touch it only at the edges.)

4. Lay the slide down with the coated side up. Spot the hydrolyzed lipid extract on the coated surface about 6 mm from the bottom. Allow the spot to dry. Then carefully place the slide in a chromatographic developing jar and cover. When the solvent front (i.e., the leading edge of the solvent) has moved to about 6 or 12 mm from the top of the slide (30–45 minutes), remove the slide from the jar. Allow the slide to dry from 4 to 5 minutes.

5. Place the slide in an iodine jar, cover, and leave until brownish spots appear.

FIG. 10-2
Hydrolysis of a lipid.

Only fatty acids migrate in the solvent used. Other components present in the extract either do not absorb on the silica gel (e.g., triglycerides, which will be found at the edge of the solvent front) or do not migrate and thus remain at the origin (e.g., phospholipids). Locate these components on your slide.

REFERENCES

Gurr, A. I., and A. T. James. 1976. *Lipid Biochemistry: An Introduction*. 2nd ed. Halstead Press.

Guthrie, R. D., and J. Honeyman. 1968. *An Introduction to the Chemistry of Carbohydrates*. Clarendon Press.

Lehninger, A. L. 1975. *Biochemistry*. 2nd ed. Worth.

Loewy, A. G., and P. Siekevitz. 1969. *Cell Structure and Function*. 2nd ed. Holt, Rinehart and Winston.

McElroy, W. D. 1971. *Cell Physiology and Biochemistry*. 3rd ed. Prentice-Hall.

Stryer, L. 1980. *Biochemistry*. 2nd ed. W. H. Freeman and Company.

White, A., P. Handler, and E. L. Smith. 1978. *Principles of Biochemistry*. 6th ed. McGraw-Hill.

A. Clean glass slide

B. Dip into silica gel solution.

C. Swirl four or five times. Then lift straight up.

Coated surface

6 mm

D. Dry 1 or 2 minutes. Remove roughest surface by wiping with paper towel. Spot with lipid extract.

FIG. 10-3
Preparation of plate for thin-layer chromatography.

Photosynthesis

The living world, with few exceptions, operates at the expense of the energy captured by the photosynthetic machinery of green plants. From the products of photosynthesis and from a small number of inorganic compounds available in the environment, living organisms are able to build up the numerous complex molecules that contribute to their cellular structure or that in other ways are essential to their existence. Furthermore, the ultimate source of the energy expended by living organisms is the converted energy of sunlight that is trapped within the newly synthesized organic molecules during photosynthesis.

Classically, the reaction taking place in photosynthesis is given as follows:

$$6\,CO_2 + 12\,H_2O \xrightarrow[\text{Chlorophyll}]{\text{Light}} C_6H_{12}O_6 + 6\,O_2 + 6\,H_2O$$
Carbon   Water   Sugar   Oxygen Water
dioxide

This equation suggests that carbohydrate synthesis is the central feature in this process. Photosynthesis, however, is not a single-step reaction, as might be indicated by this equation. It is a complex process involving the interaction of many compounds. The large number of individual reactions can be divided into two groups: (1) the light, or photochemical, reactions in which light is required; and (2) the so-called dark, or biosynthetic, reactions, so named because they do not require light for the reactions to proceed.

In the **photochemical (light) reactions**, radiant energy is used for two purposes. First, light is used to split water molecules into oxygen and hydrogen. The hydrogen is then transferred to $NADP^+$ (nicotinamide adenine dinucleotide phosphate) to form NADPH, which in turn transfers hydrogen to other molecules.

Second, light energy absorbed by chlorophyll is converted into chemical energy, which is stored in the molecule ATP (adenosine triphosphate). This conversion occurs in the chloroplast and consists of the transport of electrons from "excited" chlorophyll through a series of acceptor molecules (including the cytochromes) that constitute an electron-transport system. Thus mitochondria are not the only cytoplasmic structures capable of generating ATP. This phenomenon of light-dependent generation of ATP has been called **photophosphorylation** to differentiate it from **oxidative phosphorylation**, which occurs in mitochondria.

Thus, the light reactions result in the formation of NADPH, ATP, and the release of oxygen. In the "dark" reactions, NADPH and ATP are then used to reduce CO_2 to carbohydrate.

In this exercise, you will examine the role of light, carbon dioxide, and chloroplast pigments in the photosynthetic process.

A. ROLE OF LIGHT

1. Necessity of Light for Photosynthesis

There is no practical method in introductory courses to determine precisely the amount of sugar or oxygen produced during photosynthesis. However, it has been shown

A. Remove a leaf from a plant that has been kept in the dark for 48 hours and one from a plant that has been exposed to sunlight for 48 hours.

B. Place leaves in boiling water bath for several minutes.

C. Place leaves in beaker of hot alcohol and heat until pigment is removed.

D. Place leaves in dish containing iodine for several minutes.

E. Remove leaves. If starch is present, leaves will become deep bluish black.

FIG. 11-1
Procedure for determining the necessity of light for photosynthesis.

experimentally that during photosynthesis much of the sugar produced in the leaves is rapidly condensed into starch. Although starch is not a direct product of photosynthesis, the fact that it is a condensation product of the glucose produced during photosynthesis allows us to use its synthesis as indirect evidence for photosynthetic activity.

Your instructor will supply geranium plants that have been kept in a dark place for 48 hours. Test a leaf for the presence of starch by the following procedure (Fig. 11-1A–D).

1. Hydrolyze the cell walls by boiling in a water bath for several minutes, and then remove the pigment by putting the leaf in hot alcohol.

2. Pour iodine over the leaf in a petri dish. If starch is present, the leaf will turn a deep bluish black.

Similarly, test for the presence of starch in plants that were exposed to light for 48 hours.

From your observations, what conclusions can be made about the necessity of light for photosynthesis?

_____

_____

_____

_____

2. Effect of Light Intensity on the Rate of Photosynthesis

The intensity of sunlight striking Earth's surface varies from hour to hour, from day to day, and from season to season. Because oxygen is a by-product of photosynthesis, oxygen liberation may be used in designing an experiment to measure the effect of variations in light intensity on photosynthesis. In this study, light intensity is varied by placing an Elodea sprig at varying distances from a constant light source.

Either of the following methods may be used. Method 1 is a semiquantitative procedure in which the amount of oxygen produced is equated to the amount of water displaced in a pipet attached to a photosynthesizing sprig of Elodea. In Method 2, changes in photosynthetic rate are measured as changes in the amount of oxygen produced as bubbles, a large number of bubbles indicating greater photosynthetic activity than a small number of bubbles.

a. Method 1

1. Select a 1-ml pipet graduated in hundredths. Turn it upside down, and place a short piece of rubber tubing over the delivery end (Fig. 11-2).

A. Select a sprig of Elodea about 15 cm in length. Place it upside down in a large test tube containing 0.25% sodium bicarbonate. Before completely submerging the Elodea sprig, cut off 2–3 mm from the base of the stem with a sharp razor blade. Remove any leaves near the cut end.

B. Place a short piece of rubber tubing over a graduated (0.01's) 1-ml pipet. Aspirate the water until the tube is full. Hold your finger over the rubber tubing so that the water column does not fall, and then clamp the rubber tubing.

C. Position the pipet gently over the end of the Elodea sprig and then clamp test tube and pipet to a ring stand. Keep Elodea and pipet below water level.

D. Position a light 50 cm from the plant. Place a container of cool water between the light and the Elodea. Turn the light on and allow to stand for 7–10 minutes before taking any readings.

E. Count the bubbles produced each minute for a 5-minute period. Calculate the average bubble count per minute.

FIG. 11-2
Procedure for determining the effect of light intensity on photosynthesis.

2. Select an undamaged sprig of Elodea about 15 cm in length. Insert it upside down into a large test tube filled with a 0.25% solution of sodium bicarbonate (NaHCO₃). This solution is a source of HCO_3 for photosynthesis. Before completely submerging the plant, cut 2–3 mm from the end of the stem opposite the growing point with a sharp razor blade, being careful not to crush the stem. If there are any leaves within a few millimeters of the cut end, remove them with forceps.

3. Swab the rubber tubing on the pipet with cotton moistened with 70% ethyl alcohol. Allow to dry. Aspirate the sodium bicarbonate solution into the pipet until it is full. Hold your finger over the end of the rubber tubing to prevent the water column from dropping and attach a clamp over the tubing as shown in Fig. 11-2B and C.

4. Next, position the pipet gently over the cut end of the Elodea, and clamp in place on a ring stand, as shown in Fig. 11-2C and D. Keep the pipet and Elodea below the level of the water.

Obtain a reflector containing a 200-watt bulb and a container of cool water, and set them in the position shown in Fig. 11-2D. Why is the water container used in this system?

_____

_____

With the Elodea plant at a distance of 50 cm, turn on the lamp and allow the system to equilibrate for 7–10 minutes. Why?

_____

At beginning of equilibration

At start of timing (initial reading, 1.0 ml)

At end of timing (final reading) Amount of oxygen released, 0.5 ml

FIG. 11-3
Method of measuring oxygen evolved during photosynthesis.

Determine the total amount of oxygen given off by the plant during a 10-minute period, *by determining the amount of water in the pipet that is displaced during this time*. Fig. 11-3 illustrates how this is done.

Determine the amount of oxygen produced at distances of 50, 30, and 10 cm from the light source. Enter your results in Table 11-1, and plot your data in Fig. 11-4.

b. Method 2

Arrange materials as in Method 1. It is not necessary here, however, to use a graduated pipet. Any glass tubing that will fit closely over the cut end of the Elodea will do. Set the tube at the 50-cm distance, and allow the system to equilibrate for 7–10 minutes. Then determine the rate of photosynthesis by counting the bubbles produced each minute for a 5-minute period. Calculate the *average* num-

ber of bubbles per minute, and record your data in Table 11-1. Move the tube to the 30-cm distance, allow the system to equilibrate, and calculate the average number of bubbles. Repeat this procedure for the 10-cm distance. Plot your data in Fig. 11-4.

As light intensity increases, does the rate of photosynthesis (as measured in oxygen production) increase along with it? If not, what does this suggest?

_____

_____

_____

_____

TABLE 11-1
Effects of light intensity on photosynthetic activity.

Distance from light (cm)	Volume of oxygen (ml)	Average bubble count
10		
30		
50		

FIG. 11-4
Effect of light intensity on photosynthetic rate.

B. ROLE OF CARBON DIOXIDE

1. Necessity of CO_2 for Photosynthesis

To determine the necessity of CO_2 in photosynthesis, the apparatus in Fig. 11-5D will be used.

Select a leaf from a geranium plant that has been in the dark for 24 hours. Test the leaf for the presence of starch by immersing it in hot alcohol until it loses its green color, and then place it in a petri dish containing iodine

(Fig. 11-5A, B). Return the plant to the dark while performing the starch test. If a strong positive starch test occurs, select another plant and test the leaves until a negative or very weak starch test is obtained. Why is this step necessary?

_____

_____

_____

A. Remove a leaf from a plant kept in the dark. Place leaf in hot alcohol until pigment is removed.

B. Remove leaf from alcohol and place in dish containing iodine. If starch is present, leaf will turn bluish black.

C. Place another leaf from same plant in atmosphere lacking CO_2.

Solid KOH or NaOH

Cotton plug

Rubber stopper

Vial of H_2O

Solid KOH or NaOH

D. "Experimental" set up

E. Place a third leaf under "control" conditions.

"Control" set up

Place "experimental" and "control" set ups under bright lights for 24 hours. Then test for starch as shown in steps A and B.

FIG. 11-5
Procedure for determining the necessity of CO_2 for photosynthesis.

FIG. 11-6
Necessity of CO_2 for photosynthesis.

Select another leaf from the plant giving the negative starch test, and place the leaf in the jar as shown in Fig. 11-5D.

Place a 200-watt shielded lamp near the setup, but not close enough to heat the jar. (Better results may be obtained if this setup can be placed in direct sunlight.)

What is the "control" for this experiment?

_____

_____

Run the control simultaneously with the "experimental" setup. This experiment should be allowed to run for about 24 hours, after which time you should remove the leaf and test it for photosynthetic activity in terms of starch production.

After setting up your experiment, examine the demonstration arranged by your instructor (Fig. 11-6).

Why is there a beaker of $Ba(OH)_2$ in the bell jar?

_____

_____

What "control" would be needed for this experiment?

_____

To save time, your instructor has tested the leaves of the "experimental" and "control" plants for photosynthetic activity. Under which condition is the starch test negative?

_____

_____

If the results of your experiment do not agree with those of your instructor's, suggest reasons for this difference.

_____

_____

_____

2. Uptake of CO_2 by Aquatic Plants

That CO_2 is used during photosynthesis can be demonstrated by placing an Elodea plant in a test tube containing a chemical indicator that will change color in the presence or absence of CO_2. Phenol red is a chemical indicator that is red in an alkaline solution and yellow in an acid solution. Using this information, devise and run an adequately controlled experiment showing (1) that CO_2 is taken up by Elodea and (2) that light affects the plant's ability to take up CO_2.

C. ROLE OF CHLOROPLAST PIGMENTS

The second law of thermodynamics states that living organisms and cells create and maintain their steady-state

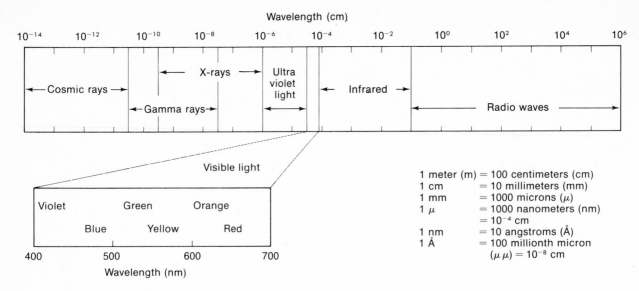

FIG. 11-7
The electromagnetic spectrum.

condition at the expense of their surrounding environment, which tends to become disordered and random (**entropy**). To maintain this steady state, a constant source of energy must be available. Energy available to cells comes in two forms: radiant (light) energy from the sun and potential energy stored in chemical bonds.

Light energy, which is a type of electromagnetic radiation (Fig. 11-7), must first be transformed into chemical (bond) energy before it can be used by the living cell. This transformation takes place in green plant cells. Because only absorbed light can transfer its energy, it seems apparent that the colored components of plant cells act to absorb visible light. Those substances that have the ability to absorb light selectively are called *pigments*. In this exercise, you will determine experimentally the necessity for chlorophyll in photosynthesis, the nature of the green color of plants, and the absorption spectrum of a chloroplast pigment solution.

1. Necessity of Chlorophyll for Photosynthesis

Select a leaf from a variegated *Coleus* and a silver-leafed geranium plant. In Row 1 of Table 11-2, draw an outline of each leaf, showing the distribution of the different pigments. The obvious pigments will be the "green" chlorophyll and the "red" anthocyanin in the *Coleus* leaf.

Place the leaves in a beaker of cold water for several minutes. Remove the leaves, and record your observa-

tions (by drawings or written comments) in Row 2 of Table 11-2.

Transfer the leaves to a beaker of boiling water for several minutes. Remove, and record any changes observed in Table 11-2. Account for the differences observed between Rows 2 and 3 in Table 11-2.

_____

_____

Next, place the leaves in hot alcohol. (CAUTION: Use a hot water bath to heat the alchol.) After several minutes, the leaves will become whitish in color. At this point, transfer them to a petri dish containing iodine. Swirl the dish gently. Outline the distribution of starch in each leaf in Row 4 of Table 11-2. How do these experiments demonstrate the necessity for chlorophyll in photosynthesis?

_____

_____

2. Isolation and Characterization of Chloroplast Pigments

Complex mixtures of chemical substances may be separated by chromatography. The separation of the mixture is based on differences in the solubilities of the constit-

TABLE 11-2
The role of chlorophyll in photosynthesis.

Row	Treatment	*Coleus*	Silver-leafed geranium
1	None		
2	Cold H_2O for several minutes		
3	Boiling H_2O for several minutes		
4	Hot alcohol for several minutes. Place in dish with iodine.		

uents of the mixture in different solvents. (See Appendix C for a discussion of the principles of chromatography.) In this study, you will use the techniques of paper or thin-layer chromatography to analyze the pigment composition of chlorophyll.

a. Paper Chromatography

In paper chromatography, filter paper is usually used to separate different kinds of mixtures. The substance to be chromatographed is placed at one end of the paper. This end is then immersed in a solvent that separates the components of the mixture as it passes upward through the spot to the top of the paper. After drying, the materials that are separated may be directly observed if they are colored, or they may be made visible using various spray reagents.

1. Prepare a "chlorophyll" extract by grinding two or three spinach leaves in 5 ml of acetone (Fig. 11-8A). Adding a small quantity of quartz sand will make the grinding easier.

2. Using a small paint brush, apply a narrow strip of chlorophyll extract to the filter paper (Fig. 11-8B). Dry thoroughly by blowing on the paper or waving it in the air. Apply the extract five or six more times. Let it dry thoroughly after each application.

3. Place the strip in a test tube containing benzene-petroleum ether as shown in Fig. 11-8. Examine the chromatogram for the next several minutes. How long does it take for the solvent to reach the top of the paper?

_____

Describe any separation that occurs.

_____

_____

_____

b. Thin-Layer Chromatography

In thin-layer chromatography, a gellike material is thinly applied to a support made of glass, aluminum, plastic, or cardboard. The gel can be prepared in several ways. In this study, commercially prepared sheets consisting of silica gel on acetate sheet backing will be used to assure uniformity of adsorbent thickness. It has the added advantage of being able to be cut to desired shape and size.

A. Using a mortar and pestle, grind 2 or 3 spinach leaves in 5 ml of acetone.

B. "Paint" a narrow band of chlorophyll extract across the paper strip. Allow it to dry. Repeat this several more times, allowing the extract to dry between each application.

C. Place the paper strip in a test tube containing 2–3 ml of benzene-petroleum ether. Do not allow the extract to become submerged.

Extract

FIG. 11-8
Procedure for separating chlorophyll pigments using paper chromatography.

A unique advantage of using thin-layer chromatography is the speed at which separation occurs. Whereas paper chromatography can require up to 24 hours to separate a complex chemical mixture, the same separation using thin-layer methods can be done in an hour.

1. Place about 0.5 cm of solvent (isooctane-acetone-diethyl ether, 2:1:1) into a chromatographic jar. Cover the jar to allow the interior to become saturated with the fumes of the solvent (Fig. 11-9).

A. Pour about 0.5 cm of solvent into chromatographic jar. Cover.

B. Apply several drops of chloroplast extract approximately 2 cm from the bottom of a silica gel thin-layer sheet. Allow to dry thoroughly between each drop.

C. Place chromatogram in solvent in jar and cover. Allow to run until solvent reaches within 2 cm of the top of the sheet.

FIG. 11-9
Procedure for thin-layer chromatography of chloroplast pigments.

2. Using a capillary hematocrit tube, apply several drops of the previously prepared chloroplast extract about 2 cm from the bottom of a strip of thin-layer silica gel. Try to keep the spot about 3 or 4 mm in diameter. Dry thoroughly between applications.

3. Insert the spotted sheet into the jar and cover. Allow to run until solvent reaches within 2 cm of the top of the sheet.

Approximately how long does it take to separate the

pigments, using the thin-layer as compared with the paper chromatographic method?

_____

3. Absorption Spectra of Chloroplast Pigments

The part of the visible spectrum that is absorbed by the chloroplast pigments can be determined by using an instrument that disperses visible light into its component colors or wavelengths (Fig. 11-10). The disappearance from the spectrum of various colors, or wavelengths, as a result of passing light through a pigment solution, indicates that those wavelengths were absorbed by the pigments. A graph of the ability of a substance to absorb light against the wavelength of light is called an **absorption spectrum**. The absorption spectrum for a hypothetical substance is shown in Fig. 11-11.

What wavelengths are strongly absorbed by this hypothetical substance?

_____

What wavelengths are weakly absorbed?

_____

In this study, you will attempt to determine the absorption spectrum of a chloroplast extract using two different methods.

a. Method 1: Spectroscopic Determination

Pipet a sample of the extract available in the laboratory into a small test tube. Your instructor will help you use the instrument for determining the absorption spectrum for your extract. In the particular instrument used here, two spectra will be projected onto a scale (400–700 nm) on the back, inside surface of the instrument. The upper reference spectrum shows the various colors (wavelengths) of light. The lower sample spectrum results from passage of the light through the sample. In the chart below indicate the wavelengths of light that are absorbed by the chlorophyll extract.

b. Method 2: Spectrophotometric Determination

In this method, a Bausch & Lomb Spectronic 20 spectrophotometer will be used to determine the absorption spectrum of the chloroplast pigments more accurately. (Refer to Appendixes A and B for a description of the theory and mechanics of using this instrument.)

1. Beginning at a wavelength of 400 nm, standardize the instrument with the acetone-ethanol solvent used to extract the chloroplast pigments. Why is this solvent used to standardize the spectrophotometer?

_____

_____

_____

2. Place the tube containing the extract into the sample holder, and determine the percent transmittance (% T).

3. Remove the sample, and reset the wavelength control to 425 nm. Restandardize the instrument to 0% and 100% transmittance, and then determine the percent transmittance of the sample.

4. Repeat the above procedure at 25-nm intervals. It will be necessary, however, to insert an accessory red filter and red-sensitive phototube for determinations above 625 nm.

5. Convert the percent transmittance (% T) into absorbance (A) using Table 11-3, and then plot your data in Fig. 11-12. At what wavelength(s) does the chlorophyll extract absorb maximally?

_____

_____

In those plants having chlorophyll as the predominant pigment, why do the leaves appear green?

_____

_____

_____

```
|          |          |          |
|          |          |          |
|          |          |          |
```
400   500   600   700
Nanometers (nm)

FIG. 11-10
(A) Dispersion of white light by a prism. (B) Determination of the absorption spectrum of chloroplast pigments by a spectroscope.

FIG. 11-11
A sample absorption spectrum.

Because the chloroplast pigments consist of both chlorophylls and carotenoids, you cannot tell from the absorption spectrum which pigments are absorbing which wavelengths. How could you determine this?

_____

_____

_____

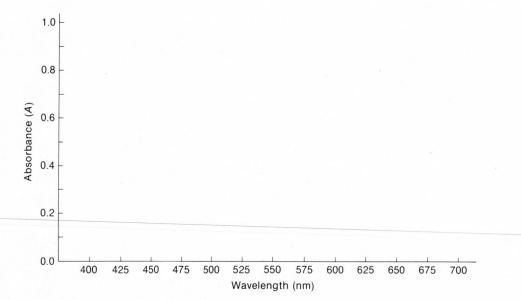

FIG. 11-12
Absorption spectrum of chloroplast extract.

TABLE 11-3
Conversion of percent transmittance (% T) to absorbance.

%T		Absorbance (A)			%T		Absorbance (A)		
		1 (.25)	2 (.50)	3 (.75)			1 (.25)	2 (.50)	3 (.75)
1	2.000	1.903	1.824	1.757	51	.2924	.2903	.2882	.2861
2	1.699	1.648	1.602	1.561	52	.2840	.2819	.2798	.2777
3	1.523	1.488	1.456	1.426	53	.2756	.2736	.2716	.2696
4	1.398	1.372	1.347	1.323	54	.2676	.2656	.2636	.2616
5	1.301	1.280	1.260	1.240	55	.2596	.2577	.2557	.2537
6	1.222	1.204	1.187	1.171	56	.2518	.2499	.2480	.2460
7	1.155	1.140	1.126	1.112	57	.2441	.2422	.2403	.2384
8	1.097	1.083	1.071	1.059	58	.2366	.2347	.2328	.2310
9	1.046	1.034	1.022	1.011	59	.2291	.2273	.2255	.2236
10	1.000	.989	.979	.969	60	.2218	.2200	.2182	.2164
11	.959	.949	.939	.930	61	.2147	.2129	.2111	.2093
12	.921	.912	.903	.894	62	.2076	.2059	.2041	.2024
13	.886	.878	.870	.862	63	.2007	.1990	.1973	.1956
14	.854	.846	.838	.831	64	.1939	.1922	.1905	.1888
15	.824	.817	.810	.803	65	.1871	.1855	.1838	.1821
16	.796	.789	.782	.776	66	.1805	.1788	.1772	.1756
17	.770	.763	.757	.751	67	.1739	.1723	.1707	.1691
18	.745	.739	.733	.727	68	.1675	.1659	.1643	.1627
19	.721	.716	.710	.704	69	.1612	.1596	.1580	.1565
20	.699	.694	.688	.683	70	.1549	.1534	.1518	.1503
21	.678	.673	.668	.663	71	.1487	.1472	.1457	.1442
22	.658	.653	.648	.643	72	.1427	.1412	.1397	.1382
23	.638	.634	.629	.624	73	.1367	.1352	.1337	.1322
24	.620	.615	.611	.606	74	.1308	.1293	.1278	.1264
25	.602	.598	.594	.589	75	.1249	.1235	.1221	.1206
26	.585	.581	.577	.573	76	.1192	.1177	.1163	.1149
27	.569	.565	.561	.557	77	.1135	.1121	.1107	.1093
28	.553	.549	.545	.542	78	.1079	.1065	.1051	.1037
29	.538	.534	.530	.527	79	.1024	.1010	.0996	.0982
30	.532	.520	.516	.512	80	.0969	.0955	.0942	.0928
31	.509	.505	.502	.498	81	.0915	.0901	.0888	.0875
32	.495	.491	.488	.485	82	.0862	.0848	.0835	.0822
33	.482	.478	.475	.472	83	.0809	.0796	.0783	.0770
34	.469	.465	.462	.459	84	.0757	.0744	.0731	.0718
35	.456	.453	.450	.447	85	.0706	.0693	.0680	.0667
36	.444	.441	.438	.435	86	.0655	.0642	.0630	.0617
37	.432	.429	.426	.423	87	.0605	.0593	.0580	.0568
38	.420	.417	.414	.412	88	.0555	.0543	.0531	.0518
39	.409	.406	.403	.401	89	.0505	.0494	.0482	.0470
40	.398	.395	.392	.390	90	.0458	.0446	.0434	.0422
41	.387	.385	.382	.380	91	.0410	.0398	.0386	.0374
42	.377	.374	.372	.369	92	.0362	.0351	.0339	.0327
43	.367	.364	.362	.359	93	.0315	.0304	.0292	.0281
44	.357	.354	.352	.349	94	.0269	.0257	.0246	.0235
45	.347	.344	.342	.340	95	.0223	.0212	.0200	.0188
46	.337	.335	.332	.330	96	.0177	.0166	.0155	.0144
47	.328	.325	.323	.321	97	.0132	.0121	.0110	.0099
48	.319	.317	.314	.312	98	.0088	.0077	.0066	.0055
49	.310	.308	.305	.303	99	.0044	.0033	.0022	.0011
50	.301	.299	.297	.295	100	.0000	.0000	.0000	.0000

Note: Intermediate values may be arrived at by using the .25, .50, and .75 columns. For example, if %T equals 85, the absorbance equals .0706; if %T equals 85.75, the absorbance equals .0667.

REFERENCES

Allamong, B. D., and T. R. Mertens. 1976. *Energy for Life: Photosynthesis and Respiration* (Self-Teaching Text). Wiley.

Björkman, O., and J. Berry. 1973. High-Efficiency Photosynthesis. *Scientific American* 229:80–93 (Offprint 1281). *Scientific American* Offprints are available from W. H. Freeman and Company, 660 Market Street, San Francisco 94104, and 58 Kings Road, Reading RG1 3AA, England. Please order by number.

Govindjee and R. Govindjee. 1974. The Primary Events of Photosynthesis. *Scientific American* 231:68–82 (Offprint 1310).

Lehninger, A. 1961. How Cells Transform Energy. *Scientific American* 205:62–73 (Offprint 91).

Levine, R. P. 1969. The Mechanism of Photosynthesis. *Scientific American* 221(6):58–70 (Offprint 1163).

Levitt, J. 1974. *Introduction to Plant Physiology.* 2nd ed. Mosby.

Price, C. A. 1970. *Molecular Approaches to Plant Physiology.* McGraw-Hill.

Rabinowitch, E. I., and Govindjee. 1965. The Role of Chlorophyll in Photosynthesis. *Scientific American* 213(1):74–83 (Offprint 1016).

Stryer, L. 1980. *Biochemistry.* 2nd ed. W. H. Freeman and Company.

Tedeschi, M. 1974. *Cell Physiology.* Academic Press.

Van Norman, R. W. 1971. *Chromatography. Experimental Biology.* 2nd ed. Prentice-Hall.

Weier, T. E., C. R. Stocking, and M. G. Barbour. 1974. *Botany: An Introduction to Plant Biology.* 5th ed. Wiley.

Carbohydrate Metabolism

In the broadest sense, metabolism includes all those events that occur in living cells. One of the more important results of these events is the formation of new cells. Concomitant with new cell formation is the active synthesis and use of carbohydrates, proteins, lipids, and other complex organic materials. In this exercise, we will confine our studies to carbohydrate metabolism and, specifically, to the hydrolysis and synthesis of starch.

Starch is a long-chain polysaccharide composed of glucose molecules linked together as shown in Fig. 12-1. Starches are frequently stored by plants and animals for use as a potentially available energy source. The breakdown of starch into its component "sugar units" is accomplished by hydrolysis. The important sugar unit we are concerned with is glucose because (1) it is a key compound in cellular metabolism (recall that it is synthesized from CO_2 and H_2O by photosynthesizing plants), and (2) it contains energy (found in the chemical bonds holding the molecule together) that can be released to do the work of the cell.

A. STARCH HYDROLYSIS

Starch hydrolysis is accomplished by amylases, which cleave the starch molecule into smaller and smaller subunits until maltose, a reducing sugar, is obtained. This sequence is shown in Fig. 12-2.

Maltose is enzymatically converted into glucose, which may then be shunted into the glycolytic and Krebs cycles, where it is further broken down into carbon dioxide, water, and energy. This process, called *cellular respiration*, will be considered in Exercise 13.

In the experiments that follow, the rate of hydrolysis of starch by salivary amylase will be measured colorimetrically under various conditions of temperature, pH, and enzyme and substrate concentrations. In these experiments, you will test for the presence of starch by adding several drops of iodine to the sample. If starch is present, the solution will turn a deep blue-black. If the starch solution is tested with iodine from 15 to 20 minutes after the addition of salivary amylase, the color obtained will

132

FIG. 12-1
Structure of a starch molecule.

Maltose unit

(↓) Amylase action

$\left[- \bigcirc - \right]$ Glucose unit

FIG. 12-2
Action of amylase on starch.

not indicate the presence of starch but will be that of the added iodine. As hydrolysis proceeds, the amount of starch in the sample will gradually be reduced. This will be reflected in the coloration of the sample on the addition of iodine, so that if the sample is tested at various intervals after adding the enzyme, a graded series of colors from deep blue to red to the color of iodine will be observed. Thus you may qualitatively measure starch hydrolysis by measuring the color changes at intervals. In this exercise, you will quantitatively measure the rate of hydrolysis by measuring the amount of light that the sample absorbs when placed in a colorimeter (refer to Appendix A for use of the Bausch & Lomb Spectronic 20 colorimeter and Appendix B for the principles of spectrophotometry).

Before beginning, carry out the following preliminary procedures for obtaining the enzyme and standardizing the colorimeter.

1. Collect 10 ml of saliva in a clean test tube. (You can stimulate the flow of saliva by chewing a small piece of paraffin.) Filter the saliva through a double layer of cheesecloth into a small beaker. This is the *stock enzyme solution*.

2. Turn on the colorimeter, and allow the instrument to warm up for 5 minutes. Check the meter needle to make sure it records 0% transmittance at a wavelength of 560 nanometers (nm) with no tube in the holder.

3. Prepare an iodine control tube by adding 3 drops of iodine to 3 ml of water in another colorimeter tube. Place the iodine control in the colorimeter, close the cover, and adjust the light control until the needle records 100% transmittance. Why is this step required?

_____

_____

1. Effect of Substrate Concentration on Activity of Salivary Amylase

In this study, you will determine the effect of altering the amount of substrate (starch) available to the enzyme.

1. Prepare a test-tube rack containing four rows of 10 colorimeter tubes each. Label the first tube in each row 1:2, 1:4, 1:8, and 1:16, corresponding to their respective dilutions of starch.

2. Label four Erlenmeyer flasks (125 ml) to correspond to the dilutions indicated, and add 50 ml of distilled water to each flask. To the first flask, add 50 ml of starch solution. Mix thoroughly, and transfer 50 ml of this mixture to the second flask. Mix thoroughly, and transfer 50 ml of the mixture to the third flask. Mix thoroughly and transfer 50 ml of the mixture to the last flask. Mix thoroughly. Remove and discard 50 ml of the last mixture.

TABLE 12-1
Effect of substrate concentration on activity of salivary amylase.

Time	Percent transmittance			
	Substrate Concentration			
	1:2	1:4	1:8	1:16

Conclusion:

3. Using a 1-ml pipet, add 0.2 ml of the stock enzyme solution to each flask, and mix thoroughly by swirling each flask. Note the time. Two minutes after adding the enzyme, transfer 3 ml of the contents of each flask to the corresponding colorimeter tube. Add 3 drops of iodine to the tubes to determine the presence of starch. Mix thoroughly and then place each tube in the colorimeter. Determine the % transmittance, and record this value in Table 12-1. Repeat this procedure at 2-minute intervals for each flask in the series. (*Note:* For these experiments, a reading of 90% T or higher will indicate that hydrolysis is complete.) Plot your data in Fig. 12-3. Interpret your results in terms of the amount of substrate available to a constant amount of enzyme.

_____

_____

_____

_____

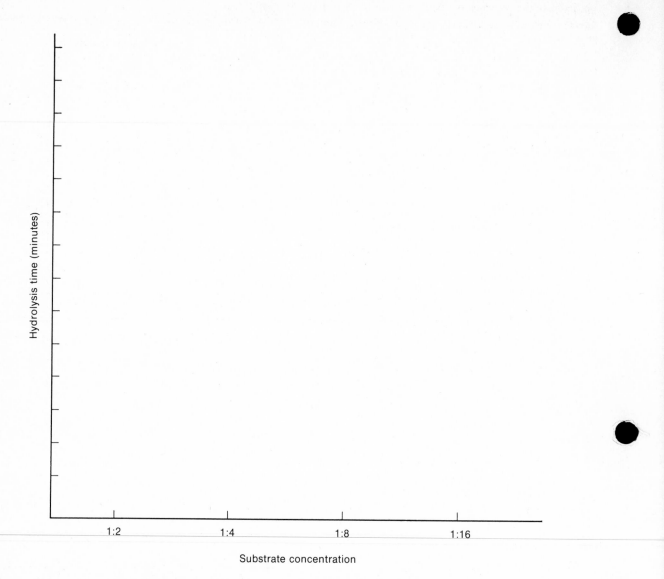

FIG. 12-3
Effect of substrate concentration on the activity of salivary amylase.

2. Effect of Enzyme Concentration on Activity of Salivary Amylase

1. Prepare a test-tube rack containing 4 rows of 10 colorimeter tubes each. Label the first tube in each row 1:5, 1:25, 1:125, and 1:625 to correspond to the enzyme dilutions that will be used in this experiment.

2. Next, set up four Erlenmeyer flasks (125 ml), each containing 20 ml of distilled water. Label each flask to correspond to the dilution series. Add 5 ml of the enzyme solution to the first flask. Mix thoroughly, and transfer 5 ml to the second flask. Repeat this procedure for the third and fourth flasks, thoroughly mixing each flask before each transfer.

3. Next add 25 ml of starch solution to each flask, starting with the first flask. Note the time.

4. Two minutes after adding the starch, remove 3 ml of solution from each flask, transfer it to the first colorimeter tube in each series, and immediately test for the presence of starch by adding 3 drops of iodine to each tube. Determine the % transmittance for each tube, and record data in Table 12-2.

TABLE 12-2
Effect of enzyme concentration on activity of salivary amylase.

Time	Percent transmittance			
	Enzyme concentration			
	1:5	1:25	1:125	1:625
Conclusion:				

TABLE 12-3
Effect of pH on activity of salivary amylase.

Time	Percent transmittance			
	pH			
	5	6	7	8.5
Conclusion:				

5. Repeat this procedure at 2-minute intervals for the remaining tubes in each series.

6. Plot your data in Fig. 12-4. Interpret your results.

3. Effect of pH on Activity of Salivary Amylase

Note: For this study, use the enzyme and substrate concentrations from Parts 1 and 2 that gave the optimum results.

1. Prepare a test-tube rack containing four rows of ten colorimeter tubes each. Label the first tube in each row to correspond to pH values of 5, 6, 7, and 8.5, respectively. To each of four Erlenmeyer flasks (125 ml), add 25 ml of buffer solutions at a pH of .5.0, 6.0, 7.0, and 8.5, respectively. Into each flask, pipet 0.5 ml of enzyme solution. Mix thoroughly by swirling each flask. Begin-

ning with the tube of lowest pH, add 25 ml of starch solution to each flask. Note the time. Thoroughly mix the contents immediately after adding the starch.

2. Two minutes after adding the starch to the first flask, quickly transfer 3 ml from each flask to the first tube in each corresponding series. Test for the presence of starch, using 3 drops of iodine. Record colorimeter readings as quickly as possible after the addition of iodine.

3. Repeat this procedure at 2-minute intervals for the remaining tubes of each series.

4. Record these times in Table 12-3, and plot your data in Fig. 12-5.

What is the optimum pH for the activity of salivary amylase?

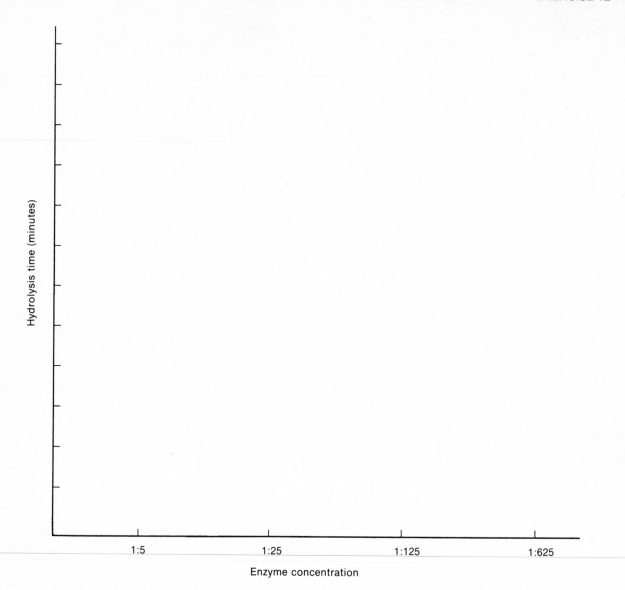

FIG. 12-4
Effect of enzyme concentration on the activity of salivary amylase.

Are your results consistent with your knowledge of where this enzyme functions in the body? Explain.

_____

_____

_____

4. Effect of Temperature on Activity of Salivary Amylase

Note: For this study, use the enzyme and substrate concentrations (from Parts 1 and 2) that gave the optimum results.

1. Into each of five Erlenmeyer flasks (125 ml), pour 50 ml of the starch solution. Immerse these containers in large beakers of water or water baths adjusted to temper-

FIG. 12-5
Effect of pH on the activity of salivary amylase.

atures of 5°, 15°, 30°, 45°, and 70°C. This may be accomplished by adding ice water or hot water to the beakers. The temperatures in the beakers should be maintained throughout the experiment and should not vary more than ±3°C.

2. While waiting for the temperature to equilibrate in the beakers, prepare a test-tube rack containing five rows of 10 or 12 colorimeter tubes each. Label the first tube in each row to correspond with the five temperature values used.

3. When the starch solution in the flasks has reached the temperature of the water bath (verify this by placing a thermometer in the starch solution), add 1 ml of enzyme solution to each flask, starting with that at 5°C. Note the time you add the enzyme to each flask. Mix each flask thoroughly as soon as the enzyme has been added, and put it back in the water bath.

4. Two minutes after the addition of the enzyme, quickly transfer 3 ml of the contents of each flask to the corresponding first colorimeter tube in each series.

Immediately test for the presence of starch by adding 3 drops of iodine to each colorimeter tube. Mix thoroughly. (At the 70°C temperature, cool the tube with tap water before adding iodine.) Repeat this procedure at 2-minute intervals for the remaining tubes of each series. Be prepared to test for starch at longer, or shorter, intervals if necessary.

5. Record this time in the appropriate space in Table 12-4. Plot your data in Fig. 12-6. What is the effect of temperature on the activity of salivary amylase?

_____

_____

_____

_____

TABLE 12-4
Effect of temperature on activity of salivary amylase.

Time	Percent transmittance				
	Temperature (°C)				
	5	15	30	45	70
Conclusion:					

B. Enzymatic Synthesis of Starch

In the first part of this exercise, you examined the hydrolysis of starch by a class of enzymes called **amylases**. However, other enzymes also function in this reaction. These enzymes, called **phosphorylases**, degrade glycogen or starch more rapidly than any known amylase.

The activity of the two classes of enzymes differs in a number of ways. The differences in their rates have already been mentioned. A second difference is that amylases cleave this polysaccharide into maltose units that require a second enzyme, called **maltase**, to complete the conversion to glucose. Phosphorylases cleave polysaccharides into glucose-phosphate units, which are further hydrolyzed to glucose and phosphoric acid through the activity of the enzyme **phosphatase**.

The most important difference in these enzymes, however, lies in the reversibility of the phosphorylase reaction, which goes readily in either direction; the amylase reaction is almost irreversible (Fig. 12-7). Explain the difference in the reversibility of these two reactions.

_____

_____

_____

_____

In this experiment, you will try to show that the phosphorylase reaction is reversible if the following conditions are met: (1) phosphorylase activity requires the presence of inorganic phosphate; (2) the reaction proceeds from glucose-1-phosphate and not glucose; (3) there must be present a small amount of primer or starter polysaccharide (this enzyme adds glucose units to the ends of preexisting polysaccharide chains).

1. Preparation of Enzyme

Phosphorylases are known to occur in many plant and animal tissues. An easily available and inexpensive source of this enzyme is potatoes. Before preparing the active enzyme, however, set up and number a series of test tubes, as shown in Table 12-5. If enzyme is called for, it is to be added immediately after it is prepared, because this particular enzyme denatures rapidly. Peel and cube a small potato, and place the cubes immediately in a beaker containing 30–40 ml of 0.01 M sodium fluor-

FIG. 12-6
Effect of temperature on the activity of salivary amylase.

ide. (CAUTION: *sodium fluoride is a poison!*) It is used here to inhibit the activity of potato phosphatase. Why?

_____

_____

_____

Transfer the cubes to a food grinder, and grind to pulp

(Fig. 12-8). Filter the pulp through a Buchner funnel, and use the extract immediately.

2. Enzymatic Synthesis of Starch by Phosphorylase

Place the enzyme preparation into the tubes called for in Table 12-5. Mix the reagents thoroughly. Immediately after adding the enzyme, remove a small sample from each tube and test it with a drop of iodine on a spot plate.

FIG. 12-7
Action of phosphorylase. (From *Experimental Biochemistry,* 2nd ed., by John M. Clark, Jr. and Robert L. Switzer. W. H. Freeman and Company. Copyright © 1977.)

TABLE 12-5
Enzymatic synthesis of starch by phosphorylases.

Tube No.	Reagents	Observations
1	3 ml of 0.01 M glucose, a small drop of 0.2% starch solution, and 3 ml of the enzyme preparation	
2	3 ml of 0.01 M glucose-1-phosphate, a small drop of 0.2% starch solution, and 3 ml of the enzyme preparation	
3	3 ml of 0.01 M glucose-1-phosphate and 3 ml of the enzyme preparation	
4	3 ml of 0.01 M glucose-1-phosphate, a small drop of 0.2% starch solution, and 3 ml of the boiled enzyme preparation	
5	3 ml of 0.01 M glucose-1-phosphate, 1 ml of 0.2 KH_2PO_4, a small drop of 0.2% starch solution, and 3 ml of the enzyme preparation	
6	3 ml of 0.2% starch solution, 1 ml of 0.2 M KH_2PO_4, and 3 ml of the enzyme preparation	
7	3 ml of 0.2% starch solution, 1 ml of 0.2 M KH_2PO_4, and 3 ml of boiled enzyme preparation	

Repeat the iodine test at 3 minute intervals thereafter. The reaction should go to completion within 30 minutes. Record your observations in Table 12-5. What is the role of KH_2PO_4 (potassium dihydrogen phosphate)?

_____

_____

What role does each test tube play in this experiment?

_____

_____

_____

_____

_____

What would have happened if the sodium fluoride were left out of the enzyme preparation?

_____

_____

_____

FIG. 12-8
Preparing the enzyme solution for synthesizing starch. (Adapted from *Plants in Action*, by Leonard Machlis and John G. Torrey. W. H. Freeman and Company. Copyright © 1956.)

REFERENCES

Giese, A. C. 1979. *Cell Physiology.* 5th ed. Holt/Saunders.

Guthrie, R. D., and J. Honeyman. 1968. *An Introduction to the Chemistry of Carbohydrates.* Clarendon Press.

Lehninger, A. L. 1971. *Bioenergetics.* 2nd ed. Worth.

Lehninger, A. L. 1960. Energy Transformation in the Cell. *Scientific American* 202(5):102–114 (Offprint 69). *Scientific American* Offprints are available from W. H. Freeman and Company, 660 Market Street, San Francisco 94104, and 58 Kings Road, Reading RG1 3AA, England. Please order by number.

McElroy, W. D. 1971. *Cellular Physiology and Biochemistry.* 3rd ed. Prentice-Hall.

Pigman, W., ed. 1972. *The Carbohydrates.* Vol. 1a. Academic Press.

Stryer, L. 1980. *Biochemistry.* 2nd ed. W. H. Freeman and Company.

White, A., P. Handler, and E. L. Smith. 1978. *Principles of Biochemistry.* 6th ed. McGraw-Hill.

Cellular Respiration

All plants and animals require a continuous supply of energy for the performance of vital activities. This is obtained in the form of the chemical bond energy locked in the nutrient molecules. The source of the chemical bond energy is the solar energy used in the photosynthetic activities of green plants. The conversion of the chemical bond energy into a readily usable form—such as the high-energy phosphate bond of adenosine triphosphate (ATP)—and its expenditure are by means of processes collectively referred to as **respiration**. Broadly speaking, respiratory processes can be classified as either **aerobic** or **anaero-**

bic. Anaerobic respiration undoubtedly evolved first, and still plays an important role in many of the metabolic activities of plants and animals. Muscular work, for example, depends in large measure on anaerobic processes. Aerobic respiration, which requires oxygen, is not only a more recent biochemical innovation (in the evolutionary sense) but also a more efficient one in terms of energy recovery from nutrient molecules. The following diagram summarizes the many steps in the respiration of the simple 6-carbon sugar, glucose, under anaerobic and aerobic conditions:

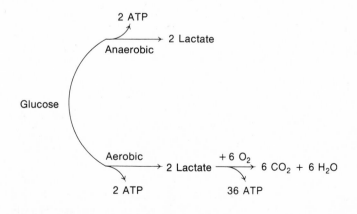

Anaerobic: Glucose → 2 ATP, → 2 Lactate

Approximately 27% of 52,000 cal/mole of glucose transferred to ATP

Aerobic: Glucose → 2 ATP, → 2 Lactate $\xrightarrow{+6 O_2}$ 6 CO_2 + 6 H_2O, 36 ATP

Approximately 42% of 686,000 cal/mole of glucose transferred to ATP

Aerobic respiration yields much more energy than does anaerobic respiration and results in the complete breakdown of glucose to carbon dioxide and water, whereas anaerobic respiration generally leads to end products, such as organic acids and alcohols, that may be toxic.

The glucose molecule is broken down and its energy released in three stages: **glycolysis**, the **Krebs cycle**, and the **electron-transport chain** (Fig. 13-1).

During glycolysis, the 6-carbon sugar molecule is converted, through a complex series of enzyme-controlled reactions, into two 3-carbon molecules of pyruvic acid. In the presence of oxygen (aerobic respiration), pyruvic acid enters another series of enzyme-mediated reactions called the **Krebs cycle**. These reactions take place in the mitochondria. In the Krebs cycle, energy in the form of ATP is generated. This is accomplished by a series of oxidation-reduction reactions that take place in the electron-transport chain. In this process, hydrogen atoms that have been removed from Krebs cycle compounds are split into positively charged protons and negatively charged, *high-energy* electrons. The electrons are transported through a series of molecules that are alternately oxidized (lose electrons) and reduced (gain electrons). During these oxidation-reduction reactions, some of the energy of the electrons is incorporated into ATP. Finally, at the end of the chain the free protons combine with the now *low-energy* electrons and oxygen to form water.

There are several ways in which respiration taking place in an organism can be demonstrated. They include measurements of energy given off in the form of heat, the amount of glucose used, the amount of oxygen consumed, and the amount of carbon dioxide released. In this exercise, you will study the external signs of respiration by indirectly determining the amount of oxygen consumed. Oxidation-reduction reactions are critical at the cellular level of respiration, so it is important that you become familiar with these kinds of chemical reactions.

A. AEROBIC RESPIRATION

Many methods used in the study of respiration depend on measuring changes in the volume or pressure of gas. Any variation in volume or pressure within a closed system in which an organism is respiring represents the net difference between oxygen consumption (which would decrease pressure and volume in the closed container) and carbon dioxide production (which would increase pressure and volume). However, if the carbon dioxide produced is absorbed in some way, any changes could be attributed to oxygen consumption.

A simple respirometer that can be used to detect changes in gas pressure and volume is shown in Fig. 13-2. This equipment consists of two vessels that can be closed to the outside. Respiring material is placed in one

FIG. 13-1
Energy, in the form of ATP, produced during glycolysis and respiration.

of the containers, along with potassium hydroxide (KOH), an agent used to absorb carbon dioxide. Because gas volume is influenced by such physical factors as atmospheric pressure and temperature, the second container (identical except for the living material) is employed as a compensation chamber. Any changes in the volume of gas in the compensation chamber must be taken into consideration when evaluating changes occurring in the respiration chamber.

In this study, you will determine the respiratory rate of germinating peas in terms of oxygen intake.

1. Following the diagram in Fig. 13-2A, fill the respiration test tube half full with germinating peas.

2. Place a loose wad of cotton over the peas. Place about 12 mm of potassium hydroxide (KOH) pellets over the cotton. The cotton keeps the KOH from contacting the living seeds; it should not be packed tightly. KOH is a substance that will remove the CO_2 from the atmosphere of the tube as fast as it is given off by respiring peas. Why is it necessary to remove the CO_2 from the tube?

_____

_____

_____

3. Prepare the compensation tube in the same way, except use glass beads in place of the peas. Why is it necessary to place the inert glass beads into the compensation tube?

_____

_____

4. Insert a rubber stopper, with attached capillary tubing, firmly into each tube (Fig. 13-2B).

5. Place the tubes in a vertical position by clamping to a ring stand (Fig. 13-2C). Using an eyedropper, add enough dye to the end of each capillary tube so that about 12 mm of the dye will be drawn into the tube (Fig. 13-2D).

6. After allowing 2–3 minutes for the gas pressures to reach equilibrium, note the position of the outer end of the dye column on the millimeter scale (Fig. 13-2E). Record this initial reading in Table 13-1. (*Note:* Because the respirometer is very sensitive to volume changes due to heat, keep it away from any heat sources such as lamps, hot plates, etc.) Then attach pinch clamps to the rubber tubing on each test tube.

7. Take readings of the location of the column at 1-minute intervals for the next 5 minutes. Record your data in Table 13-1. (*Note:* If the movement of the dye is fairly rapid, you must be prepared to take your readings at shorter intervals—20 or 30 seconds—or the column may reach the bent portion of the tube before you have enough readings to complete your data.) The dye column

A. Fill test tube half full with germinating peas. Add about 12mm layer of cotton and then potassium hydroxide (KOH).

Compensation tube

KOH
Cotton
Germinating peas
Glass beads

B. Attach millimeter ruler with tape.
Rubber tubing
Capillary tubing (20–30cm)
Insert stopper tightly into test tubes.

C. Attach tubes to ring stand. Capillary tubing must be level.

D. Add enough dye to end of tube so that 12mm of dye is drawn in.

Dye
Starting point

E. Allow 2–3 minutes for the tubes to reach equilibrium. Then mark the *starting point* on the ruler. Place clamps over rubber tubing and tighten. Take readings of the movement of the dye at timed intervals.

FIG. 13-2
Procedure for measuring oxygen consumption in germinating peas.

TABLE 13-1
Respiration data.

| Time (minutes) | Respirometer readings (in mm) | | | | | |
| | Germinating peas (Room temp: _____°C) | | | Germinating peas (_____°C) | | |
	Respiration tube (1)	Compensation tube (2)	Corrected data (1 minus 2)	Respiration tube (1)	Compensation tube (2)	Corrected data (1 minus 2)
0						
1						
2						
3						
4						
5						

can be returned to the outer end of the tube by opening the pinch clamp and tilting the capillary tube.

Why did the dye move toward the respiration chamber and not away?

_____

_____

Under what circumstances might the dye move away from the chamber?

_____

_____

8. Repeat the procedure to determine the effects of temperature on respiration and record your data in Table 13-1. Students should select different temperatures in order to reflect a variety of temperature effects.

9. Plot the data tabulated in Table 13-1 in Figs. 13-3 and 13-4. Identify each line on the graph with the appropriate label.

1. Respiration in Animals

Many factors affect respiration. Among them are the general state of health and the degree of physical activity of the organism. The activity of certain hormones also markedly affects respiration. As part of this study, you will attempt to determine what effect temperature has on the respiration of **poikilothermic** (cold-blooded) and **homeothermic** (warm-blooded) animals.

Poikilothermic animals are deficient in the necessary internal mechanisms for regulating body temperature. As a consequence, their respiratory rates tend to be *directly* related to the temperature of their environments. In contrast, homeothermic animals have the ability to maintain their internal temperatures and, therefore, are *less affected* by temperature changes in their environments.

In this exercise, you will measure the volume of oxygen consumed during respiration by using a respirometer that consists in part of a manometer. In its simplest form, a manometer is a U-tube that is partly filled with fluid. The manometer measures the difference in the pressures on the two sides of the U-tube. For example, when the pressures on both sides of the tube are equal, the fluid levels in both sides are equal (Fig. 13-5A). However, when the pressure on one side is greater than that on the other side, the fluid level is lower in the side having the greater pressure (Figs. 13-5B, C).

In the respirometer used in this exercise, the manometer is connected to two jars. These jars can be closed off from the pressure of the outside atmosphere with pinch clamps attached to the vent tubes. Any pressure changes that develop in these jars will be revealed by the vertical movement of the fluid in the manometer tube. These changes can be measured if one arm of the manometer consists of a measuring device; in this case, a pipet.

If a live animal is placed in one of the jars and the vent tubes are sealed, then the exchange of respiratory gases

FIG. 13-3
Respiratory rate of germinating peas at room temperature.

(O_2 and CO_2) will be restricted to the inside of the jar. The oxygen in the jar containing the animal will be used up and will be replaced by an equal amount of carbon dioxide. Under these conditions, there will be little or no pressure change in the jar. If, however, a compound that absorbs carbon dioxide as it is exhaled is placed in the jar, then the carbon dioxide will be removed from the atmosphere in the jar. Consequently, the total amount of gas in the jar containing the animal will be lowered. This results in a decrease in the pressure in the jar containing the animal. Why?

_____

_____

As a result, the fluid in the manometer tube moves. In which direction?

_____

_____

The empty jar attached to the other side of the manometer tube serves as a temperature-volume control. Initially, its atmosphere is identical with that of the jar containing the animal. Because no respiration is occurring in the empty jar, there will be no change in the gas pressure. Keeping both jars at the same temperature, which will vary in the source of the experiment, ensures that any changes in the height of the manometer fluid are due to pressure changes brought about by the respiratory activities of the animal in the respiration chambers.

A variety of animals are available in the laboratory.

FIG. 13-4
Effect of temperature on respiratory rate.

You are to measure their respiratory rates and, using the data obtained, determine whether the animal you have tested is poikilothermic or homeothermic.

Your instructor will determine the temperature each team of two students is to use in these experiments. Refer to Fig. 13-6A, B, C for the procedure to use to obtain that temperature. Weigh the animal to the nearest gram. Record the animal's weight in Table 13-2. Because different animals and different temperatures are being used by different teams, the data collected should be exchanged with other teams and entered in Table 13-3.

After the animal and the water bath are at the desired temperature, allow the setup to stand for 5 or 10 minutes with the vent tube open. Then attach a pinch clamp to each vent tube to seal them. Record in Table 13-2 the initial position of the fluid (in milliliters) in the pipet arm of the manometer (Fig. 13-6D).

After 5 minutes or so, record the new position of the manometer fluid in Table 13-2. (*Note:* The time interval used will depend on the respiratory rate of the animal under study. Make it long enough so that the water column rises approximately one-third the height of the pipet. It should be in whole minutes to make succeeding calculations easier.) After completing one such reading, remove the pinch clamps from the vent tubes. This will allow the fluid in the manometer to equalize. Replace the pinch clamp, and repeat the procedure twice to obtain two additional manometer readings. Calculate the average value for the three readings, and then determine how much oxygen was used per hour. For example,

$$\frac{12\,\mathrm{ml}\,O_2}{\cancel{6}\,\mathrm{min}} \times \frac{\overset{10}{\cancel{60}}\,\mathrm{min}}{1\,\mathrm{hour}} = \frac{120\,\mathrm{ml\,of}\,O_2}{1\,\mathrm{hour}}$$

$$= 120\,\mathrm{ml\,of}\,O_2\,\mathrm{per\,hr}$$

Determine the respiratory rate of each animal in terms of the milliliters of O_2 used per kilogram per hour as follows:

$$\frac{\mathrm{ml\,of}\,O_2/\mathrm{hr}}{\mathrm{wt\,in\,g}/1000} = \frac{120\,\mathrm{ml\,of}\,O_2/\mathrm{hr}}{120\,\mathrm{g}/1000}$$

$$= \frac{120\,\mathrm{ml\,of}\,O_2/\mathrm{hr}}{0.12\,\mathrm{kg}}$$

$$= 1000\,\mathrm{ml}\,O_2/\mathrm{kg/hr}$$

Record your data in Tables 13-2 and 13-3.

From your data, and from the data of other students using the same type of animal, determine whether the animal you used was homeothermic or poikilothermic. Explain.

_____

_____

_____

_____

There are several different gases in air; how could you prove that the gas being used in the tube was actually oxygen?

_____

_____

_____

B. BIOLOGICAL OXIDATION

As described in the first part of this exercise, oxidation-reduction reactions are important in releasing the energy in glucose and incorporating this energy into ATP molecules. Iron-containing compounds called **cytochromes** take part in these reactions, which are carried out in the mitochondria. In these reactions, oxidation takes place

FIG. 13-5
Operation of a simple manometer. (After *Investigations of Cells and Organisms*, by P. Abramoff and R. G. Thomson. Prentice-Hall, 1968.)

Respiration jar — Thermometer

Frog or mouse

Wire screen

Cotton

Add hot or cold water

Solid potassium hydroxide (KOH), or sodium hydroxide (NaOH)

A. *Room Temperature:* After setting up the respiration jar, place the animal in it. Then place animal and jar in water bath maintained at room temperature by addition of hot and cold water.

Respiration jar

Thermometer

Respiration jar

Mouse

Ice in water bath

Ice

Ice bath in large beaker

B. *High Temperature:* Place respiration chamber and animal in water bath maintained at 30° or 35°C, adding hot or cold water as needed. Wait from 5 to 10 minutes before beginning experiment.

C. *Low Temperature:* Place respiration jar with animal in ice from 10 to 15 minutes. Meanwhile reduce the temperature of the water bath to 5° or 10°C, using ice. Then place respiration jar in cooled water bath.

Vent tubes closed off by pinch clamps

D.

Inverted 5- or 10-ml pipet

Manometer

3 ml

Rubber tubing

Water level before

Water level after

FIG. 13-6
Procedure for determining respiration rate of an animal. (After *Investigations of Cells and Organisms,* by P. Abramoff and R. G. Thomson. Prentice-Hall, 1968.)

TABLE 13-2
Calculation of respiratory activity.

Treatment	Trial	Initial manometer reading (ml)	Final manometer reading (ml)	Volume of O_2 used (ml)	Time interval (min)	Calculated average ml of O_2/hr	Calculated average respiratory rate (ml of O_2/kg/hr)
Room temperature ____°C	1						
	2						
	3						
High temperature ____°C	1						
	2						
	3						
Low temperature ____°C	1						
	2						
	3						

Type of animal _____ Weight (kg) _____

Poikilothermic _____ Homeothermic _____

TABLE 13-3
Respiratory data of other animals.

Type of animal	Temperature treatment	Respiratory rate (ml of O_2/kg/hr)	Type of animal	Temperature treatment	Respiratory rate (ml of O_2/kg/hr)

in the presence of oxygen. An example of an oxidation-reduction reaction is

$$(1)$$

in which $A \cdot H_2$, the hydrogen donor, is called the **reductant**; B, the hydrogen acceptor, is called the **oxidant**. Thus every oxidation must be accompanied by a simul-taneous reduction. The energy required for the removal of hydrogens in oxidation reactions is supplied by the accompanying reduction. In order for this type of reaction to proceed, specific enzymes called **dehydrogenases** are required.

Specific dehydrogenases called **oxidases** use oxygen as a hydrogen acceptor. Most oxidases are enzymes that contain a metal, such as copper, iron, or zinc, and a riboflavin-containing complex. The transfer of hydrogen from the substrate (the reductant) to oxygen by the oxidase usually results in the formation of hydrogen peroxide (H_2O_2) (see Reaction 2). Although H_2O_2 is toxic to the tissues, its toxic effect is prevented by two important enzymes: **peroxidase** and **catalase**.

$$A \cdot \boxed{H_2} \quad \underset{\text{Oxidase}}{\overset{O_2}{\diagdown}} \quad \overset{B \cdot \boxed{H_2}}{\diagup} \tag{2}$$

$$A \diagup \quad \boxed{H_2}\boxed{O_2} \quad \diagdown B$$

Peroxidase, as shown in Reaction 2, splits off the oxygen, which then acts to accept hydrogen from another substrate molecule. During the same reaction, another molecule (B in Reaction 2) is reduced. Thus the toxic potential of hydrogen peroxide has been removed. In this exercise, you will examine an oxidation-reduction reaction in which peroxidase is a catalyst.

Guaiacol is a substance that is oxidized to a colored product by H_2O_2 in the presence of peroxidase. Thus, Reaction 3 can be used to follow an oxidation-reduction reaction as a function of peroxidase activity, which can be determined by colorimetrically measuring the amount

of light that oxidized guaiacol absorbs. (Refer to Appendix A for the use of the Bausch & Lomb Spectronic 20 Colorimeter and Appendix B for the principles of spectrophotometry.)

$$\underset{\text{Guaiacol (reduced)}}{\text{OCH}_3\text{,OH}} + H_2O_2 \xrightarrow{\text{Peroxidase}} \underset{\text{Guaiacol (oxidized colored complex)}}{\text{O,O}} + 2H_2O \tag{3}$$

With a paring knife, peel a turnip and cut it into small cubes; place the cubes in a homogenizer and grind for 30 seconds. Alternatively, place the cubes in a mortar containing silica sand, and grind to pulp with a pestle (Fig. 13-7). Filter the homogenate through a double layer of

FIG. 13-7
Apparatus for extracting the enzyme peroxidase.

TABLE 13-4
Peroxidase activity in turnip tissue.

Time (seconds)	% transmittance				
	1 ml of turnip extract	0.5 ml of turnip extract	2.0 ml of turnip extract	1 ml of boiled turnip extract	1 ml of extract + 0.5 ml NaCN
20					
40					
60					
80					
100					
120					

cheesecloth into a beaker. Squeeze out as much of the liquid as you can. Dilute 1 ml of the juice to 200 ml with distilled water.

Add 0.01 ml of liquid guaiacol, together with 0.2 ml of 0.9% H_2O_2 and 4.7 ml of distilled water, to a test tube. Put 1.0 ml of the diluted turnip extract and 4 ml of water into a colorimeter tube. Pour the guaiacol-H_2O_2 solution into the colorimeter tube. To mix, pour the mixture quickly back into the empty test tube and then back into the colorimeter tube. Wipe the colorimeter tube clean and immediately place it in the Spectronic 20 colorimeter. The wavelength to be used is 500 nanometers (nm). What solution should you use to standardize the colorimeter for this test?

_____

_____

Start the stopwatch, and read the % transmittance. Take readings every 20 seconds, and record the data in Table 13-4. Plot these readings against time in Fig. 13-8. Repeat the determination, using one-half and then twice as much extract. Also measure the effect of extract that has been placed in a bath of boiling water for several minutes and then cooled. Then test the effect of adding 0.5 ml of 0.01 M sodium fluoride (CAUTION: Poison!) to the reaction mixture.

From these data, what can you conclude about peroxidase activity in turnip tissue?

_____

_____

_____

Fill in the blanks in Reaction 4. Indicate oxidants, reductants, the reaction catalyzed by peroxidase, and reactions catalyzed by dehydrogenases.

In oxidation-reduction reactions, what component of the hydrogen atom is actually being shunted through the various carrier molecules?

_____

(4)

154

FIG. 13-8
Peroxidase activity in turnip tissue.

REFERENCES

Allamong, B. D., and T. R. Mertens. 1976. *Energy for Life: Photosynthesis and Respiration* (Self-Teaching Text). Wiley.

Giese, A. C. 1979. *Cell Physiology*. 5th ed. Holt/Saunders.

Green, D. E. 1964. The Mitochondrion. *Scientific American* 210(1):63–74.

Hinkle, P. C., and R. E. McCarty. 1978. How Cells Make ATP. *Scientific American* 238:104–123 (Offprint 1383). *Scientific American* Offprints are available from W. H. Freeman and Company, 660 Market Street, San Francisco 94104, and 58 Kings Road, Reading RG1 3AA, England. Please order by number.

Kimball, J. W. 1978. *Cell Biology*. 2nd ed. Addison-Wesley.

Lehninger, A. L. 1960. Energy Transformation in the Cell. *Scientific American* 202(5):102–114 (Offprint 69).

Lehninger, A. L. 1961. How Cells Transform Energy. *Scientific American* 205(3):62–73 (Offprint 91).

Racker, E. 1968. The Membrane of the Mitochondrion. *Scientific American* (Offprint 1101).

Stephenson, W. K. 1978. *Concepts in Cell Biology: A Self-Instruction Text*. Wiley.

Stryer, L. 1980. *Biochemistry*. 2nd ed. W. H. Freeman and Company.

Tedeschi, M. 1974. *Cell Physiology*. Academic Press.

White, A. W., P. Handler, and E. L. Smith. 1978. *Principles of Biochemistry*. 6th ed. McGraw-Hill.

Transport in Biological Systems

The movement of water, metabolic wastes, food, hormones, minerals, gases, and many other materials within the organism is extremely important to higher plants and animals. Almost every metabolic activity of the organism depends ultimately on the exchange of materials between cells and between the organism and its environment.

Nutrient molecules must be absorbed, body wastes removed, and oxygen obtained to support cellular respiration. A variety of substances, including such diversified materials as chemical regulators (hormones) and defensive materials (antibodies), must be exchanged if the organism is to function coherently. Basically, exchange depends on physical processes such as diffusion, osmosis, and pinocytosis and on biochemical processes such as active transport. Because these phenomena can affect rapid movement over short distances, very small organisms (i.e., protozoa) or organisms with most of their cells in contact with the environment (sponges) rely almost entirely on them to achieve exchange (Fig. 14-1A).

Larger and more complex organisms require supplementary systems. With only a small fraction of their cellular mass in direct contact with the environment, exchanges based solely on diffusion would not occur rapidly enough to meet their needs. In larger organisms, cellular exchanges take place in an internal environment (the extracellular fluid system), and a way must be developed to transport these fluids throughout the organism. Exchange between the organism and the environment than takes place through the body wall or some specialized part of it. These mechanisms constitute the transport system of plants and the circulatory systems of animals.

A. TRANSPORT IN ANIMALS

Circulatory systems in animals vary enormously in complexity. In the simplest cases, movement of extracellular fluids is achieved by the compressive action of body wall muscles or by ciliary activity (Fig. 14-1B).

157

A. Direct exchange between
cells and environment

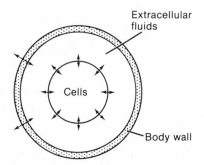

B. Circulation of extracellular
fluids in the absence of a
defined circulatory system

C. Open circulatory system

D. Closed circulatory system

FIG. 14-1
Types of exchange and circulatory systems.

Those only slightly more complex, however, have some type of pumplike heart. The pump may consist simply of a group of pulsatile vessels, as in the earthworm, or it may take the form of a simple membranous chamber, as in insects. In many molluscs and vertebrates, the heart is a complex, chambered structure. The evolution of a heart is normally associated with the development of vessels that direct the flow of extracellular fluids to specific areas of the body. In insects and several other invertebrates, the system of such vessels is incomplete in that the fluids carried by the vessels empty into irregular cavities and return to the heart through the body spaces (Fig. 14-1C). Such circulatory systems are said to be "open," and there is no distinction between the fluids within the heart and vessels and those outside.

In vertebrates, the circulatory system is completely closed and consists of a pump and a continuous series of vessels. The blood carried in these vessels is different from the extracellular fluid in many respects (Fig. 14-1D). Blood flow takes place within this tubular system, and exchange between the blood and other extracellular fluids takes place through the smallest vessels (capillaries) and irregular cavities (sinuses).

In the early 1600s, William Harvey, an English physician, discovered the pattern of circulation of blood. He subsequently concluded that the blood carries nutrients, oxygen, and various other materials to the body tissues, and carbon dioxide and other waste products away from the tissues. Harvey, however, never saw one of the more important parts of the circulatory system—the capillaries. These blood vessels are important because it is in the capillaries that the exchange of materials in the circulatory system and in the cells takes place. In this exercise, you will examine the circulation of blood through the capillaries in the fish tail *or* the web of a frog's foot.

1. Capillary Circulation

a. In the Fish Tail

Obtain a small (5-cm) goldfish from the aquarium in your laboratory (Fig. 14-2). Wrap the fish (except for the mouth and tail) in dripping wet cotton. (*Note: Do not allow the cotton around the fish to dry out.*) Place it in the bottom half of a petri dish (Fig. 14-2B, C). If the fish moves around too much, place it in a container of chloretone solution to anesthetize it. After a minute or two, the fish will roll over on its side and will remain anesthetized for about one hour.

Place a cover slip (or glass slide) over a thin region of the tail. Then position the petri dish on your microscope so that the fish's tail is over the hole in the stage (Fig. 14-2D). Focus on the tail with the low-power objective of your microscope. Note the movement of blood through

A. Remove a 5-cm goldfish from the aquarium.

B. Wrap the fish (except for the head and tail) with dripping wet cotton.

C. Place fish in bottom half of Petri dish. Place cover slip or glass slide over thin part of tail.

Cotton

Cover slip

D. Place dish on microscope so that fish's tail is over hole in stage.

E. Examine with low and high power objectives of your microscope.

F. Capillary circulation. Label capillaries, venules, and arterioles.

FIG. 14-2
Examination of capillary circulation in the goldfish tail. (After *Investigations of Cells and Organisms*, by P. Abramoff and R. G. Thomson. Prentice-Hall, 1968.)

the blood vessels. The smallest vessels you see are the capillaries. They are just wide enough to permit the passage of a single file of blood cells. What is the advantage of having red blood cells pass through the capillaries in single file?

_____

_____

Change to high power to examine the capillaries and blood cells more closely.

Blood enters the capillaries from small arteries called **arterioles**. Trace a capillary back to an arteriole. Does the blood flow more rapidly in the arterioles or in the capillaries?

_____

Follow a capillary in the direction in which the blood is flowing. It will join a slightly larger blood vessel called **a venule**. Is the rate at which the blood flows greater in the venules or in the capillaries?

_____

What is the relation between the diameters of the red blood cells and the capillaries?

_____

_____

What significance might this relation have with regard to exchange of gases and other products?

_____

_____

_____

Does the red cell seem to be a rigid or a flexible structure?

_____

What are the advantages and disadvantages of this?

_____

_____

_____

Why are exchanges between the surrounding tissues and the blood more likely to occur in the capillaries than in the arteries or veins?

_____

_____

_____

_____

_____

Record your observations of capillary circulation with a drawing in Fig. 14-2F.

b. In the Web of a Frog's Foot

Carefully wrap a live frog in a wet towel tightly enough to keep it from moving very much. Leave one foot exposed. Now spread and pin the web of the foot over a hole in a balsa board. Keep the skin of the frog moist with tap water. By supporting the whole preparation on the stage of your microscope, the actual circulation of cells in the blood vessels can be seen. Select a very small field and observe carefully the size of the vessels, the thickness of their walls, and velocity of blood flow. As you look at the demonstration, keep in mind the three comparisons that you wish to make between arterioles, capillaries, and venules: (1) relative size, (2) comparative speed of flow of blood, (3) amount of pulsation. Stroke the web lightly in the field of view. Record your observations.

Observe the vascular bed in the web with the low-power lens of a compound microscope or with a stereoscopic microscope at a magnification of $40 \times$ or more.

Blood enters the capillaries from small arteries called *arterioles*. Trace a capillary back to an arteriole. Does the blood flow more rapidly in the arterioles or in the capillaries?

_____

Follow a capillary in the direction in which the blood is flowing. Is the flow of blood greater in the venules or in the capillaries?

_____

What is the relation between the diameters of the red blood cells and the capillaries?

_____

What significance might this relation have with regard to exchange processes?

_____

_____

_____

Does the red blood cell appear to be a frigid or a flexible structure?

_____

What are the advantages and disadvantages of this?

_____

_____

Why are exchanges between the surrounding tissues and the blood more likely to occur in the capillaries than in the arteries or veins?

_____

_____

_____

_____

_____

2. Factors Affecting Capillary Circulation

The flow of blood is affected by a variety of factors, most of which operate to ensure that blood is delivered at adequate rates to various sections of the body. The effects on capillary circulation of ethyl alcohol, nicotine, and lactic acid are given in Table 14-1. Determine the effects of temperature and adrenalin on the capillary circulation of the frog mesentary or fish tail, following the directions given below. After you have finished, return the fish to the aquarium and the frog to your instructor.

a. Temperature

Carefully examine the capillary network at room temperature to determine the normal blood flow. Then, using an eye-dropper, apply several drops of chilled frog or fish Ringer's solution (isotonic salt solution) to the surface of the capillary network. Does the blood flow rate increase or decrease?

_____

Record your results in Table 14-1. Rinse off the tissue using warm (room temperature) Ringer's solution, and then apply Ringer's solution heated to 40°C. Record your results in Table 14-1.

b. Adrenalin

Wash the tissue with warm Ringer's solution. Then place one drop of 1:50,000 adrenalin solution on the capillary bed. Record your observations in Table 14-1. Rinse the tissue with warm Ringer's solution.

From the data recorded in Table 14-1, answer the following questions concerned with the effect of these factors on peripheral circulation.

TABLE 14-1
Factors that affect blood flow in capillaries.

Regulator	Diameter decreases (constricts) Blood flow rate decreases	Diameter increases (enlarges) Blood flow rate increases
Ethyl alcohol	+	(−)
Nicotine	(−)	+
Lactic acid	(−)	+
Adrenalin		
Temperature	Cold ringer's:	Warm ringer's:
Animal used:		

Why is the temperature of the fingers of a nonsmoker higher than that of those who smoke?

_____

_____

_____

It is known that the lactic acid content of muscle tissue increases during exercise. Why, then, would you expect more oxygen to be delivered to the muscle tissue of a person who is exercising than to that of a person who is resting?

_____

_____

_____

Suggest a reason why a drunk person might more easily die from cold exposure than a sober person.

_____

_____

_____

_____

Adrenalin is released into the bloodstream at times of stress. Why might a person who is frightened become pale rather than flushed and red?

_____

_____

_____

3. Factors Affecting Heartbeat

Anesthetize the frog that was used in Part A1b, and cut from A to B as shown in Fig. 14-3A. (*Note: If you used a fish in Part 1, your instructor will give you an anes-*

thetized frog.) Extend the incision forward to the shoulder girdle. Lift upward and forward with each cut to avoid damaging the underlying organs. Cut through the bones of the shoulder girdle. Then at Points X and Y cut laterally and pull back the skin to expose the internal organs (Fig. 14-3B). Use clean filter paper to sponge up any blood in the area.

Note that the heart is enclosed in a membrane, the **pericardium**. Observe the volume of the heart during its diastolic (expansion) and systolic (contraction) phases. Carefully slit the pericardium, and note any changes in volume during **diastole** and **systole**. There are two anterior chambers and a posterior third chamber; the anterior chambers are the **auricles**. The single posterior chamber is the **ventricle**. Note any differences in the texture of its wall relative to those of the atria. Observe the groove marking the boundary between the auricles and ventricle. This is the **atrioventricular groove**. Observe the **truncus arteriosus**, a thick-walled tube that arises dorsally from the ventricle and divides into two **aortic arches**. With fine-nosed forceps, lift the ventricle by its apical tip and reflect it forward. Note the narrow V-shaped **sinus venosus**, which opens into the right auricle.

Finally, observe the main veins, which return blood to the heart. The right and left **anterior venae cavae**, or caval veins, enter the sinus venosus from the anterior part of the body. A single **posterior vena cava**, or caval vein, empties into the posterior part of the sinus venosus.

Carefully observe the sequence of contraction of all parts of the heart and the veins and truncus arteriosus. List the order in which these parts contract.

_____

_____

Using the second hand of a watch, or using a stopwatch, determine the number of contractions per minute made by the auricles, ventricle, truncus arteriosus, and sinus venosus.

Left auricle	_____/minute
Right auricle	_____/minute
Ventricle	_____/minute
Truncus	_____/minute
Sinus	_____/minute

Are the rates equal or different? What can you conclude from this?

_____

_____

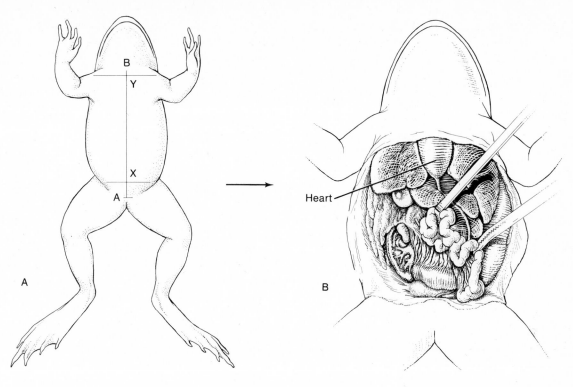

FIG. 14-3
Dissection of frog to expose the heart.

_____

_____

_____

Observe and record the rate of contraction of the heart: _____/minute. Decerebrate the frog as outlined in Appendix D, Part C. After 5 minutes, observe and record the rate of contraction again: _____/minute. Destroy the midbrain and hindbrain areas by pithing the animal as described in Appendix D, Part B. After 5 minutes, observe and record the rate of contraction: _____/minute.

Finally, insert a dissecting needle into the part of the vertebral column containing the spinal cord, and complete the destruction of the central nervous system by forcing the needle down as far as it will go. After a recovery period of 5 minutes, observe and record the rate of contraction of the heart: _____/minute.

Do your observations suggest that the central nervous system plays a role in governing heart action?

_____

If so, which part of the central nervous system seems to be the most important?

_____

Did the heart cease beating with complete destruction of the central nervous system?

_____

What conclusions are suggested by this?

_____

_____

_____

Chill several glass or metal rods in a beaker of ice water, and apply the rods one at a time to the ventricle. When it has cooled, record the contraction rates of the auricles, ventricle, and sinus venosus in Table 14-2. Restore the heart to room temperature with frog Ringer's solution. Repeat, cooling the atria and then determining

TABLE 14-2
Effects of differential cooling on heart contraction.

Portion cooled	Rate (contractions/minute)		
	Ventricle	Auricles	Sinus venosus
Ventricle			
Auricles			
Sinus venosus			

the contraction rates as before. Again warm the heart. Finally, cool the sinus venosus, and determine the rate of contraction of each chamber. (It will be necessary to tip up the ventricle to reach the sinus venosus.)

Do your observations suggest that one part of the heart has a greater effect on heart rate than the other parts?

_____

How do you account for this?

_____

_____

_____

To examine this aspect of heart control further, remove the heart from the body by lifting the ventricular apex and cutting through the anterior and posterior vena cavae and the right and left aortae. Be careful not to stretch the heart, and do not damage the chambers, particularly the sinus venosus. In addition, be careful not to puncture the gall bladder, a small, dark green sac lying close to the heart near the liver.

Place the heart in a watch glass containing Ringer's solution at room temperature. After 2 or 3 minutes, the heart should begin to contract again. Does this support your earlier conclusions? Explain.

_____

_____

_____

Determine the rate of contraction of the whole isolated heart: _____/minute. Carefully separate the sinus

venosus from the right auricle, without damaging either one. After 2 or 3 minutes, determine the contraction rate of the sinus venosus and of the atrioventricular part: sinus venosus:_____/minute;atrioventricular:_____/minute. As a last step, separate the auricles from the ventricle. It may be necessary to wait a few minutes for the ventricle to resume contractions. If it shows no sign of contracting after 5 or 10 minutes, stimulate it by touching it with a dissecting needle. After it resumes beating, determine the contraction rate of each segment: sinus venosus: _____/minute; auricles: _____/minute; ventricle; _____/minute.

Summarize your conclusions regarding the control of heart activity in the frog.

_____

_____

_____

_____

_____

_____

_____

4. Function of Hemoglobin

Almost all of the oxygen carried in the blood is transported in combination with hemoglobin. In vertebrate animals, hemoglobin is contained within red blood cells. It consists of a protein called **globin** to which is attached a prosthetic group called **heme**. Heme is a complex consisting of protoporphyrin and ferrous iron (Fe^{2+}).

To function, hemoglobin depends on its ability to reversibly combine with oxygen:

$$Hb + O_2 \rightleftharpoons HbO_2$$

Hemo-   Oxyhemoglobin   globin

Hemoglobin combines with oxygen in the lungs, where oxygen concentration is high. Oxygen is then released in the tissues, where the oxygen concentration is low. The iron of the heme group is the site of the reversible reactions involving oxygen. Part of the carbon dioxide released from the tissues by cellular respiration is then transported by the hemoglobin to the lungs, where carbon dioxide levels are low, and is exchanged for oxygen. It has been suggested that carbon dioxide is transported in combination with the amino groups of the globin molecule.

a. Absorption Spectrum of Hemoglobin

Hemoglobin possesses a distinct absorption spectrum, as does each of its derivatives (i.e., oxyhemoglobin, deoxyhemoglobin, carboxyhemoglobin). In this study, you will determine the spectrum of hemoglobin, as well as those of some of its alternate forms. The part of the visible spectrum that is absorbed by hemoglobin can be determined by using an instrument called a **spectroscope**, which disperses visible light into its component colors, or wavelengths (Fig. 14-4). The disappearance from the spectrum of various colors, or wavelengths, as a result of passing light through a pigment solution, indicates that those wavelengths were absorbed by the pigments. The absorption spectra of hemoglobin and its derivatives will be visible as shadows in the yellow and green regions. These are **absorption bands**. The wavelength at which the shadow is darkest is the wavelength of maximum absorption (λ_{max}).

1. *Oxyhemoglobin:* A major physiological function of hemoglobin resides in its ability to react reversibly with oxygen. Under optimal conditions 1 g of hemoglobin will combine with 1.36 g of oxygen. Oxyhemoglobin is quite stable as long as there is sufficient oxygen present to prevent the reverse reaction from occurring.

To determine the absorption spectrum of oxyhemoglobin, pipet a sample of defibrinated blood (diluted 1:100) into a small test tube. Your instructor will demonstrate the use of the instrument for determining the absorption spectrum of your sample. In the particular instrument referred to here, two spectra are projected onto a scale (400–700 nm) on the back, inside surface of the instrument. The upper reference spectrum shows the colors (wavelengths) of light. The lower spectrum results from passage of the light through the sample. In the first chart below, indicate the wavelengths of light that are absorbed by oxyhemoglobin.

2. *Reduced hemoglobin:* To the test tube you have just examined, add a small amount of sodium dithionite (sodium hydrosulfite), a reducing agent. Reexamine the blood and determine its absorption spectrum; draw it in the second chart below.

You should see that the two bands of oxyhemoglobin have been replaced by a single broad band.

Shake the tube vigorously, and then reexamine the absorption spectrum. How do you account for what you observed?

_____

_____

_____

_____

_____

_____

FIG. 14-4
Spectroscope for demonstrating the absorption spectrum of hemoglobin.

Scale (400–700 nm) on *inside* surface of instrument.

3. *Carboxyhemoglobin:* In addition to its ability to combine with oxygen, hemoglobin will also react with a variety of other substances such as hydrogen sulfide, ferricyanide, nitric oxide, and carbon monoxide (CO). The product in most cases is a colored compound that can also be characterized by its absorption spectrum. The combination of hemoglobin and carbon monoxide is of particular interest because carbon monoxide is found in city air, in the exhaust of motor vehicles, and in industrial gases and because it has about 200 times as much affinity for hemoglobin as does oxygen. In addition, the formation of carboxyhemoglobin (HbCO) prevents hemoglobin from combining with oxygen, probably because the two gases compete for the same spot in the hemoglobin molecule. The reaction between oxyhemoglobin and carbon monoxide is

$$HbO_2 \; + \; CO \; \rightleftharpoons \; HbCO \; + \; O_2$$

Oxy-   Carbon   Carboxy-   Oxygen
hemoglobin   monoxide   hemoglobin

Examine a sample of blood through which carbon monoxide has been bubbled. Determine its spectrum and draw it on the chart below.

b. Hemoglobin Crystals

Hemoglobin and its derivatives can be crystallized if treated with acid and gently heated. Although the shapes of the crystals are very characteristic and can be used as a reliable and delicate test for the presence of blood, they cannot be readily distinguished from one animal species to another.

FIG. 14-5
Normal red blood cells (above) and red blood cells of a person who has sickle-cell anemia (right). (Photomicrographs by Anthony C. Allison.)

To observe the presence of hemoglobin crystals,

1. Place a drop of blood in the center of a clean glass slide, and allow it to air-dry.

2. Cover the dried blood with one or two drops of glacial acetic acid, and mix thoroughly with a toothpick.

3. Add a cover glass. *Note:* The entire area under the cover glass should be filled with acid.

4. Heat the slide *gently* over a low flame until bubbles are observed in the acid.

5. Allow the slide to cool, examine it microscopically, and locate the hemoglobin crystals, which are generally rhomboid in shape, although they may have other forms.

c. Abnormal Hemoglobin (Sickle Cell)

Sickle-cell anemia was first discovered by J. B. Herrick in 1910. In this inherited disease (predominantly, but not exclusively, found in blacks and Latin Americans), a defective hemoglobin molecule (Hemoglobin S) causes the red blood cells to assume an elongated, sickled shape. Not only do these cells have a low oxygen-carrying capacity, but their abnormal shapes also cause a slowing and sludging of the cells in the capillaries, with resultant anoxia (lack of oxygen) in the tissues. In some cases, tissue may be destroyed. This disease is particularly harmful to normally sedentary people who exercise vigorously only occasionally. Examine microscope slides of normal and sickled red blood cells. Compare them with the normal red blood cells and the sickled cells shown in Fig. 14-5.

In sickle-cell anemia, the protein (globin) part of the normal hemoglobin molecule (Hb A) has been slightly altered by a mutation of a gene. When the abnormal genes

(Hb^S) are inherited from both parents, the resulting homozygous condition ($Hb^S Hb^S$) causes a severe disability known as **sickle-cell disease**. When only one abnormal gene is inherited, resulting in the heterozygous condition ($Hb^A Hb^S$), the offspring is said to possess **sickle-cell trait**, a condition considerably less severe.

The two types of homoglobin, Hb A and Hb S, can be distinguished from each other by electrophoresis, a procedure in which proteins migrate along an electrical gradient. The difference in the charges of each hemoglobin causes them to separate from each other (Fig. 14-6). This procedure can be used to distinguish between people whose hemoglobin is normal, those having sickle-cell disease, and those having sickle-cell trait.

Recall that all proteins consist of chains of smaller units called amino acids. The hemoglobin molecule has four polypeptide chains: two beta chains and two alpha chains. Each alpha chain consists of 141 amino acids in a known specific sequence. Each beta chain has 146 amino acids. In sickle hemoglobin, glutamic acid is replaced by valine at one position in each chain (Fig. 14-7).

Until recently there was no effective treatment for this debilitating disease. However, intravenous treatment with glucose and urea, which blocks and reverses sickling, has shown some promise.

B. TRANSPORT IN PLANTS

Water is one of the basic raw materials of photosynthesis. It is the major component of plant tissues, making up 90% of the plant body. Water is the substance in which

SS sample ——————— Hb S

AS sample ——————— Hb S
——————— Hb A

AA sample ——————— Hb A

−
Cathode

+
Anode

FIG. 14-6
An example of electrophoretic separation of hemoglobins: SS
and AS contain abnormal hemoglobin S; AA is normal.

Normal ($Hb^A Hb^A$)	Leucine—Threonine—Proline—**Glutamic acid**—Glutamic acid—Lysine
	Leucine—Threonine—Proline—**Glutamic acid**—Glutamic acid—Lysine
Sickle disease ($Hb^S Hb^S$)	Leucine—Threonine—Proline— **Valine** —Glutamic acid—Lysine
	Leucine—Threonine—Proline— **Valine** —Glutamic acid—Lysine
Sickle trait ($Hb^A Hb^S$)	Leucine—Threonine—Proline—**Glutamic acid**—Glutamic acid—Lysine
	Leucine—Threonine—Proline— **Valine** —Glutamic acid—Lysine

FIG. 14-7
Sequences of amino acids in peptide of beta chains of
hemoglobin A and hemoglobin S.

most materials enter and leave the cells of plants, and it
is the solvent for the various biochemical reactions that
occur in living cells.

The amount of water used by plants is far greater than
that used by animals of comparable weight. The reason
for this is that a large amount of the water used by the
animal is recirculated in the form of blood plasma or
tissue fluid. In plants, over 90% of the water taken in by
the root system is evaporated into the air as water vapor.
This process, which largely occurs through the leaves, is
called **transpiration**. Consequently, plants not only have
developed extensive and efficient transport systems but
also have evolved numerous morphological adaptations

to conserve water. In this study, you will become familiar
with some of the factors that regulate transpiration.

1. Effect of Environmental Factors on Transpiration Rate

1. Cut a branch from a geranium or *Coleus* plant and
insert it into a rubber stopper as shown in Fig. 14-8. Place
the branch and stopper in a potometer flask that was previously filled with distilled water. Insert the stopper
slowly to avoid creating bubbles. If this is done properly,
water will be forced out of the end of the capillary tubing.

169

Hole slightly smaller than stem

Rubber stopper

Cork borer

B. Hold branch under water and cut off about 2 cm of stem.

A. Cut branch from plant.

C. Select a rubber stopper having a hole slightly smaller than diameter of stem. Insert a cork borer as shown, and place stem far enough into cork borer so that when borer is removed the stem will project about 1 cm below the stopper. Carry out this procedure under water, but do not allow leaves to become wet.

D. Lower tube so it is parallel to the surface of the table before taking measurements.

Disposable syringe

Millimeter ruler

Sample starting point

Capillary tube

Rubber tubing

Potometer flask covered with aluminum foil.

If water column recedes, it may be returned to starting point by injecting water into rubber tubing with syringe.

FIG. 14-8
Procedure for determining the rate of transpiration.

However, when the pressure on the stopper is released the fluid in the capillary tube will tend to recede. If this should occur, fill a 5-ml syringe with water and insert the needle into the rubber coupling between the flask and the capillary tubing. Slowly inject water until it comes out of the end of the tubing. If the apparatus has been properly set up, the water in the tube will begin to recede slowly. The rate at which the meniscus moves along the tubing is a measure of the rate of water uptake by the branch and may be used as a measure of the rate of transpiration. Determine the transpiration rate by recording the distance the meniscus moves each minute for a period of 10 minutes. If the meniscus goes beyond the graduated scale at the right, it may be returned to the zero mark by injecting water into the rubber coupling as previously described. Record your results in Table 14-3. Plot your data in Fig. 14-9.

2. Design and perform experiments to show the effects (if any) of light intensity, air movement, and humidity and the role of the leaves in the process of transpiration. Record the experimental conditions and your results in Table 14-3. Plot your data in Fig. 14-9. What would be the control for these various experiments?

_____

What is the reason for covering the potometer flask with aluminum foil?

_____

_____

_____

All aerial parts of plants may lose water by transpiration. In most herbaceous and woody plants, a large proportion of the water is lost through openings called **stomates**. Discuss the effects of the various environmental factors as they affect transpiration in terms of their effects on the activity of the stomates.

_____

_____

_____

_____

Why is it important that ornamental evergreen plants be thoroughly watered before winter sets in?

_____

_____

_____

In what way is transpiration a beneficial process to the plant?

_____

_____

_____

TABLE 14-3
Potometer data.

Experimental conditions	Time (minutes)									
	1	2	3	4	5	6	7	8	9	10
	Distance (mm)									
Control										
Light intensity										
Air movement										
Humidity										
Effect of leaves										

FIG. 14-9
Comparison of transpiration rates under various environmental conditions.

2. Movement of Minerals

The study of relationships between structure and function in plants and animals has been aided by the use of radioactive substances called **radioisotopes** (see Appendix F). Radioisotopes can be used to trace the pathways of substances during their movement throughout an organism. When used in this way, they are called **tracers**. For example, biologists using radioactive carbon dioxide ($C^{14}O_2$) have been able to identify the various intermediate compounds that carbon becomes associated with in the photosynthetic process.

In this part of the exercise, a radioactive compound, uranyl nitrate, will be used to determine if the minerals that are absorbed by roots are distributed throughout the plant.

Carefully remove two young bean seedlings from their container (Fig. 14-10A). Try not to damage the roots. Wash the roots with tap water (Fig. 14-10B). Place one of the plants in a flask containing a solution of uranyl nitrate so that the roots are completely submerged (Fig. 14-10C). Label this flask "experimental." The second plant should be set up as your control (Fig. 14-10D). What solution should be put in the control flask?

Cover both flasks with aluminum foil, and place them on a widow ledge in the light for one to two hours. Next lift the plants out of the flasks just high enough so that the root can be cut off at the base of the stem. Allow the roots to fall back into the flasks (Fig. 14-10E). Return the containers to your instructor for disposal. Place each plant on a separate x-ray film pack. Spread the leaves so they do not overlap, and tape the plants to the film packs (Fig. 14-10F). Mark each film pack with your name and the date, and indicate whether it is the "experimental" or the "control" plant. Now place each film pack between two pieces of blotting paper (or paper towels). Add a heavy weight (two or three heavy books), and allow to remain this way for 10–15 days. At the end of this time (they may be left for a longer period), develop each film according to the directions given by your instructor. Discard the plants and blotting paper in the container provided for this purpose.

The radioactive uranyl nitrate is emitting high-energy particles. When these strike the emulsion of the film, latent images are formed, which, when treated with photographic developing solution, are reduced to metallic silver. This produces a black spot on the film. In this way you will be able to show the distribution of the radioactive uranyl nitrate in the plant. This procedure is called **autoradiography**. The picture you obtain is an **autoradiograph**.

172

A. Remove 2 plants from the container.

B. Wash the roots with tap water to remove soil.

Cotton

C. "Experimental" (Solution: Radioactive uranyl nitrate)

D. "Control" (Solution: _____)

E. Cut the roots from the stem. Allow the roots to fall back into the flask. Give the flask to your instructor.

F. Tape the plants to an X-ray film pack. Cover with blotting paper. Place 2 or 3 heavy books on top for 10 to 15 days.

G. Develop film.

FIG. 14-10
Procedure for preparing an autoradiograph.

REFERENCES

Allison, A. C. 1956. Sickle Cells and Evolution. *Scientific American* 195:87–94 (Offprint 1065). *Scientific American* Offprints are available from W. H. Freeman and Company, 660 Market Street, San Francisco 94104, and 58 Kings Road, Reading RG1 3AA, England. Please order by number.

Baker, D. A. 1978. *Transport Phenomena in Plants*. Wiley.

Biddulph, S., and O. Biddulph. 1959. The Circulatory System of Plants. *Scientific American* 200:44–49 (Offprint 53).

Galston, A. W. 1980. *The Life of the Green Plant*. 3rd ed. Prentice-Hall.

Guyton, A. C. 1976. *Medical Physiology*. 5th ed. Saunders.

Hoar, W. S. 1975. *General and Comparative Physiology*. 2nd ed. Prentice-Hall.

Lassen, N. A., D. H. Ingvar, and E. Skinhøj. 1978. Brain Function and Blood Flow. *Scientific American* 239:62–71 (Offprint 1410).

Leopold, A. C. 1975. *Plant Growth and Development*. 2nd ed. McGraw-Hill.

Lerner, I. M., and W. J. Libby. 1976. *Heredity, Evolution, and Society*. 2nd ed. W. H. Freeman and Company.

Luttge, U., and N. Higginbotham. 1979. *Transport in Plants*. Springer-Verlag.

Macey, R. I. 1975. *Human Physiology*. 2nd ed. Prentice-Hall.

Perutz, M. F. 1978. Hemoglobin Structure and Respiratory Transport. *Scientific American* 239:92–125 (Offprint 1413).

Ray, P. M. 1972. *The Living Plant*. 2nd ed. Holt, Rinehart and Winston.

Zimmerman, M. H. 1963. How Sap Moves in Trees. *Scientific American* 208:132–142 (Offprint 154).

Biological Coordination in Plants

As organisms become more complex and individual cells become more specialized, the various activities within the organism must be coordinated. Furthermore, organisms need effective ways to respond to physical and chemical changes in their environment. Thus, all organisms must become adapted to receive various internal and external stimuli and to respond to these stimuli in a coordinated manner.

Although higher plants do not have nervous systems, the coordination of many activities is a necessity if the plant is to grow and develop. There are two types of mechanisms that bring about coordination in plants. One, consisting of a system of chemical messengers, directs the cells of the plant to carry out different functions. This group includes the various plant hormones and other growth regulators. A second coordinating system consists of various physical forces; for example, electrical gradients, gas-exchange gradients, and metabolic or pressure differences throughout the plant. The end product of these controls is a highly complex plant body having localized areas of growth, special regions of photosynthetic activity, and the ability to translocate and accumulate the nec-

essary raw materials for growth and differentiation into reproduction of other functions to assure the continuation of the species.

A. PHOTOTAXIS

The ability to respond to a stimulus (a chemical or physical change in the environment) is a striking characteristic of living organisms. The response of the organism to any stimulus serves to coordinate the activities of the organism so that equilibrium with the environment is maintained. In this study, you will examine the effects of various wavelengths of light in orientating movements of the green alga, *Euglena*.

Following the directions outlined in Fig. 15-1, expose a tube of *Euglena* to various wavelengths of light. The *Euglena* will tend to concentrate and adhere to the sides of the tube, depending on the wavelength to which they are most sensitive. At the conclusion of the study, carefully decant off the liquid in the tube, and remove the black paper sleeve. Record your observations in

Approximately 25 mm longer than length of test tube

Black paper

A. Approximately 6 mm longer than circumference of test tube

B. Draw a line through center of paper and then punch out six equally spaced holes.

(Clear)
(Red)
(Blue)
(Green)
(Yellow)
(Orange)

C. Cover each hole with colored cellophane, using Scotch tape. (Note: Use two thicknesses of red.)

Light source

D. Wrap paper around test tube and tape tightly to eliminate light leaks. Seal end.

E. Fill with *Euglena* culture. Cork, and place in sunlight or near light source consisting of fluorescent and incandescent lights from 1.5 to 2 hours.

FIG. 15-1
Procedure for studying the effect of different wavelengths of light on the movements of *Euglena*.

Fig. 15-2 by shading the appropriate circles to represent the density of *Euglena* found associated with each colored filter. What wavelength of light is most effective in attracting *Euglena?*

_____

Prepare a wet mount of *Euglena,* and locate a red-pigmented "eye-spot" near the flagella. Suggest a role for this structure in the response just studied.

_____

_____

_____

Of what survival value to *Euglena* is the response observed?

_____

_____

_____

B. GEOTROPISM

The effect of gravity in determining the direction of growth in various plant parts is called **geotropism**. Stems generally grow in a direction opposite the force of gravity. Is this negative or positive geotropism?

_____

Characterize the response of roots in regard to their reaction to gravity.

_____

In the following parts of this study, special attention will be given to the geotropic response of *Coleus* or *Iresine* shoots. For convenience, each team will be assigned one aspect of the problem. Because the response of the plant usually requires several hours, set the experiment aside for examination during the next laboratory period. In Table 15-1, fill in the expected results and then compare these with the actual results.

1. What is the effect of gravity on stem orientation? Remove three *Coleus* or *Iresine* branches, keeping the

Filter

Clear

Red

Blue

Green

Yellow

Orange

Record density of *Euglena* at each wavelength by shading as indicated below:

None   Moderate

Light   Heavy

FIG. 15-2
Effect of wavelengths of light on the orienting movements of *Euglena.*

surface moist during the cutting operation. Set them up as indicated in Fig. 15-3. What is the "control" in this experiment?

_____

_____

_____

2. Does defoliation affect the geotropic response of *Coleus* or *Iresine* shoots? Design and perform an experiment to answer this question. Complete Table 15-2.

TABLE 15-1
Geotropism data.

Results	Stem position		
	Vertical	Horizontal	Inverted
Expected			
Observed			
Conclusions			

FIG. 15-3
Experimental setup to show effect of gravity on growth.

Rubber stopper with hole slightly smaller than stem diameter

Tube filled with water (Note: Check water level daily. Refill as necessary to keep cut end in water.)

Ring stand and clamps

3. Does the shoot apex exert any effect on the geotropic response of *Coleus* or *Iresine?* Design and perform an experiment to answer this question. Complete Table 15-3.

4. Will replacing the shoot apex with auxin have any effect on the geotropic response of *Coleus* or *Iresine?* Design and perform an experiment to answer this question. Complete Table 15-4.

C. CHEMOTROPISM

The response of nonmotile cells to chemical stimulation, in which growth occurs toward or away from the chemical stimulus, is called **chemotropism**. In this part of the exercise, the chemotropic response of lily pollen tubes to various materials (pistils, auxin, and gibberellic acid) will be studied. Petri dishes containing a nutrient medium will be used in these experiments. Pollen and the materials to be tested for chemotropic activity can be obtained from the instructor. A small piece of material to be tested is placed on the surface of the nutrient medium and the pollen positioned around it, using a camel-hair brush and a binocular microscope. For best results, distribute the pollen in small clumps within 2 or 3 mm of the material to be tested. To test the chemotropic activity of liquids, cut a well in the medium with a cork borer, place the liquid in the well, and position the pollen around the rim.

1. Is chemotropic activity exhibited by the lily pistil? Obtain petri dishes, pollen, and lily pistils from the instructor. Determine if chemotropic activity is exhibited by all parts of the pistil. Design and perform an experiment to answer this question. Test for chemotropic activity as described. What controls should be used?

_____

_____

What criteria would be used to determine if positive or negative chemotropism is indicated?

_____

_____

_____

Complete Table 15-5.

2. Is the chemotropic activity of pistils altered by heat? Design and perform an experiment to answer this question. Complete Table 15-6.

3. Is chemotropic activity exhibited by auxin or gibberellic acid? Design and perform an experiment to test the chemotropic activity of each of these known plant growth substances. It will be necessary to know the solvents for each of these substances so that adequate controls can be established.

_____

_____

_____

_____

If one (or both) of these substances shows chemotropic activity, determine its optimum concentration by testing with a series of concentrations—for example, 1, 10, 50, and 100 parts per million (ppm). Complete Table 15-7.

REFERENCES

Baron, W. M. M. 1979. *Organization in Plants*. 3rd ed. Wiley.

Galston, A. W. 1980. *The Life of the Green Plant*. 3rd ed. Prentice-Hall.

Galston, A. W., and P. J. Davies. 1970. *Control Mechanisms in Plant Development*. Prentice-Hall.

Krishnamoorthy, H. N. 1975. *Gibberellins and Plant Growth*. Wiley.

Machlis, L., and J. G. Torrey. 1956. *Plants in Action: A Laboratory Manual of Plant Physiology*. W. H. Freeman and Company.

Salisbury, F. B. 1957. Plant Growth Substances. *Scientific American* 196:125–134 (Offprint 110). *Scientific American* Offprints are available from W. H. Freeman and Company, 660 Market Street, San Francisco 94104, and 58 Kings Road, Reading RG1 3AA, England. Please order by number.

Van Overbeek, J. 1968. The Control of Plant Growth. *Scientific American* 219:75–81 (Offprint 1111).

Went, F. W. 1962. Plant Growth and Plant Hormones. In W. H. Johnson and W. C. Steere, eds., *This is Life*. Holt, Rinehart & Winston.

TABLE 15-2
Data on the effect of defoliation on the geotropic response.

Procedure:
  1. Experimental treatment
 	
  2. Control treatment

Expected results:
Observed results:
Conclusions:

TABLE 15-3
Data on the effect of the shoot apex on the geotropic response.

Procedure:
  1. Experimental treatment

  2. Control treatment

Expected results:

Observed results:

Conclusions:

TABLE 15-4
Data on the effect of replacing the apex with auxin on the geotropic response.

Procedure:
  1. Experimental treatment
 	
  2. Control treatment

Expected results:
Observed results:
Conclusions:

TABLE 15-5
Data on the chemotropic activity of lily pistils.

Procedure:
  1. Experimental treatment

  2. Control treatment

Results:

Conclusions:

TABLE 15-6
Data on the effect of heat on the chemotropic activity of lily pistils.

Procedure:
1. Experimental treatment

2. Control treatment

Results:

Conclusions:

TABLE 15-7
Data on the chemotropic activity of auxin and gibberellic acid.

Procedure:
  1. Experimental treatment

  2. Control treatment

Results:

Conclusions:

Biological Coordination in Animals

The intact animal has functional capabilities that exceed those characteristic of its constituent cells, tissues, organs, and organ systems. This observation is the basis for the generalization that "the organism is more than a simple sum of its parts." Each subunit of the body has a specific contribution to make, but the proper functioning of the whole organism depends on the integration of a wide spectrum of individual processes into a coherent unit. Such integration in turn depends on the exchange of information between parts of the body, and in this vital process the nervous system and endocrine organs play a central role. Although structurally quite different, they exert their effects in an essentially similar fashion—through the production and release of molecules that modify cellular activity. The effects produced by the nervous system are normally quite localized in that the materials released at nerve endings (such as acetylcholine or norepinephrine) act on specific targets—other nerve cells, muscle cells, and secretory cells. The effects of the endocrine glands, on the other hand, are more generalized in that their secretions (hormones) are distributed throughout the body by the circulatory system. Specificity of hormonal effects is achieved by variations in the sensitivity of different types of cells to particular hor-

mones. In a general sense, the nervous system contributes to organismic coordination by providing rapid and highly specific but short-term control, whereas long-term modifications of physiological activity are normally the province of the endocrine system.

The nervous system is divided into the **central nervous system**, composed of the brain and spinal cord, the **peripheral nervous system**, consisting of the cranial and spinal nerves (those nerves originating in the brain and spinal cord, respectively), and the **autonomic nervous system**, which regulates those parts of the body under involuntary control (i.e., intestines and blood vessels). In this exercise, you will become familiar with the anatomy and physiology of the nervous system of the frog.

A. THE BRAIN

Carefully remove the skin from the top of the head. Then remove any muscles present on the posterior part of the skull. The brain occupies that part of the skull extending from between the eyes to the foramen magnum. Using a scalpel (or fine scissors) and forceps, carefully remove the thin bone on the roof and lateral margins of the skull and expose the brain and anterior part of the spinal cord. Take care in doing this, because brain tissue is fragile and easily damaged.

Note that the brain is covered by a layer of membranous tissue, called the **meninges**: the outer nonvascular meningeal membrane is called the **dura mater**; the inner layer, called the **pia mater**, is highly vascularized and is tightly bound to the surface of the brain. In human beings, inflammation of the meninges is called **meningitis** and can affect the brain or the spinal cord, or both. It can be caused by bacteria, fungi, or viruses. One of the more common agents of this disease is the bacterium *Neisseria meningitidis,* frequently called *meningococcus.* Carefully remove these meninges to obtain an unobstructed view of the surface features of the brain.

1. Features of the Dorsal Surface

The brain is composed of five regions. In the frog, these regions are in a linear arrangement. The most anterior region, the **telencephalon**, is subdivided into the **olfactory bulbs** and the **cerebral hemispheres** (Fig. 16-1A). Locate the **olfactory nerves**, which lead from the external nares to the olfactory bulbs. These nerves carry odor stimuli to the olfactory bulbs and cerebral hemispheres. The cerebral hemispheres are predominantly olfactory in the frog, but in human beings they involve reasoning, memory, foresight, emotion, personality, intelligence, and speech mechanisms.

Immediately posterior to the cerebral hemispheres is the **diencephalon**, the second region in the linear arrangement of the brain. Locate the **pineal body** protruding from the surface. The function of the pineal is unknown, although it does contain light-sensitive and secretory cells.

Just anterior to the pineal, the roof of the diencephalon is quite thin and vascularized. Careful removal of this membranous roof reveals a cavity in the brain, the **third ventricle**. Just lateral to the third ventricle, the walls of the diencephalon make up the **thalamus**.

The third region, the **mesencephalon** (or midbrain), is posterior to the diencephalon and is chiefly composed of the **optic lobes**. These structures receive sensory impulses from the eyes, as well as from many other sense organs. It is thought that the optic lobes carry out many of the functions associated with the cerebrum in higher vertebrates.

The **cerebellum**, located just behind the optic lobes, constitutes the major part of the fourth region of the brain, called the **metencephalon**. In the frog, as in all vertebrates, this region functions in the coordination of such motor activities as walking, twisting, and kicking.

The fifth region, the **myelencephalon** consists of the **medulla oblongata**, which continues into the spinal cord. The medulla contains control centers regulating breathing, heart rate, visceral activity, and swallowing. The roof of the medulla covers the fourth ventricle. If you carefully remove the membranous roof, you should see the **choroid plexus**, a series of vascular folds of tissue, attached to its inner surface.

2. Features of the Ventral Surface

The brain must be removed from the cranium in order to view the various regions and attachments of nerves on the ventral and lateral surfaces. To do this, first place the frog in a tray of water (to minimize damage) and then sever the olfactory nerves and the medulla oblongata, leaving as much of these structures attached to the brain as possible. Then, as you carefully lift the brain, cut the various cranial nerves (see Fig. 16-1B) extending from the ventral surface.

As you lift out the brain, look for a small bulbous structure projecting from the ventral surface in the region of the optic lobes. This structure, called the **hypophysis** (pituitary gland), lies in a small depression in the bone on the floor of the skull. You may have to chip some bone away to remove this structure.

With the aid of Fig. 16-1, locate the optic nerves and chiasma and the hypothalamus. The **optic nerves** cross as they reach the brain and form the **optic chiasma** from which they continue as optic tracts to the optic lobes. Thus the optic nerve from the right eye stimulates the sight centers of the left side of the brain and vice versa.

The **hypothalamus** makes up the floor of the diencephalon just posterior to the optic chiasma. Extending from the hypothalamus is the hypophysis (if you do not find it on the brain, it may have broken off and may still be in the bone pocket). The hypothalamus in the frog and other vertebrates regulates the **autonomic nervous system**, which controls such activities as blood pressure, salt balance, water balance, peristaltic movements of the intestines, and secretions of the pituitary gland.

The pituitary gland, often called the "master gland," secretes hormones that affect growth, activities of the adrenal and thyroid glands, and the production of hormones in the testes and ovaries. In humans, the pituitary has posterior (**neurohypophysis**) and anterior (**adenohypophysis**) lobes. A description of the hormones secreted by these lobes and their functions in humans follows:

a. Hormones of the Anterior Lobe

In human beings, the adenohypophysis produces several hormones, called **tropic** hormones, because they act largely on other endocrine glands.

Somatotropin, or **growth hormone**, promotes growth (particularly of bones and muscles) by increasing protein

DORSAL

VENTRAL

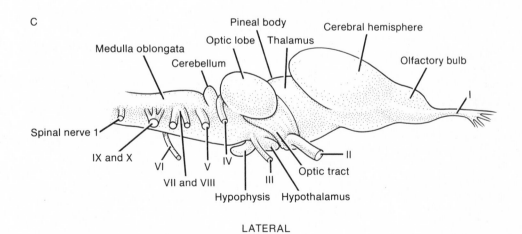

LATERAL

FIG. 16-1
The frog brain and the stumps of the cranial nerves: (A) dorsal, (B) ventral, and (C) lateral views.

synthesis until puberty. *Hypersecretion* of somatotropin (due to a pituitary tumor, for example) results in giantism in children and acromegaly in adults. *Hyposecretion* results in dwarfism. Secretion of growth hormone is regulated by a somatotropin-releasing factor (SRF) secreted by the hypothalamus.

Adrenocorticotropic hormone (ACTH) stimulates the outer cortical part of the adrenal gland to produce its hormones (cortisone, aldosterone, and others). Production of ACTH is curtailed when the levels of adrenal cortical hormones are adequate. Conversely, when these levels decrease, the pituitary is stimulated to produce ACTH.

Thyroid-stimulating hormone (TSH, or thyrotropin) stimulates the thyroid gland to produce thyroxin and triiodothyroxine, which function to regulate the rate of metabolism, the level of calcium in the blood, and the level of phosphate in bone.

Follicle-stimulating hormone (FSH) stimulates the growth of the ovarian follicles in females and the seminiferous tubules in the testes during spermatogenesis in males. Pituitary hormones that affect the gonads are called **gonadotropic hormones**.

After FSH has acted, **luteinizing hormone (LH)** stimulates the development of ovarian follicles and the corpus luteum, ovulation, and the production of estrogens (which are important in the development of secondary sex characteristics and regulation of the menstrual cycle). The hypothalamus secretes a luteinizing hormone-releasing factor (LRF), which is thought to regulate the production of LH.

The **interstitial cell-stimulating hormone (ICSH)** is produced only in males. This hormone promotes the secretion of **testosterone** by the interstitial cells of the testes. Testosterone affects secondary sex characteristics of the male.

Lactogenic hormone (prolactin) promotes the production of milk by the mammary glands. There is evidence that the hypothalamus produces a prolactin-inhibiting factor (PIF) that suppresses prolactin production until it is needed.

Melanocyte-stimulating hormone (MSH) stimulates the deposition of the pigment melanin in the skin after exposure to sunlight. A similar condition is produced if the adrenal cortex atrophies, as in Addison's disease.

b. Hormones of the Posterior Lobe

Oxytocin causes the smooth muscles in the uterus to contract during child birth and stimulates smooth muscles of the mammary glands during nursing. This hormone is secreted by the hypothalamus and then moves into the pituitary before it is released.

The **antidiuretic hormone (ADH, or vasopressin)** promotes reabsorption of water by the kidney. Like oxytocin, ADH is secreted by the hypothalamus when osmoreceptors that are present there detect an increase in the osmotic pressure of the blood following a loss of water. ADH thus conserves water by decreasing urine output.

B. THE CRANIAL NERVES

Cranial nerves are those nerves that are attached to the brain. Using Fig. 16-1, locate as many of their stumps as you can. Although there are 10 pairs of cranial nerves in the frog (identified by Roman numerals in Fig. 16-1), some are very small and may not be found. A description of each nerve follows:

I **Olfactory.** Sensory in function. Has nerve endings in the lining of the nasal cavity. Interpreted as odor in the cerebral hemispheres.

II **Optic.** Sensory in function. Has nerve endings in the retina of the eye. Stimulates vision centers in optic lobes.

III **Oculomotor.** Primarily a motor nerve that innervates the muscles that move the eyeballs. A branch of this nerve regulates the ciliary body of the eye, which in turn regulates the size of the pupil. There are also a few sensory fibers in the nerve that give feedback information on the intensity of muscle contractions during eye movement.

IV **Trochlear.** A motor nerve that sends impulses to the muscles of the eyes.

V **Trigeminal.** Motor and sensory in function. Receives sensory stimuli from the skin of the head and the lining of the mouth. Carries motor stimuli to the region of the jaw.

VI **Abducens.** Primarily a motor nerve that innervates the muscles of the eyes.

VII **Facial.** Motor and sensory in function. It carries sensory stimuli from the taste buds, lining of the mouth cavity, and the tongue. Motor impulses control the hyoid apparatus. In human beings, this nerve is sometimes called the "nerve of facial expression" because it supplies motor fibers to all muscles that affect expression.

VIII **Acoustic.** Sensory in function. Sometimes called *auditory nerve,* it functions in equilibrium and hearing.

IX **Glossopharyngeal.** Sensory and motor in function. Sensory fibers return stimuli from the tongue, taste buds, and lining of the buccal cavity. Motor fibers innervate some throat muscles.

X **Vagus.** Has both sensory and motor fibers affecting the heart, lungs, laryngotracheal chamber, bronchi, esophagus, stomach, intestine, and many of the abdominal organs.

Human beings have two pairs of nerves in addition to the aforementioned ones: spinal accessory nerves (XI) and hypoglossal cranial nerves (XII). One branch of the vagus nerve in the frog has the function of the human spinal accessory nerve and supplies motor fibers to the shoulder muscles. Part of the olfactory nerve in the frog serves the same function as that of the human hypoglossal nerve and supplies motor fibers to the tongue.

To help you remember the order in which the 10 cranial nerves in the frog, plus the 2 additional nerves in humans, are arranged, you might want to use the following rhyme, in which the first letter of each word corresponds to the first letter of the name of a nerve:

> On Old Olympus' Towering Top,
> A Finn And German Vended Some Hops.

C. THE SPINAL CORD AND SPINAL NERVES

The spinal cord continues posteriorly from the brain into the vertebral column (Fig. 16-2). To expose the spinal cord, remove the skin and muscle from the dorsal surface of the frog. Then insert fine-pointed scissors into the vertebral column, lateral to the midline, and carefully cut through the neural arch of the first vertebra. Repeat this on the other side, and then lift off the top of the vertebra. Repeat this procedure for all remaining vertebrae (Fig. 16-2). Locate the various spinal nerves along the length of the spinal cord. Note that they pass through an opening in the vertebral column, called the **intervertebral foramina**. Observe that the spinal cord is uniformly cylindrical except where the nerves to the fore and hindlimbs emerge. There the spinal cord enlarges into the **brachial** (fore) and **lumbar** (hind) enlargements. These swellings are due to the presence of large numbers of neurons that send branches to the muscles of the limbs.

If you carefully cut away additional bone and muscle surrounding one of the nerves, you will see that it, like the others, branches as it enters the spinal cord. The upper branch, usually swollen, is called the *dorsal root* and contains neurons of sensory nerves. Motor neurons leave the spinal cord through the ventral root. The frog has 10 pairs of spinal nerves. Using a dissecting microscope, attempt to find one of each pair. A description of each nerve follows:

Spinal Nerve 1. Usually destroyed during dissection. Emerges between the first and second vertebra. Innervates the muscles in the buccopharyngeal cavity.

Spinal Nerve 2. One of the largest nerves. With branches of the first and third spinal nerves, it forms the **brachial plexus**. Supplies muscles of the shoulder and arm.

Spinal Nerves 3, 4, 5, and 6. Innervate the muscles and skin of the abdomen.

Spinal Nerves 7, 8, and **9.** Together, these nerves form the **sciatic plexus**, sending branches to the skin and muscles of the posterior part of the abdomen, the pelvic region, and the muscles of the hind leg. The largest nerve, the sciatic nerve, runs parallel to the sciatic artery and vein into the thigh.

Spinal Nerve 10. A very small nerve that leaves the urostyle through a small opening. It supplies the urinary bladder and cloaca.

D. SPINAL CORD ANATOMY

Study a stained slide of a cross section of mammalian spinal cord passing through the dorsal root ganglia. You will notice that it is not a perfect circle but has notches in its circumference (Fig. 16-3). The deeper notch is the **ventral fissure**. Rotate your slide so that this fissure is toward you.

The brain and spinal cord are surrounded by membranous coverings called **meninges.** There are three such membranes in mammals: an outer **dura mater** next to the skull and vertebral bones, an inner **pia mater** fitting tightly to the brain and spinal cord, and a median **arachnoid membrane.**

In the center of the cord, locate a small, clear space, the **central canal.** This canal runs the length of the cord and, at its anterior end, is continuous with the fourth ventricle of the medulla oblongata. It is filled with **cerebrospinal fluid**, as are all the cavities within and around the central nervous system. Looking at the cross section of the cord, you will notice an H-shaped area of **gray matter** occupying much of the central region. The gray matter contains many cell bodies and looks gray in fresh tissue. In the outer area of the cord is the more uniformly colored **white matter**, containing fewer nuclei. The white matter is made up mostly of fibers that appear white in fresh tissue, owing to the glistening white sheaths around them. In your slide, the white matter has a granular appearance because almost all of its fibers run lengthwise and thus are cut transversely in the slide, each fiber end appearing as a dot.

192

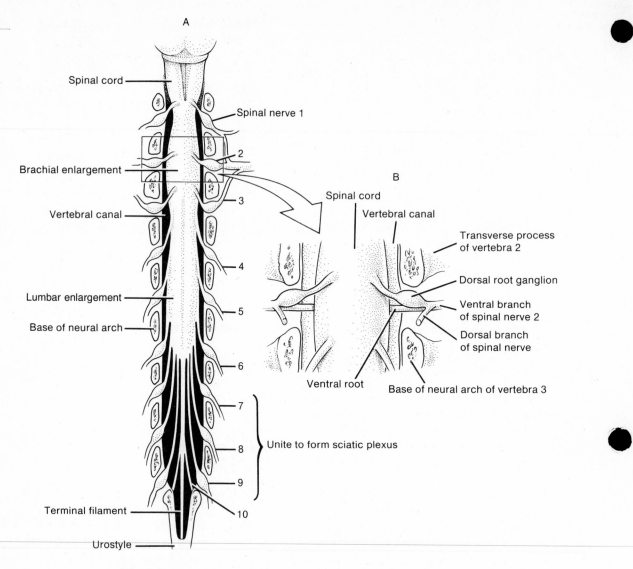

FIG. 16-2
(A) Dorsal view of the spinal cord and the origins of the 10 spinal nerves.
(B) Enlargement of the origin of the second spinal nerve.

The gray matter shows some differentiation. In the lower corners of the H-shaped area are extralarge cells—the cell bodies of **efferent (motor) neurons**. Locate their position in Fig. 16-3. Because their processes (cytoplasmic extensions) are normally very irregular, they are seldom visible in their entirety in a thin section. If you could trace them, the axons of these large neurons would be found to run out through the ventral root into the spinal nerve.

Besides the large motor neurons, numerous other cells will be found. The smallest belong to a special type of supporting cell characteristic of the central nervous system; these cells are not neurons. The intermediate-sized cells are called **association (adjustor) neurons** because they take impulses from the incoming sensory fibers and switch them to other adjustors, or up to the brain by long fibers in the cord, or directly to the motor neurons. Because the axons of adjustor neurons often branch, they can transmit an impulse to a number of other cells and these in turn to several more. Thus, in the end, hundreds of cells may be stimulated by one entering impulse.

E. REFLEX ARCS

Each spinal nerve is attached to the spinal cord by two connections, a **sensory (dorsal)** and a **motor (ventral) root** (Fig. 16-3). The dorsal root has an enlargement

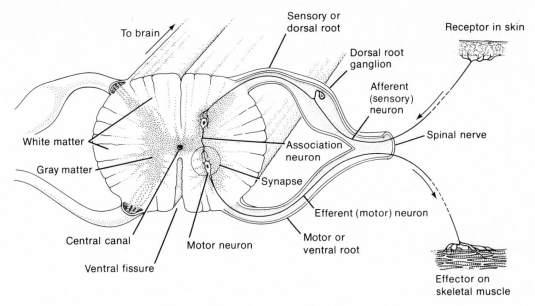

FIG. 16-3
Diagrammatic representation of the relationship of spinal cord, spinal nerves, and the simple reflex arc.

called the **dorsal root ganglion**, containing numerous cell bodies. The dorsal root contains only those fibers that carry impulses toward the spinal cord; the impulses originate in sense organs from all parts (internal and external) of the body. The ventral root contains no cell bodies.

The process transmitting the nerve impulse from the sense organ to the nerve-cell body is the **dendrite**. Another process, the **axon**, transmits the impulse from the cell body and in this case to the dorsal region of the gray matter of the spinal cord. The nerve cell (neuron) that carries impulses into the spinal cord from the sense organs—for example, skin and stomach smooth muscle—is called an **afferent (sensory) neuron**.

The axon of the afferent neuron usually synapses with an **association (adjustor) neuron** found within the gray matter of the spinal cord. The parts of the association neuron are similar to those of the afferent neuron, but it has several short dendrites and a short axon that ends close to the ventral region of the gray matter.

If the reaction produced is of a simple type, the axon of the association neuron synapses with the dendrites of an **efferent (motor) neuron**. The cell body, as well as the short dendrites of motor neurons, is found in the ventral part of the gray matter. A long axon proceeds from the cell body of the motor neuron and passes ventrally out of the spinal cord into the ventral root; it then enters the spinal nerve. It passes through the spinal nerve and terminates in an effector organ, which in this case is

FIG. 16-4
Typical reflex arcs.

always a striated, skeletal muscle. The pathway that the impulse takes from the sense organ through the afferent, association, and efferent neurons to the effector is known as a **reflex arc**.

Reflex arcs vary considerably in their complexity. For example, among very primitive animals, **direct effector** systems are found in which a nerve cell responds directly to stimulation and transmits directly to an effector (Fig. 16-4A). However, in vertebrates, a specialized sensory organ detects stimuli and activates nerve cells. The nervous pathway from sense organ to effector unit may consist of a sensory-motor neuron (Fig. 16-4B), or separate sensory and motor nerve cells (Fig. 16-4C), or one or more association neurons may be interpolated to increase the number of circuits possible (Fig. 16-4D).

A nervous reflex can be defined as a coordinated response by effectors to a stimulus applied to a receptor, mediated through two or more neurons. Much animal behavior can be interpreted in terms of the activity of reflex circuits in the spinal cord, but this activity is modified by influences from higher centers, to the extent that the brain has achieved physiological dominance.

1. Reflexes in the Living Frog

a. Blinking

Hold a live frog securely in one hand by grasping the hind legs. Place a blunt probe or a glass rod close to one eye, and observe that the frog blinks. In fact, the response at times is so strong that the eye is pulled into the throat region. Note the "lids" covering the eyes.

b. "Scratch" Reflex

Grasp the head and forelimbs securely in one hand. Wash off any mucus present on the back of the frog. With forceps, place a small (6-mm square) piece of filter paper moistened with dilute acetic acid on the lower surface of the back. Notice how the hind leg attempts to brush off the irritant. This is the "scratch" reflex. A stronger acid would produce a more violent response, with the animal trying to use both legs to brush off the irritating substance. Wash off the acid with water.

c. Other Reflexes

Lay the frog on its back, and stroke the throat and belly regions. When first stroking a male (a male has a large, swollen "thumb"), watch the distinct clasping reflex in the forelimbs. Notice the quieting, almost hypnotic, effect on the frog as stroking is continued.

2. Spinal Reflexes in the Decerebrate Frog

The frog is an excellent animal for the study of **spinal reflexes** because of the brevity of the period of spinal shock following destruction of the brain, the small blood loss in decerebration, and the adequacy of the cutaneous respiration for supporting metabolism. (See Appendix D for frog pithing and decerebration techniques.)

Holding the frog firmly in your left hand, quickly sever the spinal cord at the neck (on a line just posterior to the eardrums) with a probe. Then, using scissors, cut off the head, but leave the lower jaw. Wipe off the blood, and suspend the frog from a ring stand with the hook through the lower jaw, with the frog's back toward you. Wash off the mucous covering, but remember to keep the skin moist. If spinal shock has occurred, the animal does not respond; wait 5 or 10 minutes for recovery before proceeding. Such a preparation is known as a **decerebrate frog**. Because it lacks a brain, it is completely without consciousness. Does the scratching reflex remain in this "decerebrate frog"?

_____

Pinch the toe of one foot with a forceps. What happens?

_____

_____

What does the other foot do?

_____

Stimulate the toe of the other foot in a similar manner. Be sure to allow the frog to recover for a minute or so before applying the next stimulus. Now pinch the toe of one foot, holding it tightly with forceps so that it cannot be withdrawn. Describe what happens.

_____

_____

How do you think the nerve impulse reached the unstimulated leg?

_____

_____

F. STIMULATION OF MUSCLE THROUGH NERVE

Cells are, in general, subject to stimulation from a variety of impulses. In studying the different agencies that can cause a muscle to react, remember that the muscle cell differs only in degree, not in kind, in the way it responds to a stimulus. Cells that are specialized to perform other functions may respond to the same forms of stimulation that muscle cells do, but in a different way. A nerve will transmit an impulse in response to an adequate stimulus. If the nerve is in physiological connection with an excit-

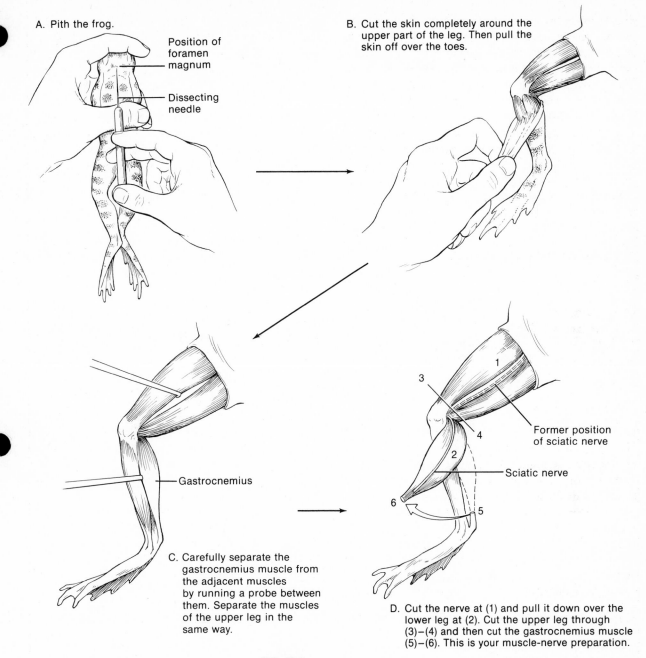

A. Pith the frog.

Position of foramen magnum

Dissecting needle

B. Cut the skin completely around the upper part of the leg. Then pull the skin off over the toes.

Gastrocnemius

C. Carefully separate the gastrocnemius muscle from the adjacent muscles by running a probe between them. Separate the muscles of the upper leg in the same way.

Former position of sciatic nerve

Sciatic nerve

D. Cut the nerve at (1) and pull it down over the lower leg at (2). Cut the upper leg through (3)–(4) and then cut the gastrocnemius muscle (5)–(6). This is your muscle-nerve preparation.

FIG. 16-5
Frog muscle-nerve preparation.

able muscle, the muscle will contract on receiving that impulse. Adequate stimulation of the nerve will have been attained when the muscle that it innervates contracts. In this part of the exercise, we will examine the effects of several factors on the nerve impulse, using an isolated **muscle-nerve preparation**. Usually an isolated gastrocnemius muscle and its nerve are used.

To obtain your muscle-nerve preparation, kill a frog by pithing both the brain and spinal cord (see Appendix D). Remove the skin from the legs. This can be easily done if the skin is cut completely around the "thigh" of

the frog leg. The entire skin of the leg may then be pulled off in the same way that you would strip a glove from your hand (Fig. 16-5). Place the animal, dorsal side up, on moist filter paper. Keep the animal moist with physiological saline. Note the large "calf" muscle of the lower leg. This is the gastrocnemius muscle and is the one to be used. Run a blunt probe (the end of a forceps will do) between this muscle and the long bone of the leg, noting how easily it is freed in the region between the two ends.

Next, notice the fairly well marked groove running along the upper leg. This groove marks the position of the sciatic nerve, which innervates the gastrocnemius muscle and which must be freed from the rest of the upper leg. With two pairs of forceps, pull the muscles apart on either side of the groove. If you do this carefully, you will expose the sciatic nerve along with blood vessels. The nerve is the faintly yellowish strand; the blood vessels are red. Without touching or pulling the nerve, remove the muscles (or pull them aside) so that the nerve is exposed from a point near the knee up to the hip. Then, with a forceps, grasp the hip end of the nerve and, cutting across the nerve on the hip side of the forceps, gradually free the nerve of connective tissue down to a point near the knee joint. This is the most delicate operation of the whole dissection. You should not stretch the nerve or touch it with metal *except where it is held at the hip end.* Lay the free nerve down on top of the lower leg. Using scissors, cut through the middle of the upper leg. Cut through everything, including bone and muscle, but be sure that the nerve is laid back so you do not cut through it. Sever the tendon at the lower end of the gastrocnemius muscle. Cut the lower leg bone near the knee. Your muscle-nerve preparation is now ready to use. Place it on filter paper moistened with physiological saline, or, if you are not ready to use it at once, place it in a beaker of the solution.

1. Effect of Mechanical Stimulation

Tap the nerve lightly near its distal (cut) end with a small glass rod. What is the result?

_____

Repeat the procedure with a harder tap. Does the muscle respond more fully than the first time?

_____

Pinch the nerve sharply with forceps about 0.5 cm from its cut end. Is the response any greater?

_____

Pinch the nerve approximately 1 cm from the cut end. What is the result?

_____

Account for the results you observed.

_____

_____

_____

2. Effect of Thermal Stimulation

Touch the nerve with the pointed end of a small glass rod so gently that there is no response. Heat the end of the rod until it is rather warm to the touch, and again touch the nerve as gently as before. What is the result?

_____

3. Effect of Chemical Stimulation

Cut off the part of the nerve that has already been used. Put a drop of 1 N HCl on the end of the nerve. Describe the response, if any.

_____

Wash off the terminal part of the nerve.

4. Effect of Electrical Stimulation

When two different metals are connected and their free ends are in contact with a salt solution, a current of electricity will flow in the way that it does in a battery. Scrape the ends of a piece of iron and copper wire (12–15 cm in length) with a knife or an emery cloth. Twist them together tightly at one end to make a V-shape. Making sure that the nerve-muscle preparation is moistened with physiological saline solution, touch the uninjured part of the nerve with the free ends of the wires. Repeat several times. Describe the response observed.

_____

Place one end of the V-shape on a nerve and the other on a muscle. What is the result?

_____

_____

Reverse the positions of the wires. What difference in the response, if any, is observed?

_____

Repeat the foregoing procedures, stimulating the muscle directly. Describe the response.

_____

_____

_____

Contrast this with the response obtained when stimulation is via the nerve.

_____

_____

_____

Would you say that nervous tissue is a better conductor than muscle? Why?

_____

REFERENCES

Baker, P. F. 1966. The Nerve Axon. *Scientific American* 214:74–82 (Offprint 1038). *Scientific American* Offprints are available from W. H. Freeman and Company, 660 Market Street, San Francisco 94104, and 58 Kings Road, Reading RG1 3AA, England. Please order by number.

Guyton, A. C. 1977. *Basic Human Physiology*. 2nd ed. Saunders.

Katz, B. 1966. *Nerve, Muscle, and Synapse*. McGraw-Hill.

Levi-Montalcini, R., and P. Calissano. 1979. The Nerve-Growth Factor. *Scientific American* 240:68–77 (Offprint 1430).

Luria, A. R. 1970. The Functional Organization of the Brain. *Scientific American* 222:66–78 (Offprint 526).

Macey, R. I. 1975. *Human Physiology*. 2nd ed. Prentice-Hall.

Marrazzi, A. S. 1957. Messengers of the Nervous System. *Scientific American* 196(2):86–94.

Merton, P. A. 1972. How We Control the Contraction of Our Muscles. *Scientific American* 226:30–37 (Offprint 1249).

Patterson, P. H., D. D. Potter, and E. J. Furshpan. 1978. The Chemical Differentiation of Nerve Cells. *Scientific American* 239:50–59 (Offprint 1393).

Schmidt-Nielsen, K. 1970. *Animal Physiology*. 3rd ed. Prentice-Hall.

Stent, G. 1972. Cellular Communication. *Scientific American* 227:42–51 (Offprint 1257).

Storer, T. I., R. L. Usinger, R. C. Stebbins, and J. W. Nybakken. 1979. *General Zoology*. 6th ed. McGraw-Hill.

Vander, A. J., J. H. Sherman, and D. Luciano. 1980. *Human Physiology: The Mechanism of Body Function*. 3rd ed. McGraw-Hill.

Mendelian Genetics

Like many subjects, genetics can be studied through the use of lectures and books without laboratory work. However, the personal experience of performing experimental procedures, collecting and analyzing data and drawing conclusions gives insights and appreciation of a discipline that cannot be achieved by simply reading about the subject.

Modern genetics, and indeed much of contemporary evolutionary theory, has as its basis the sturdy foundations of experimental evidence established by Gregor Mendel. His genius in studying the inheritance of single and multiple characteristics led to the discovery of his principles (now laws) of **segregation** and **independent assortment**. From these simple beginnings have evolved the studies leading to the characterization of DNA ("the stuff of life") and to the forefront of modern molecular biology and studies involving recombinant DNA.

In this exercise, you will become familiar with basic studies involving Mendelian genetics; that is, the laws of **segregation** and **independent assortment** as observed through studies involving monohybrid and dihybrid crosses. For demonstrating Mendel's laws, a variety of organisms may be used. We will study the fruit fly, *Drosophila*, and maize (corn), because these are probably the two eucaryotic organisms for which substantial genetic knowledge has accumulated. Before beginning these studies, read Appendix G for a discussion of Mendel's laws of inheritance.

A. GENETIC STUDIES USING *DROSOPHILA*

The most widely used organism for genetics studies is the common vinegar, or fruit fly, *Drosophila melanogaster*. This fly is easily cultured, and its generation time is only 9 or 10 days at normal room temperature (25°C). Because *Drosophila* is small, the cultures occupy little space; it is therefore a convenient and inexpensive organism with which to work.

Drosophila is well understood genetically and is therefore used more than any other organism for laboratory experiments concerning the basic principles of Mendelian genetics. Wild-type (normal) and mutant strains of *Drosophila* can be easily obtained for instructional purposes.

199

An enormous number of spontaneous mutations have been found, and many others have been induced by radiation, thus making *Drosophila* highly suitable for the investigation of genetic crosses.

Before performing genetics experiments with *Drosophila*, refer to Appendix H to learn some basic facts about the biology and culture of this organism.

1. Examination of Wild-Type Drosophila

In this part of the exercise, you will become familiar with the characteristics of the wild type and some of the common mutants of *Drosophila*. Then you will be given several flies whose mutant traits you are to identify.

Obtain a vial of wild-type fruit flies from your instructor and etherize them according to the procedure outlined in Fig. 17-1. When all of the flies have stopped moving, turn them onto a white card and carefully examine them with a dissecting microscope or hand lens. Become familiar with male and female characteristics by recording your observations in Table 17-1.

Obtain from your instructor a numbered vial containing a mixture of the following mutant flies:

Vestigial—a wing mutant characterized by highly reduced, withered wings.

White—a mutant whose eyes look white.

Bar—an eye mutant in which the number of facets of the eye is reduced, resulting in the appearance of a "bar" down the middle of the eye.

Black—a mutant whose body is black.

Other mutants

Etherize the flies and determine the nature of the mutant flies in your vial. Record your observations in Table 17-2.

2. Experimental Genetic Crosses

In making these genetic crosses, you will use methods essentially similar to those used by scientists doing research on *Drosophila*. You will be supplied with pedigreed stocks, maintained in the laboratory, that carry mutant genes. Flies in these cultures tend to breed true as long as they mate among themselves. Very rarely, however, new hereditary variations (i.e., spontaneous new mutations) do occur, and you should be on the lookout for these.

For these studies, flies having readily recognizable differences (traits) will be used. Names and symbols used to identify the mutant genes carried by the flies are those

TABLE 17-1
Comparison of male and female fruit flies.

Characteristic observed	Comparison	
	Male (♂)	Female (♀)
Which is relatively larger in overall size?		
What is the difference in banding on the abdomen?		
What is the shape of the tip of the abdomen?		
Are sex combs present or absent?		

TABLE 17-2
Unknown mutant flies.

Mutation	Sex

derived by research workers. Breeding stocks will be conveniently designated by symbols indicating the particular mutant gene(s) carried. Flies that exhibit traits that may be considered standard or normal are designated as wild: a plus sign (+) indicates wild type with reference to any gene. A lowercase letter indicates that the mutant allele is recessive to the wild-type allele. A capital letter designates a wild-type allele. The symbol *e*, for example, represents the recessive mutant allele for ebony body color and $e+$ ($+^e$ or E) the dominant allele for the wild-type gray body; B symbolizes the dominant allele for bar eye and B^+ ($+^B$ or b) the recessive allele for the wild-type eye. Homozygous ebony flies are symbolized *ee* and homozygous wild-type, e^+e^+.

When making a cross between two varieties of fruit flies, only those characters in which the parent flies differ should be considered. For example, in crossing flies having vestigial wings and those having sepia eyes, only wing shape and eye color should be observed carefully.

A. Gently tap the culture bottle to force the flies to the bottom.

B. Remove the cotton plug and in its place quickly insert the etherizing bottle.

C. Reverse the two bottles so that the etherizer is now on the bottom. Shake the flies into the etherizer.

D. Remove the culture bottle and quickly replug. Simultaneously plug the etherizer with its cork.

E. Transfer the flies to a white card. Examine them with a hand lens or dissecting microscope. Move flies around with a toothpick.

FIG. 17-1
Procedure for etherizing flies.

B. MENDEL'S LAW OF SEGREGATION

According to Mendel's first law, the **law of segregation**, genes do not blend, but behave as independent units. They pass intact from one generation to the next, in which they may or may not produce visible traits, depending on their dominant characteristics. Furthermore, genes segregate at random, thus producing predictable ratios of traits in the offspring.

1. In *Drosophila*

In this experiment, you will make several crosses to demonstrate Mendel's law of segregation—either crosses given in the following table or others suggested by your instructor. If time is limited, your instructor may have prepared the necessary matings for you.

Parent (P_1)

Female (♀)	×	Male (♂)
1. Sepia eye color *(se)*	×	Wild-type (red eye color)
2. Dumpy wings *(dp)*	×	Wild-type (long wings)
3. Vestigial wings *(vg)*	×	Wild-type (long wings)
4. Ebony body color *(e)*	×	Wild-type (gray-brown body color)

However, if you are to make the necessary crosses, you will be supplied with appropriate fly cultures by your instructor. As you make these crosses, complete the information indicated in Table 17-3. Isolate an etherized male of one variety and an etherized virgin female of the other, using the procedures described in Appendix H. While holding a culture bottle on its side, place these flies in the bottle. Be sure to add some dry yeast granules or yeast suspension to the medium *before* introducing the flies. Keep the bottle on its side until the flies have recovered from etherization, to prevent them from becoming stuck in the medium. After 7 or 8 days, remove the parent flies. Flies of the first filial generation (F_1) will begin to appear about 10 days after mating. After several F_1 flies have appeared, etherize them and examine under low-power magnification. Separate the flies by sex and record the phenotypes in Table 17-3.

To establish an F_2 generation, select three F_1 flies of each sex to be mated and place them in a fresh bottle of medium, using the mating procedure described for the first mating. It is not necessary that the F_1 female flies be virgins for this mating. Why?

_____

_____

Remove the F_1 flies in 7 or 8 days. About 14 days after mating, etherize the F_2 flies, separate them by sex, and record the phenotypes in Table 17-3. Record the results of the F_2 cross you made by entering the genotypes of the parent, F_1, and F_2 generations.

From this data, indicate the F_2 phenotypic ratio you obtained.

_____

What F_2 genotypic ratio was observed?

_____

Which trait is dominant in your crosses?

_____

2. Chi-Square Analysis of *Drosophila* Data

In general, when you carry out crosses involving one or more pairs of alleles, the results are fairly predictable. For example, if you carry out the following crosses you expect the typical 3:1 monohybrid ratio in the F_2 generation:

P_1:		$AA \times aa$	
F_1:		Aa	
F_1: (self-fertilized P_1's for F_2's) $Aa \times Aa$			
F_2:	AA	Aa	aa
	1	2	1	Genotypic ratio
	3		1	Phenotypic ratio

The same expectation could be made for a dihybrid cross where the expected 9:3:3:1 phenotypic ratio would be expressed.

The ratios just given are the *expected* ratios. In natural populations, the *expected values* rarely are identical to the *experimental* or *observed* values you get when counting the numbers of individuals expressing the characteristic in which you are interested.

The purpose of the **chi-square test** is to determine whether the experimentally obtained data (i.e., the *observed* data) are a good fit for, or satisfactory approximation of, the *expected* data for a given ratio. In other words, this test determines whether any deviations from the expected values are due to something other than chance.

Record the data obtained in Part B1 in Table 17-4. Carry out a chi-square analysis of the data (read Appendix E for a description of how to do a chi-square analysis).

TABLE 17-3
Monohybrid crosses in *Drosophila*.

————————————	———————————— ×	————————————
Student name	P₁ female	P₁ male

Date P₁ mated _____   Date P₁ removed _____

Phenotype of F₁ females _____   Phenotype of F₁ males _____

———————————— ×	————————————	————————————
F₁ female	F₁ male	Date F₁ mated

————————————	————————————
Date F₁ removed	Date F₂ examined

F₂ males		F₂ females	
F₂ phenotypes	Number	F₂ phenotypes	Number
Total =		Total =	

	Male	Female
	————————————	————————————
Genotype of P₁	————————————	————————————
Genotype of F₁	————————————	————————————
Genotypes of F₂	————————————	————————————
	————————————	————————————
	————————————	————————————
	————————————	————————————

TABLE 17-4
Data for chi-square analysis of monohybrid cross in *Drosophila*.

Phenotype	Genotype	Observed *(O)*	Expected *(E)*	*(O − E)*	*(O − E)²*	*(O − E)²/E*
Totals						
Conclusion:						

Are the observed values you obtained small enough to be within the limits expected by chance alone?

_____

If not, what factors, other than chance, could account for the larger deviations of the observed values from the values you expected to obtain?

_____

_____

_____

_____

_____

What is the F_2 ratio obtained?

_____

Is the ratio you obtained in your tray the same or different from that obtained when you count the plants of the entire class? Explain any differences.

_____

What phenotypes are expressed in the F_2 generation?

_____

What genotypes are expressed in the F_2 generation?

_____

What would be the phenotype and genotype of the F_1 generation?

_____

What would be the phenotypes and genotypes for the original parents (i.e., the P_1 generation)?

_____

_____

Would it be possible to have had sexually mature P_1's for each of the traits expressed in the F_2 generation? Explain.

_____

3. In Maize (Corn)

You will be given F_1 corn seeds that, when planted, will grow into F_2 plants that will exhibit an obvious deficiency. Your instructor will give you planting and watering instructions. It takes about 7–10 days for the seedlings to emerge from the soil. When they are 50–75 mm tall, count the two different types of seedlings in your own tray and in those of the rest of the class. You may use whatever symbols you feel are appropriate to distinguish one allele from the other. Set up appropriate tables, properly labeled, to tabulate your data.

What is the deficiency expressed by one of the alleles?

_____

_____

_____

_____

_____

Analyze your results using the chi-square test (see Appendix E). Are your experimental values consistent with what you would expect to obtain? If not, suggest why the deviation from the expected value could have occurred.

_____

_____

_____

_____

C. MENDEL'S LAW OF INDEPENDENT ASSORTMENT

Mendel's second law was derived from his studies involving crosses dealing with two gene pairs. He demonstrated that, whether you are dealing with one, two, three, or more alleles, each acts independently of the others and is not changed in transmission from one generation to the next. However, we now know that this is valid only if the genes involved are located on different chromosomes, as was the case in all Mendel's studies. Thus Mendel always obtained the classical 9:3:3:1 dihybrid ratio. Subsequent studies have shown other ratios for dihybrid crosses in which the genes are linked, that is, located on the same chromosomes. In the space below, give examples of other dihybrid ratios (i.e., 9:7) and the circumstances under which they would be obtained (i.e., linkage).

_____

_____

_____

1. In *Drosophila*

The gene for ebony body color *(e)* is located on the third chromosome and the gene for vestigial wings *(vg)* is located on the second chromosome. Reciprocal crosses should be made from these stocks as follows:

$$\text{vestigial } \male \ (vgvg;\ e^+e^+) \times \text{ebony } \female \ (vg^+vg^+;\ ee)$$

and

$$\text{vestigial } \female \ (vgvg;\ e^+e^+) \times \text{ebony } \male \ (vg^+vg^+;\ ee)$$

Note: Make certain only virgin females are used in these crosses. Why?

_____

_____

After about eight days, remove the parental stock and discard them. When the F_1 flies emerge, count them and determine the characteristic(s) which they express. Record the data you obtain in Table 17-5 or 17-6. What do you predict the F_1 phenotype and genotype to be?

_____

Mate the F_1 males and F_1 females in new bottles. Again, after eight days, remove and discard all F_1 flies. When the F_2-generation flies have emerged, count them and determine the numbers and ratios for the characteristics being studied. Record this information in Table 17-5 or 17-6.

Also, fill in Table 17-7 and then carry out a chi-square analysis to determine if your experimental values are consistent with what you would theoretically expect to obtain. (See Appendix E for a discussion of chi-square analysis.)

2. In Maize (Corn)

Your instructor will provide you with F_2 maize seeds removed from an ear of corn similar to the one shown in Fig. 17-2.

FIG. 17-2
Example of a dihybrid cross in maize. Typical 9:3:3:1 ratio expressed for genes located on different chromosomes.

206

TABLE 17-5
Dihybrid cross in *Drosophila.*

| Student name | P₁ female | × | P₁ male |

Date P₁ mated   Date P₁ removed

Phenotype of F₁ females   Phenotype of F₁ males

| F₁ female | × | F₁ male | Date F₁ mated |

Date F₁ removed   Date F₂ examined

F₂ males		F₂ females	
F₂ phenotypes	Number	F₂ phenotypes	Number
Total =		Total =	

	Male	Female
Genotype of P₁		
Genotype of F₁		
Genotypes of F₂		

TABLE 17-6
Dihybrid cross in *Drosophila* (reciprocal cross).

Student name	P₁ female	×	P₁ male

Date P₁ mated   Date P₁ removed

Phenotype of F₁ females   Phenotype of F₁ males

F₁ female	×	F₁ male	Date F₁ mated

Date F₁ removed   Date F₂ examined

F₂ males		F₂ females	
F₂ phenotypes	Number	F₂ phenotypes	Number
Total =		Total =	

	Male	Female
Genotype of P₁		
Genotype of F₁		
Genotypes of F₂		

TABLE 17-7
Data for chi-square analysis of dihybrid cross in *Drosophila*.

Phenotype	Genotype	Observed (O)	Expected (E)	(O − E)	(O − E)²	(O − E)²/E
Totals						
Conclusion:						

Determine the four different phenotypes being expressed. Count the number of kernels represented by each phenotype and record them in the space below. Select the symbols you feel would represent the phenotypes being expressed.

Allele	Phenotype
_____	_____
_____	_____
_____	_____
_____	_____

Which characteristics are recessive?

_____

Which characteristics are dominant?

_____

Give the phenotype _____ and genotype _____ of the F_1 generation.

Give the phenotype and genotype of the original P_1, homozygous parents.

_____

Complete Table 17-8 and carry out a chi-square analysis to determine if the experimental values are consistent with what you would expect to obtain in this dihybrid cross.

D. INHERITANCE OF HUMAN BLOOD GROUPS

The discovery of human blood groups was reported by Dr. Karl Landsteiner in 1900. This important discovery, for which Landsteiner received a Nobel Prize, led to the establishment of four blood groups: O, A, B, and AB. The basis for these groups is the presence of **antigens**, which are molecules that form part of the surface coating of red blood cells. These antigens stimulate lymphocytes to produce a class of globular protein molecules called **antibodies**. These antibodies combine with the red blood cell antigens to cause agglutination (clumping) and subsequent elimination from the circulation by macrophages.

The two antigens discovered by Landsteiner are glycoproteins and are designated A and B. If you have Type A blood, then the surface of your red blood cells has the specific Glycoprotein A; if you have Type B, then you have Glycoprotein B on your blood cells; if you have Type AB, your blood cells have both types of antigens; and if you have Type O you have neither A nor B antigens on your red blood cells. Furthermore, an organism's serum contains antibodies against whichever antigen is not present on its red cells. Thus human beings with Type A blood have antibodies against Type B red cells in their blood. Similarly, Type B people have antibodies against A, Type O have antibodies against both A and B, and Type AB have neither antibody in their blood.

If a patient having blood type A is given a transfusion of Type B or AB blood, the anti-B antibodies in his or her blood will agglutinate the Type B or AB red blood cells almost immediately, with severe—perhaps fatal—consequences. In practice, blood types are cross-matched before transfusion. Thus a person who has Type A can be safely transfused with Type O cells because those who

TABLE 17-8
Data for chi-square analysis of dihybrid cross in maize.

Phenotype	Genotype	Observed (O)	Expected (E)	(O − E)	(O − E)^2	(O − E)^2/E
Totals						
Conclusions:						

TABLE 17-9
Human blood groups.

Phenotype	Genotype	Antigen found on surface of red blood cells	Antibody found in serum
O	OO	none	anti-A and anti-B
A	AA or AO	A	anti-B
B	BB or BO	B	anti-A
AB	AB	A and B	none

have Type A carry no antibodies against O. Similarly, Type O can be transfused to a person who has Type B or AB. For this reason, those who have Type O blood are known as **universal donors**. In practice, it has been found best to use a donor of the same blood type as the recipient, and the universal donor is used only in an emergency.

If you have Type AB red blood cells, you are a **universal recipient** because you have no naturally occurring antibodies to Type A or B red blood cells, and therefore neither A nor B antigens will be foreign to your blood.

The antigens that determine the four blood groups are the result of the expression of three alleles for Phenotypes O, B, and A. Alleles for Phenotypes A and B are apparently dominant over that for O. The distribution of the antigens and antibodies in the human blood groups is shown in Table 17-9.

Many blood groups have been identified in addition to the O, A, B, and AB series. These include the MNS, Pp, Lutheran, Kell, Lewis, Duffy, Kidd, and the Rh series—the last being very important in certain pregnancies. If a woman is Rh negative (i.e., she lacks the Rh antigens on her red blood cells) and her husband carries the Rh anti-

gens on his cells, then some of the children born to these parents may be Rh positive. Should any of the blood of an Rh-positive fetus cross the placenta, antibodies against the Rh antigens on the fetal red blood cells will form in the woman. Some of these antibodies will then recross the placenta into the fetus, where they will react with the Rh-positive red cells, producing anemia and jaundice. The anemic condition causes the fetus to produce immature red blood cells (**erythroblasts**) at a high rate, leading to the condition known as *erythroblastosis fetalis*.

The degree of agglutination depends largely on the concentration of antibodies in the serum. Thus when blood is transfused, the antigen of the donor and the antibody of the recipient are all that matter because the antibodies in the blood of the donor are extensively diluted by the blood of the recipient and thus are essentially ineffective in agglutinating the recipient's blood.

To determine your own blood type, it is necessary to have only two reagents: one containing anti-A antibodies and the other containing anti-B antibodies. Each of the two antibodies should agglutinate the red blood cells containing the corresponding antigen. Table 17-10 shows the results that will be obtained if cells of the four differ-

A. Place 2 or 3 drops of each solution on a clean slide.

B. Add a drop of alcohol to the tip of your finger. Allow to dry.

C. Prick the finger with a sterile lancet. (CAUTION: Do not exchange lancets with other students!) Discard after use.

D. Discard the first drop of blood. Then add a drop of blood to each circle. (CAUTION: Allow blood to drop onto the fluid. Do not touch finger to antiserum.)

E. Quickly stir each drop with a separate toothpick. Note clumping in circle A, indicating blood type A.

FIG. 17-3
Procedure for determining human blood group phenotypes.

ent blood types are used. A plus sign (+) indicates agglutination of cells and a minus sign (−) indicates no agglutination.

Draw three circles with a wax pencil on a clean microscope slide. Label one circle "A" (for anti-A), one "B" (for anti-B), and the third "C." Add a drop of anti-A serum (colored blue for identification purposes) to circle A, and a drop of anti-B (yellow) to circle B.

Add a drop of 0.9% saline to circle C (Fig. 17-3). Why is this control needed?

_____

_____

Apply alcohol to the tip of the finger to be pricked. Prick that fingertip with a sterile, disposable lancet supplied by the instructor. Squeeze the finger and wipe off the first drop of blood. Continue to squeeze the finger, and apply a large drop of blood to each circle. Quickly stir each drop with a separate toothpick to get a uniform mixture, and after a few minutes note whether any reactions have taken place. After obtaining the blood, clean your finger with alcohol.

If agglutination has occurred only in Circle A, your blood type is A; if only in Circle B, your blood type is B. If agglutination has occurred in both Circle A and Circle B, your blood type is AB; and if there is no agglutination in either Circle A or Circle B, your blood type is O. What is your blood group phenotype?

_____

What is your blood genotype? _____

_____

If you are typing your blood as part of a class project, tabulate the blood types of other students in Table 17-11. Compare the incidence (%) of blood types in your class with the incidence of human blood types in the United States that are listed in Table 17-12.

A knowledge of the blood groups is of considerable importance in medicine, biology, and forensic (legal) medicine dealing with paternity. What blood types are not possible for the children of two Type AB or two Type O parents?

In a case of disputed paternity, the child is Type O, the mother Type A, and the putative father is AB. What inference can be drawn from this knowledge?

_____

TABLE 17-10
Determination of human blood groups.

Unknown red blood cells from individual	Serum used and reaction		Phenotype
	Anti-A	Anti-B	
1	+	−	A
2	+	+	AB
3	−	−	O
4	−	+	B

TABLE 17-11
Summary of class blood types.

Blood type	Number of students with this blood type	Incidence (%)
A		
B		
AB		
O		

TABLE 17-12
Incidence of blood types in several populations in the United States.

Type	Incidence (%) among			
	Whites	Blacks	Chinese	American Indians
O	45	48	36	23
A	41	27	28	76
B	10	21	23	1
AB	4	4	13	1

What if the putative father were Type B?

Suppose that the identities of the children in a hospital nursery become mixed up. How might blood typing help straighten out the matter?

REFERENCES

Crow, J. F. 1979. Genes that Violate Mendel's Rules. *Scientific American* 240:134–146 (Offprint 1418). *Scientific American* Offprints are available from W. H. Freeman and Company, 660 Market Street, San Francisco 94104, and 58 Kings Road, Reading RG1 3AA, England. Please order by number.

Demerec, M., and B. P. Kaufman. 1969. *Drosophila Guide: Introduction to the Genetics and Cytology of Drosophila.* 8th ed. Carnegie Institution.

Flagg, R. O. 1971. *Drosophila Manual.* Carolina Biological Supply Co.

Lerner, I. M., and W. J. Libby. 1976. *Heredity, Evolution, and Society.* 2nd ed. W. H. Freeman and Company.

Ortho Diagnostics. 1967. *Blood Group Antigens and Antibodies as Applied to Compatibility Testing.*

Ortho Diagnostics. 1969. *Blood Group Antigens and Antibodies as Applied to the ABO and Rh Systems.*

Singer, S. 1978. *Human Genetics.* W. H. Freeman and Company.

Srb, A. M., R. D. Owen, and R. S. Edgar, eds. 1970. *Facets of Genetics: Readings from Scientific American.* W. H. Freeman and Company.

Stern, C. 1973. *Principles of Human Genetics.* 3rd ed. W. H. Freeman and Company.

Stern, C., and E. R. Sherwood, eds. 1966. *The Origin of Genetics.* W. H. Freeman and Company.

Strickberger, M. W. 1962. *Experiments in Genetics with Drosophilia.* Wiley.

Biochemical Genetics

The science of genetics has passed through several phases during the past seventy years. Each period was initiated by some important event.

The first period began with the rediscovery of Mendel's papers in 1900. The results of this period demonstrated the universal application of the laws of heredity; that is, the transmission of heritable characteristics is brought about by the same mechanism that regulates Mendelian segregation.

The second period, beginning around 1910, saw the introduction of a new "tool" to be used in genetic research—the fruit fly, *Drosophila melanogaster*. From this period came the experimental evidence that genes are located in linear order on the chromosomes.

Further studies on the structure of chromosomes and the discovery that radiation (such as X rays) caused mutations (a potentially transmissible change in a gene or chromosome) marked the beginning of the third period of activity. This information was developed further during the succeeding years.

The fourth period introduced microorganisms in genetic studies and provided evidence that the genes regulated the activities of cells by controlling the production of enzymes.

The formulation of the Watson-Crick model of the molecular structure of deoxyribonucleic acid (DNA) opened the present era of molecular genetics. DNA is unique in three respects. First, it is a very large molecule, having a certain uniformity of size, rigidity, and shape. Despite this uniformity, however, it has almost infinite internal variety that gives it the complexity required for information-carrying purposes. The second characteristic of DNA is its capacity to make copies of itself with remarkable exactness. The biologist or chemist would say that such a molecule can **replicate** itself. The third characteristic is its ability to transmit information to other parts of the cell. The behavior of the cell reflects the information transmitted.

The past several years have shown that this genetic information (carried in the chemical structure of DNA) consists of a four-letter alphabet of which the "words" and "sentences" of the genetic material and the role it plays in determining the structure of proteins will be regarded as one of the greatest discoveries of all time.

A. CHROMATOGRAPHIC SEPARATION OF *DROSOPHILA* EYE PIGMENTS

In 1941, George W. Beadle and Edward L. Tatum presented experimental evidence supporting the concept that genes control the chemical activities of the cell by controlling the production of biochemical catalysts called *enzymes*. Enzymes, in turn, catalyze the numerous chemical reactions taking place in cells that are ultimately expressed morphologically, physiologically, biochemically, or in the behavior of an adult organism.

Eye pigmentation in the fruit fly *Drosophila melanogaster* is under genetic control. The "normal" eye color of this insect is correlated with the presence of a characteristic series of substances called **pteridines** (derived from the Greek word *pteron,* meaning wing). This term was chosen because the first substances in this class of compounds were extracted from butterfly wings. These compounds are readily separated by chromatography and, if viewed under ultraviolet light, produce seven distinctive fluorescent patterns in wild-type *Drosophila* (Fig. 18-1). Pteridines are present in many invertebrates, in certain pigment cells of amphibians and fishes, and in plants where they may participate in photosynthesis. The pathway of pteridine synthesis is not well understood; however, certain steps have been identified:

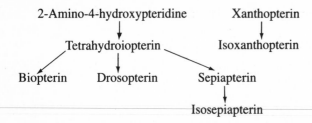

Flies with mutant eye colors have pteridine patterns that are distinctly different from that of the wild-type flies. Certain "normal" wild-type pteridines may be completely missing, whereas others may be present in abnormally large quantities.

Recessive mutations (e.g., X-linked *w,* white eyes) affect the pteridine profiles of wild-type heterozygotes. Although a wild-type heterozygote may appear to have normal eye color, it can be shown chromatographically to be not fully normal at all.

Two mutants that have been independently isolated have dull, reddish brown eyes in contrast with the bright red of normal flies. The two genes producing this trait have been found to reside in two locations in the *Drosophila* genome. One of them, termed *maroonlike (mal),* is located on the first (or sex) chromosome (Chromosome I), whereas the other, termed *rosy (ry),* is located on the third chromosome (Chromosome III). Both of these genetic loci must be wild-type in order for normal wild-

type pigmentation to occur; thus flies that are *mal/mal*$^+$:ry^- have the same phenotype as flies that are genotypically *mal/mal:ry*$^+$/ry^-. Enzymatic analysis has revealed that both mutant types are deficient in xanthine dehydrogenase, the enzyme that converts 2-amino-4-hydroxypteridine into isoxanthopterin. As a result of the enzymatic deficiency, mutant flies accumulate 2-amino-4-hydroxypteridine, whereas the wild-type flies have no or little substrate but do contain considerable quantities of the product isoxanthopterin. This particular example supports the generalization that genes produce their effects through the action of enzymes.

In this study, you will analyze chromatographically the pteridines in the normal (wild-type) fruit fly and compare the wild type with several eye-color mutants to establish the eye-color mutations are accompanied by differences in pteridine patterns. (See Appendix C for a discussion of chromatography.)

1. On a 20-by-20-cm silica gel plate, draw a pencil line parallel to, and about 25 mm from, one edge (Fig. 18-2). Lightly pencil in several evenly spaced dots along the origin line. The number of dots will depend on the number of flies supplied by your instructor. Handle the silica gel plate as little as possible because fingerprints may interfere with separation.

2. Obtain three wild-type flies, three each of the eye-color mutants rosy *(ry)* and maroonlike *(mal),* and three each of one or more of the following mutants:

Sepia *(se)*	Cinnabar *(cn)*
Brown *(bw)*	Vermillion *(v)*
Plum *(Pm)*	Eosin *(w*^{e}*)*
Scarlet *(st)*	Apricot *(w*^{a}*)*
	White *(w)*

Because sex differences exist with respect to the pteridines, the following analyses should be made using flies of the same sex. Choose adult males or females.

The wild-type fruit fly has dark red eyes, a tannish, bristle-covered body, and a long, straight pair of wings reaching just beyond the tip of the abdomen (Fig. 18-3). The adult males are differentiated from females by their somewhat smaller bodies; a rounded, heavily pigmented abdomen; and a "sex comb" (a tuft of bristles) on the forelegs. The abdomen of the female is somewhat pointed, is traversed by several dark stripes, and may have a terminal tuft of short bristles.

3. Etherize three wild-type flies and place them in a vial containing about 0.25 ml of the chromatographic solvent. Crush the flies with a glass rod to dissolve the pigments. Using a capillary tube, add several drops of the extract to the silica gel, as shown in Fig. 18-2. Allow the spot to dry between applications. Be careful not to

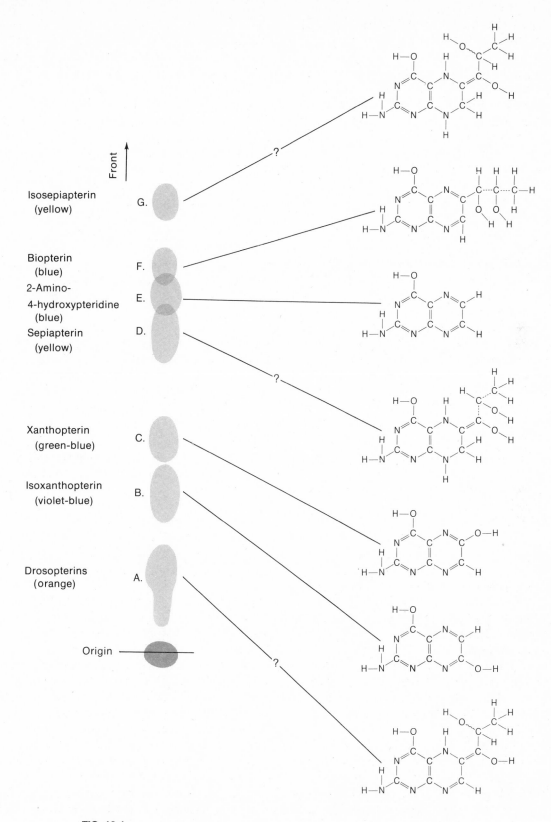

FIG. 18-1

Pteridines of the wild-type fruit fly. The chemical structures were worked out by Max Viscontini, Institute of Organic Chemistry, University of Zurich. (From *Fractionating the Fruit Fly,* by Ernst Hadorn. Copyright © 1962 by Scientific American, Inc. All rights reserved.)

A. Tap vial to force flies to bottom.

B. Remove cotton plug and quickly insert cork. Etherize flies until they are dead. Remove cotton.

Cork with cotton containing ether

Origin line

25 mm

WILD TYPE

C. Thoroughly crush three flies in a small amount of solvent and add several drops of extract to silica gel plate using a capillary tube.

Cover

Solvent "front"

About 1 cm of solvent

WILD TYPE

D. Place silica gel plate in jar containing 1 cm of chromatographic solvent. Cover and develop in a dark room. Remove when solvent front reaches to within 3.5 cm of the top of the plate.

WILD TYPE

E. Dry chromatogram and examine in darkened room with ultraviolet light.

FIG. 18-2
Procedure for chromatographic separation of pteridines.

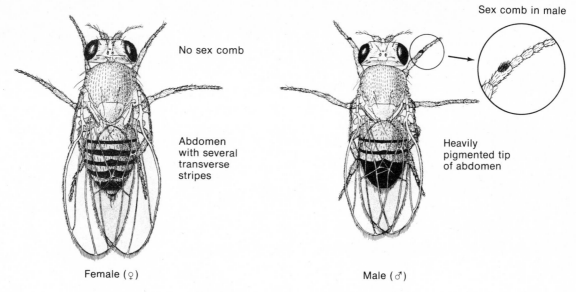

No sex comb

Abdomen
with several
transverse
stripes

Female (♀)

Sex comb in male

Heavily
pigmented tip
of abdomen

Male (♂)

FIG. 18-3
The adult fruit fly, *Drosophila melanogaster.*

disturb the silica gel coating any more than necessary. Label for identification. Repeat this procedure for each of the eye-color mutants. What is one control that should be used?

_____

Add this control to the thin-layer sheet.

4. Allow the spots to dry for several minutes. Then place the silica gel sheet in the solvent in the chromatographic jar (Fig. 18-2). Because the pteridines are light sensitive, the chromatograms should be developed in a dark room (or the jar should be covered with foil).

5. Allow the chromatogram to develop until the solvent front reaches to within 3.5 cm of the top of the sheet.

6. Remove the plate from the tank, mark the solvent front with a pencil, and air-dry for several minutes. Examine the sheet, using ultraviolet (UV) light of "long" wavelengths (360 nm). (CAUTION: Do not look directly into the UV lamp and wear goggles to protect your eyes from UV reflection from the laboratory table.) Note the fluorescent colors of the various pteridines (Fig. 18-1). Outline each spot with a pencil. The pteridines are listed in Table 18-1 in the order in which they are separated on the chromatogram, with the pteridine listed last being found at the bottom of the chromatogram, nearest to the origin. Indicate which pteridines are present in the flies you examined by checking the appropriate boxes in Table 18-1.

Calculate the R_f values, and record them in Table 18-2 for each of the pteridines isolated on your chromatogram, using the procedure outlined in Appendix C.

Does your chromatogram of sepia-eyed flies show any pteridines present in excess of those found in wild-type? _____ . If so, what pigments?

_____

What pteridines did you or your classmates observe in male and female rosy and maroonlike eye-color mutant flies?

_____

_____

_____

_____

Explain any differences you may have observed.

_____

_____

_____

_____

Discuss the eye-color mutations in terms of the genetic control of enzyme synthesis and activity.

_____

TABLE 18-1
Distribution of pteridines in the wild-type *Drosophila* and in eye-color mutants.

Pteridine (color)	Fruit fly eye type					
		Mutants				
	Wild type Sex: ___	Rosy Sex: ___	Maroonlike Sex: ___	_____ Sex: ___	_____ Sex: ___	_____ Sex: ___
Isosepiapterin (yellow)						
Biopterin (blue)						
2-Amino-4-hydroxypteridine (blue)						
Sepiapterin (yellow)						
Xanthopterin (green-blue)						
Isoxanthopterin (violet-blue)						
Drosopterins (orange)						

TABLE 18-2
Calculation of R_f values for pteridine pigments of a wild-type *Drosophila melanogaster*.

Pigment	Distance from base line to center of spot	Distance from base line to solvent front	R_f values
Isosepiapterin			
Biopterin			
2-Amino-4-hydroxypteridine			
Sepiapterin			
Xanthopterin			
Isoxanthopterin			
Drosopterins			

_____

_____

_____

_____

If time permits, you might consider using this technique to answer the following questions.

1. Do adult male and female flies have the same pteridine patterns?

2. Do the patterns of pteridine synthesis change during the development of the fly from egg to the adult?

3. Will there be pigment differences in body-color mutants similar to those seen in eye-color mutants?

B. INDUCTION OF MUTATION BY ULTRAVIOLET LIGHT

The capacity for mutation is inherent in the genetic material of all living organisms, as well as in viruses. Although mutations may occur spontaneously, the frequency with which mutations occur can be increased by a variety of agents called **mutagens**. One of the more commonly used mutagenic agents is ultraviolet light. Ultraviolet light produces its effects (at least in part) by causing breaks in chromosomes that result in the loss or rearrangement of parts.

In this experiment, ultraviolet radiation will be used to study the mutation rate of the antibiotic-producing mold *Penicillium*. This study will be limited to such obvious mutations as shape and pigmentation of the colony and the effects on growth rate.

1. Working in pairs, obtain two petri dishes containing nutrient medium. Label one "Control" and the other "UV," and add your names, date, and laboratory section number.

2. Add 1 ml of a *Penicillium* spore suspension to each of the plates as follows (Fig. 18-4).

a. Gently shake the flask containing the spores to make the contents uniformly suspended.

b. Fill the pipet in the flask to the 1-ml mark. Add the spore suspension to the surface of the agar in the control dish. Then, holding the agar plate at eye level, tilt the plate, allowing the suspension to run to the far edge. (CAUTION: Do not tilt it so far that the spore suspension runs over the lip of the plate.) Then hold the plate horizontally and gently jerk it toward you. Repeat this several times, rotating the plate part-way between "jerks." In this way, the spore suspension will cover the entire surface of the agar.

c. Repeat Steps a and b for the UV plate.

3. Set the plate aside for $\frac{3}{4}$ to 1 hour, so that the spores settle onto the agar. Do not move the plates during this period.

4. Irradiate the UV plate as follows (Fig. 18-4).

a. Turn the UV lamp on several minutes before irradiation.

b. Place the plate, cover on, under the UV lamp.

c. Remove the cover and expose the plate to the UV light for 35–40 seconds. Replace the cover and remove the plate.

5. Incubate the plates for one week at 28°C. Then count the number of *Penicillium* colonies that have grown on the control and irradiated plates. (Each colony arises from one spore.) Record your data in Table 18-3.

6. Carefully study the appearance of the colonies on the control plate. These are the normal or wild-type colonies. They should be bluish black in color, with a narrow white fringe. If available, examine color transparencies of wild-type colonies to aid you in your identification of the normal condition. If any of the colonies on the control plate deviate from the wild-type (for example, in colony size, margin width, color, or surface appearance), consider them to be mutants. Would you expect to find mutant colonies on the control plate? Explain.

_____

_____

_____

What evidence is there that UV radiation is indiscriminate in its ability to induce mutations?

_____

_____

_____

220

A. Shake spore suspension.

B. Add 1.0 ml of suspension to surface of agar.

C. Tilt plate, allowing suspension to run to edge.

D. Rotate, and jerk plate to spread spores over surface of agar.

Ultraviolet lamp

Cover

E. Irradiate for 35 seconds after removing cover.

FIG. 18-4
Ultraviolet irradiation of *Penicillium* spores. (Adapted from *Plants in Perspective,* by Eldon H. Newcomb, Gerald C. Gerloff, and William F. Whittingham. W. H. Freeman and Company. Copyright © 1964.)

TABLE 18-3
Effects of ultraviolet radiation on *Penicillium*.

Penicillium	Class data		Team data	
	Control	UV	Control	UV
Total number of colonies				
Number of mutant colonies				
Percentage of mutant colonies				
Percentage of spores surviving irradiation				

The mutations studied in this exercise were expressed as gross visible changes. Is it possible that some of the wild-type colonies are carrying UV-induced mutations? Explain.

_____

_____

_____

_____

_____

_____

C. MOLECULAR AND MORPHOLOGICAL BASIS OF HEREDITY

At the turn of the century, the rediscovered classical work of Mendel laid the foundations of modern genetics. The nature of the gene—the functional unit of inheritance—was defined. Subsequently, as a result of many ingenious experiments, the Mendelian laws of inheritance and the chromosome theory of inheritance were developed.

Much is known about the structure of chromosomes from visual observations. Chromosomes change in morphology during the various stages in the process of cell growth and multiplication. In general, these changes are cyclic: As the cell prepares for division and proceeds to divide, the chromosomes pass through a regular progression of structural changes until, at the completion of division, the characteristics of the original cell are restored in the daughter cells.

In addition to reproducing themselves, chromosomes direct and regulate metabolic activities by means of var-

ious messenger molecules (i.e., the several types of RNA), form nucleoli, segregate, compact themselves at certain times, and govern differentiation at the intracellular, cellular, tissue, organ, and organism levels. Thus, whereas some aspects of chromosomal structure and function are well known and understood, others need clarification.

In this study, you will become familiar with the molecular structure of DNA, with evidence that DNA is the genetic material, and with the morphology of the giant, salivary gland chromosomes.

1. The Molecular Structure of DNA

In the early 1950s, Watson and Crick formulated their classic model of the molecular structure of deoxyribonucleic acid—DNA. A three-dimensional model based on the Watson-Crick formulation probably is available in your laboratory.

On the DNA model (and Fig. 18-5A) note that the molecule consists of nitrogen compounds, phosphates, and sugars, which are joined in two coiling strands that form a double helix. Note that each strand consists of alternating sugar and phosphate molecules linked together. Attached to each sugar, toward the inside, is a nitrogen base. The bases of the two strands are paired and are connected to one another by hydrogen bonds. There are four different bases: adenine (A), thymine (T), cytosine (C), and guanine (G). What pattern of base pairing is evident?

_____

The base-sugar-phosphate combination constitutes a nucleotide (Fig. 18-5B). The distance between successive base pairs is 3.4 Å units. How many base pairs are there in one complete turn of the helix?

_____

How many Å units would one turn be?

_____

Label the model of the DNA molecule diagrammed in Fig. 18-5. This model represents only a very small segment of the DNA molecule. Indeed, if it were possible to remove the DNA from a cell and stretch it out as a single, fine thread, it would cover a length of about 3 feet (1 meter).

Each plant or animal begins life as a single cell that undergoes mitosis to form the multicellular adult. This suggests that DNA must also be able to replicate itself. In Fig. 18-6, suggest (by drawing) a method of DNA replication.

222

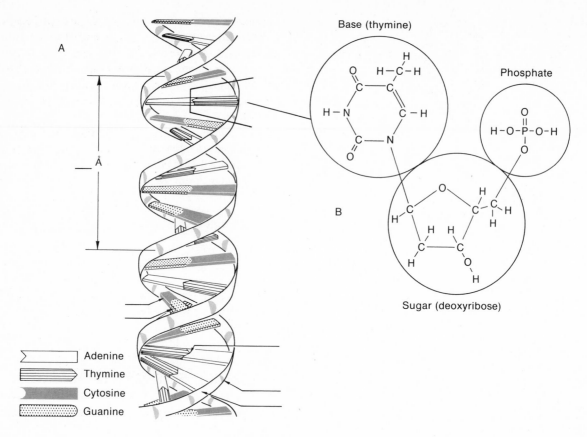

Base (thymine)

Phosphate

B

Sugar (deoxyribose)

Adenine
Thymine
Cytosine
Guanine

FIG. 18-5
Molecular structure of DNA.

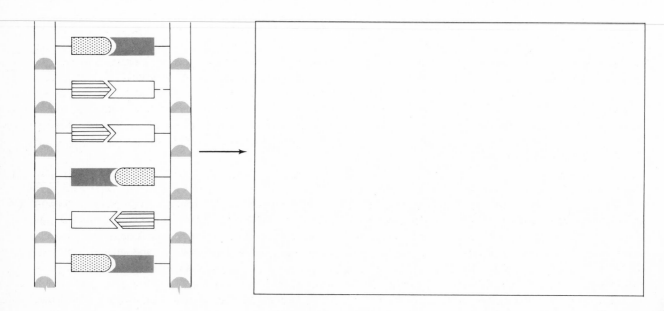

FIG. 18-6
Suggested method of DNA replication.

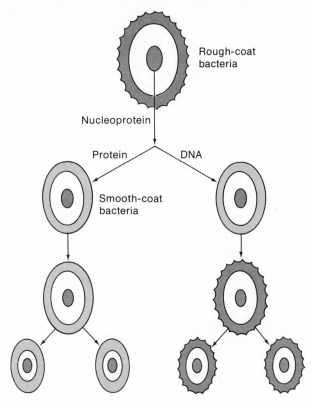

FIG. 18-7
Bacterial transformation by DNA.

In terms of your knowledge of the structure of DNA, suggest a possible mechanism of mutation at the molecular level.

_____

_____

_____

2. Bacterial Transformation

About 20 years ago, studies showed that, through the mediation of a certain chemical substance, the parental cell passes its own characteristics to its daughter cells; that is, the daughter cells inherit the capacity to become nerve cells or muscle cells or to secrete hormones from "information" supplied by the parent cell. This "genetic information" was found to lie in the structure of the chemical compound known as DNA (deoxyribonucleic acid). The first evidence that DNA was the "genetic material" came from experiments using bacteria.

The chromosomes contain a **nucleoprotein complex**, which consists of DNA, RNA (ribonucleic acid), and several types of protein. It is possible to extract the nucleoproteins from bacterial cells and to separate them into DNA and protein fractions. If these fractions are added to a medium in which other bacteria are growing, the foreign DNA and protein will be absorbed by the bacteria. Avery, MacLeod, and McCarty provided evidence for the link between DNA and the genetic material, using two different strains of bacteria—one having a rough coat and the other having a smooth coat. The nucleoprotein of the rough-coated bacteria was extracted and separated into DNA and protein fractions. Each fraction was added to separate cultures of smooth-coated bacteria. The results showed that the smooth-coated bacteria, to which DNA had been added, acquired the rough-coated characteristic (Fig. 18-7). Moreover, the offspring of these bacteria gave rise to more rough-coated bacteria. This **bacterial transformation** was brought about specifically by DNA.

3. Chromosome Morphology

a. Salivary Gland Chromosomes In *Drosophila*

The giant salivary gland chromosomes of *Drosophila* and other flies afford an excellent opportunity to study the components of the nucleus in relation to chromosomal structure. Although it is true that these cells are highly specialized and that certain aspects may not readily apply to other tissues, they are like most other cells in terms of their major nucleoprotein components. They are unlike many other tissues, however, in that from the time the first gland primordium is formed in the embryo the cells do not divide. The larval salivary gland thus contains a constant number of cells from before the egg is hatched until the gland degenerates during formation of the puparium. The gland grows entirely through cell enlargement, and, as the cell enlarges, the nucleus and its chromosomes also enlarge.

Giant salivary gland chromosomes occur primarily in dipteran flies. The chromosomes attain their maximum size just before pupation. The salivary gland undergoes degeneration (histolysis) in *Drosophila* during the formation of the puparium, although in other species (e.g., *Sciara*) gland degeneration occurs about 30 hours after pupation. An important physiological function of these glands is the secretion of "silk" or a similar protein, which can be used to spin a web or a cocoon or to attach the puparium to a substratum. Salivary glands also secrete digestive enzymes during the active ingestion phase of

224

A. Select largest larva and place on slide lightly moistened with saline.

Microscope field

Mouth parts

B. Examine with dissecting microscope and locate head end, including mouth parts.

C. Pierce head and hold in place. Grasp rear end with forceps and gently pull head and attached parts away from the body and onto the slide.

Salivary gland

D. Remove excess material and stain the glands as directed.

Digestive tract

Fat body

"Head"

FIG. 18-8
Procedure for removing *Drosophila* salivary glands.

larval growth and are well developed in some dipteran larvae that do not appear to secrete silk. Large, multi-stranded, or **polytene,** chromosomes are not confined to the dipteran salivary gland, but are also present in cells of the gut epithelium, in Malpighian tubules of the larva, and in the foot pads of adult flies. Chromosomes of these tissues are usually not as large as those of the salivary gland. The micromorphology of chromosome structure is ideally studied in giant chromosomes of the salivary gland.

In this exercise, you will study the morphology of salivary gland chromosomes from a slide that you will prepare from the fruit fly *Drosophila melanogaster*.

1. Examine a culture and locate wormlike larvae. Select one of the larger, slower-moving ones, preferably one that is crawling up the side of the culture container. Gently remove it with forceps and place it on a glass slide lightly moistened with saline solution. Examine it with your dissecting microscope. Note that it has a blunt rear end and a pointed head end that contains black mouth parts. To obtain the salivary glands, the head end must be dissected away from the rest of the body (Fig. 18-8).

2. With a finely pointed needle (which has been dipped into saline solution), pierce the head as close to the anterior end as possible. The larva wriggles, so you will probably have to make several attempts before you are successful.

3. After the head has been secured, grasp the rear end with a pair of finely pointed forceps and with one smooth, quick motion at the anterior end stretch the larva until the mouth parts are torn off and pulled onto the moist slide. All of this can be done while observing the operation with the dissecting microscope.

4. The salivary glands, when pulled out, will probably be accompanied by the digestive tract and fat bodies. Add a drop of saline to the slide. When you are sure that you have the salivary glands, remove the digestive tube and any other extraneous parts with a sharp razor blade or scalpel. Discard these parts, leaving only the salivary glands on the slide.

5. The salivary glands are now ready to be stained. Remove the excess saline solution from the slide by soaking it up with a small piece of paper toweling or filter paper. Try not to touch the glands with the paper because they might adhere to it. Cover the glands with a drop of aceto-orcein stain.

6. After staining for 5 minutes, carefully place a plastic cover slip over the glands. Then place a small piece of paper toweling over the cover slip and press down hard with your thumb. Examine the preparation with your compound microscope. If properly squashed, the cells of the gland will be separated from each other. You should be able to see a nucleus in most of the cells.

7. If your preparation has been adequately stained, you should be able to see banding along the length of the chromosomes. The bands may be better observed if the chromosomes are released from the nuclei. To do this, firmly tap the cover slip with a pencil eraser several times. Examination under the high power of the microscope should now show the chromosomes separated and the bands sharply stained. Compare your preparation with that of the *Sciara* chromosomes shown in Fig. 18-9.

b. Chromosome "Puffs"

In your studies of mitosis and meiosis, the chromosomes appeared as heavily stained bodies that apparently lacked distinct morphology. However, when you examined the giant chromosomes found in the salivary glands of *Drosophila* larvae (and of certain other flies), you became aware of a great deal of structural detail that is not apparent in "ordinary" chromosomes.

a. Examine Fig. 18-10. This is a photograph of the giant salivary gland chromosomes of the "midge" fly, *Chironomus*. (If they are available, supplement your studies with specially prepared slides of these chromosomes.) Note the darkly stained bands that are separated from each other by lighter areas.

These bands are areas of DNA and show up when these chromosomes are stained by Feulgen's reagent, a dye that stains DNA.

b. In the center of the photograph, note the appearance of a chromosome "puff." It has been shown that the pattern of "puffing" changes during the development of this organism. Recent experimental evidence suggests that these puff regions are sites of special gene activity, where a special "message-carrying" chemical is formed.

It has further been shown that the hormone involved in the insect molting process can induce puffing. This hormone, called **ecdysone,** appears to act on specific genes, which in turn generate a "message" that is transferred to the cell proper, where it initiates the synthesis of specific protein. It has also been demonstrated that one of the plant growth regulators—**gibberellin**—will accelerate molting and that ecdysone, when used in one of the standard gibberellin bioassays, brings about a growth response similar to that of gibberellin.

FIG. 18-9
Salivary gland chromosomes of *Sciara coprophila,* showing distinct longitudinal differentiation.
(Photomicrograph courtesy of Dr. Ellen M. Rasch, East Tennessee State University.)

Chromosome puff

FIG. 18-10
Giant salivary gland chromosomes of *Chironomus.* (Photomicrograph by Claus Pelling, Max Planck Institute for Biology.)

REFERENCES

Avery, O. T., C. M. MacLeod, and M. McCarty. 1944. Studies on the Chemical Nature of the Substance Inducing Transformation of Pneumococcal Types. Induction of Transformation by a Desoxyribonucleic Acid Fraction Isolated from Pneumococcus, Type III. *Journal of Experimental Medicine* 79:137–157.

Demerec, M., and B. P. Kaufmann. 1969. *Drosophila Guide.* 8th ed. Carnegie Institution, 1530 P Street, N.W., Washington, D.C.

DuPraw, E. J. 1970. *DNA and Chromosomes.* Holt, Rinehart and Winston.

Flagg, R. O. 1971. *Drosophila Manual.* Carolina Biological Supply Company.

Hadorn, E., and H. K. Mitchell. 1951. Properties of Mutants of *Drosophila melanogaster* and Changes During Development as Revealed by Paper Chromatography. *Proceedings of the National Academy of Sciences* 37:650–665.

Leitenberg, M., and E. L. Stokes. 1964. *Drosophila melanogaster* Chromatography, I. *Turtox News* 42:226-229.

Leitenberg, M., and E. L. Stokes. 1964. *Drosophila melanogaster* Chromatography, II. *Turtox News* 42:258–260.

Szekely, M. 1979. *From DNA to Protein: The Transfer of Genetic Information.* Wiley.

Tomasz, A. 1969. Cellular Factors in Genetic Transformation. *Scientific American* 220:38–44 (Offprint 1130). *Scientific American* Offprints are available from W. H. Freeman and Company, 660 Market Street, San Francisco 94104, and 58 Kings Road, Reading RG1 3AA, England. Please order by number.

Van Norman, R. W. 1971. Chromatography. *Experimental Biology,* 2nd ed., Chap. 11. Prentice-Hall.

Wacker, A. 1963. Molecular Mechanisms of Radiation Effects. *Progress in Nucleic Acid Research* 1:369–399. Academic Press.

Wagner, R. P., B. R. Judd, B. G. Sanders, and R. N. Richardson. 1979. *Introduction to Modern Genetics.* Wiley.

Watson, J. D., and F. H. C. Crick. 1953. Genetical Implications of the Structure of Deoxyribonucleic Acid. *Nature* (London) 171:964–967.

Watson, J. D. 1976. *Molecular Biology of the Gene.* 3rd ed. Benjamin.

Fertilization and Early Development of the Sea Urchin

The development of a fertilized egg into the complex, interdependent systems of tissues and organs that make up an adult animal is one of the more fascinating studies in developmental biology. In this exercise and the two that follow, the patterns of early development in an echinoderm (the sea urchin), an amphibian (the frog), and a bird (the chick) will be studied.

An important factor that determines the type of development an embryo undergoes is the amount of yolk in the egg. Not only the amount, but the position and distribution of the yolk will markedly affect the patterns of cleavage and subsequent events in early development. In the more primitive eggs, the amount is small and the yolk is evenly distributed throughout the cytoplasm. This type of egg, called **isolecithal** (equal yolk), is found in the sea urchin. Another type of egg has a large amount of yolk that is displaced toward the vegetal pole, the cytoplasm being concentrated at the animal pole. This type of egg, called **telolecithal** (end yolk), is found in the frog and chick.

In this exercise, you will observe fertilization and the early stages of embryonic development of a marine echinoderm, the sea urchin. This animal, related to the starfish, can be induced to shed its gametes either by injecting potassium chloride into the body cavity or by stimulating it with a weak electric current. Each female will lay approximately one billion eggs and each male will eject several billion sperm.

A. FERTILIZATION

Before the laboratory meeting, your instructor will have obtained living eggs and sperm from female and male sea urchins. The procedure used is shown in Fig. 19-1.

Obtain a depression slide and cover slip as shown in Fig. 19-1. With a clean pipet, transfer a drop of the egg suspension to the slide and examine microscopically.

Add 1 drop of dilute sperm suspension to the eggs on the slide, and examine immediately under high power of

229

Inject 2.0 ml of 0.5 M KCl into body cavity
through soft membrane surrounding mouth.

♀

Mouth
(oral surface)

♂

Place oral surface down on clean glass plate
until animal begins to shed gametes from
gonopores on aboral surface.

Aboral
surface

Invert ♀ over beaker
containing 25 ml of sea
water and allow eggs to
drain into water.
When eggs have settled,
pour off the water.
Add fresh water and
repeat the washing
procedure three times.

Invert ♂ over dry Petri
dish to collect sperm.

Cover and store
sperm dry in cool
place until used.

Prepare dilute egg
suspension by adding
5 drops of concentrated
egg solution to graduate
cylinder and bring to
100-ml volume with sea
water. Eggs will last
5 or 6 hours at 40°F.

To use: Dilute 1 or 2
drops of dry sperm
with 10 ml of sea
water. The sperm
must then be used
within 20 or 30 minutes.

Add 1 drop eggs
and 1 drop sperm.

Wax to hold cover
slip away from slide

This   or this

Depression slide

FIG. 19-1
Preparation of sea urchin egg and sperm suspensions for
observing fertilization and early development.

TABLE 19-1
Approximate time sequence for the development of fertilized sea urchin eggs.

Formation of fertilization membrane	2–5	minutes
First cleavage	50–70	minutes
Second cleavage	78–107	minutes
Third cleavage	103–145	minutes
Blastula	6	hours
Hatching of blastula	7–10	hours
Gastrula	12–20	hours
Pluteus larvae	24–48	hours

the microscope. Note the time so that you will know when to expect the cleavage stages (see Table 19-1). The rate of development varies with temperature; therefore the eggs should be kept at temperatures not to exceed 25°C. What response do the sperm exhibit with respect to the eggs?

_____

_____

What might be the cause of this response?

_____

_____

Soon after a sperm penetrates an egg, a **fertilization membrane** begins to lift from the egg's surface and completely surrounds the egg. The entire process—from the time the sperm touches the egg to the formation of the fertilization membrane—takes from 2 to 5 minutes.

The first cleavage does not occur until from 50 to 70 minutes after the formation of the fertilization membrane. The changes taking place within the egg during this time are difficult to observe in living material. After the sperm enters the cell, the male nucleus migrates toward the female nucleus and unites with it, reestablishing the diploid number of chromosomes. Subsequently, the chromatin is organized into chromosomes, and the first nuclear division, followed by cell division, occurs.

B. CLEAVAGE

The process by which the fertilized egg develops into a multicellular embryo is called **cleavage**. During this process, complex events occur within the nucleus and cytoplasm. You will only be concerned with the more readily observable external changes.

While waiting for the first division, examine prepared slides of sea urchin or starfish eggs. How can you tell if an egg on a slide is fertilized or unfertilized?

_____

_____

Next, prepare a slide of the living sperm. By reducing the light, you may be able to observe the flagellum by which the sperm moves. If, at this point, the fertilized eggs have not reached the first cleavage stage, continue with Part C.

From your study of meiosis (Exercise 3), you will recall that, in the development of the egg, polar bodies are formed during the first and second meiotic divisions. In the sea urchin, the first cleavage begins in the region where the polar bodies are formed—the animal pole. If you carefully observe the egg, you should notice that it begins to elongate slightly before it divides. The second cleavage occurs from approximately 15 to 20 minutes after the first cleavage. Describe the plane of this division with respect to the first cleavage.

_____

_____

Describe the plane of the third cleavage with respect to the first two cleavages.

_____

_____

If your preparation does not attain this stage of development, examine fertilized eggs that were prepared earlier by your instructor or examine your slide later in the day.

C. LATER STAGES OF DEVELOPMENT

Before the eight-cell stage is reached, the cleavages are uniform. Subsequent to the eight-cell stage, the four cells of the vegetal pole divide unequally, resulting in four large cells (**macromeres**) and four small cells (**micromeres**). Then the four cells of the animal pole divide into eight cells of equal size (**mesomeres**) (Fig. 19-2).

1. Blastula

As the cells of the embryo undergo additional cleavage, a spherical mass containing a fluid-filled central cavity,

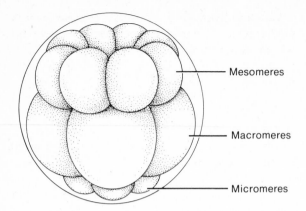

FIG. 19-2
Unequal cell division in the sea urchin (fourth division).

FIG. 19-3
Blastula and gastrula of the sea urchin.

the **blastocoel,** is formed. With further cleavages, the cavity increases in size until the embryo, now called a **blastula,** consists of several hundred cells that become arranged in the form of a single-layered hollow ball. At this stage in the sea urchin, the embryo begins to rotate within the fertilization membrane. Approximately 8 hours after fertilization, the bastula breaks through the membrane by secreting a "hatching enzyme," which apparently digests the fertilization membrane. If you are unable to observe a living blastula, examine slides of this stage in the sea urchin or in related forms such as the starfish Fig. 19-3A.

2. Gastrula

For several hours after "hatching," the blastula swims actively. About 15 hours after fertilization, the single-layered blastula changes into a double-layered **gastrula** (Fig. 19-3C). In the sea urchin, this process begins when cells at the lower, or vegetal, pole begin to pulsate intensely, particularly on the inner surfaces facing the blastocoel. This causes some of the cells to be forced into the blastocoel forming a slight indentation called the **blastopore**. These cells then send out long cytoplasmic extensions that become attached to the opposite wall near the animal pole. Contraction of these cytoplasmic strands results in a deepening of the blastopore; ultimately forming an invagination that will become the **archenteron**, or primitive gut, of the embryo. The blastocoel remains, but is soon invaded by other cells. The invagination continues forward to the animal pole, where it will eventually meet the opposite wall. At this junction the mouth will form. The opening of the blastopore will become the anus in the adult.

At the conclusion of gastrulation, the embryo consists of an outer presumptive ectoderm and an inner presump-tive endoderm that lines the archenteron. A third layer, the mesoderm, will develop between the ectoderm and endoderm from the proliferation of cells arising in the endodermal layer. These embryonic germ layers develop into the various tissue and organ systems of the adult animal. The skin, sense organs, and nervous system arise from the ectoderm. The muscles, skeletal elements, and blood originate in the mesoderm. The endoderm gives rise to the alimentary canal and its various derivatives: the pharynx, esophagus, stomach, liver, intestine, pancreas, and endocrine glands.

Examine living gastrulae or slides of this stage of development.

3. Pluteus Larva

In the later stages in the development of the gastrula, the skeletal elements begin to form as pairs of rodlike structures on either side of what will become the anus. Twenty-four hours after fertilization, the larva is well formed. Examine slides or living specimens of the pluteus larva (Fig. 19-4A). When 2 or 2½ months old, the larva metamorphoses into the adult sea urchin (Fig. 19-4B). Examine specimens of the adult animal. Echinoderms are characterized by having numerous "tube feet." Where on the sea urchin are these feet located?

_____

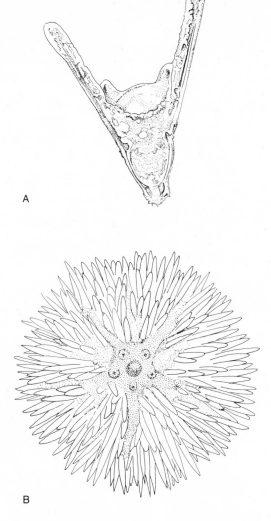

FIG. 19-4
Sea urchin: (A) pluteus larva and (B) adult.

What seems to be their function?

_____

_____

_____

_____

D. ARTIFICIAL PARTHENOGENESIS

Eggs of sea urchins, and of numerous other organisms, have the ability to develop **parthenogenetically** (from the

Greek words *parthenos,* for "virgin," and *genesis,* "birth"); that is, without being fertilized by sperm. Sea urchins, in particular, are very susceptible to the action of external substances. For example, various concentrations of electrolytes such as magnesium chloride ($MgCl_2$) and potassium chloride (KCl), as well as nonelectrolytes such as urea and sucrose, induce parthenogenetic cleavage in sea urchin eggs. In the following study, you will attempt to determine if hypertonic seawater will induce cleavage in nonfertilized eggs.

1. Prepare petri dishes containing the following concentrations of seawater:

Normal concentration

1.5 × normal

2 × normal

4 × normal

2. Transfer samples of washed, unfertilized eggs (as prepared in Part A) to each of the dishes.

3. After treatment for 5 minutes, wash the eggs in four changes of normal seawater and then leave them in the fourth change.

4. Examine the eggs for the presence of fertilization membranes, which appear more slowly in parthenogenetically induced eggs than in normal eggs. Check further development, noting particularly if the development of any of the eggs is arrested at a given cleavage stage.

_____

_____

E. DEVELOPMENT OF EMBRYOS FROM ISOLATED BLASTOMERES

In 1892, Hans Dreisch separated sea urchin blastomeres (cells) in early embryonic stages and followed the development of these isolated cells. He was able to do this because, immediately after fertilization, the fertilization membrane is quite fragile and can be removed by vigorously shaking the test tube containing the eggs. Without the membrane, the two cells can then be separated. You will attempt to duplicate this procedure in this study.

1. Place a sample of unfertilized eggs into a test tube half full of seawater. Add a drop of sperm suspension, and seal with a clean rubber stopper. Mix the contents by gently inverting the test tube once or twice.

2. After 1 minute, vigorously shake the test tube for 2 minutes. This should rupture a large number of fertilization membranes.

3. Transfer the contents of the test tube to a petri dish. After an hour, examine the eggs for the appearance of the first cleavage. If cleavage has begun, watch carefully until the first cleavage is just completed. Then, using a clean pipet, vigorously squirt seawater into the culture several times. Then allow the eggs to settle to the bottom and examine microscopically for isolated blastomere pairs.

4. Transfer the isolated blastomeres to finger bowls of seawater and observe development for the next several days.

Compare "normal" development with that of isolated "half embryos." Consider such things as rate of development and size of pluteus larvae.

_____

_____

_____

_____

F. VITAL STAINING OF SEA URCHIN EGGS

Many chemical and structural components of cells can be "visualized" through the use of vital stains, which do not kill the cells in the course of staining. Several of these stains are listed as follows, together with the cellular constituents with which they react:

Toluidine blue stains mucopolysaccharides pink and nucleic acids (mostly RNA) blue.

Janus green B, Rhodamine B, and Methylene blue stain mitochondria.

Nile blue sulfate stains phospholipids.

Acridine orange stains DNA yellow and RNA deep orange (these are fluorescent colors under ultraviolet).

Brilliant vital red stains acid and neutral proteins.

Using these stains and the following procedure (you may have to modify the staining time), treat samples of unfertilized sea urchin eggs and locate the various constituents just listed.

1. Using a marking crayon, label the depressions in a spot plate to correspond to the various stains listed above. Use one depression as a control.

2. Add 1 ml of seawater and four or five unfertilized sea urchin eggs to each depression.

3. Add 1 drop of stain to each depression. Add nothing to the control.

4. Stain from 1 to 2 hours. Then carefully pipet off the staining solution, and add fresh seawater. Examine the eggs microscopically, and "describe" your results by drawing them in Fig. 19-5.

Toluidine blue
Comment:

Janus green B
Comment:

Rhodamine B
Comment:

Methylene blue
Comment:

Nile blue sulfate
Comment:

Acridine orange
Comment:

Brilliant vital red
Comment:

Control
Comment:

FIG. 19-5
Vital staining of sea urchin eggs.

REFERENCES

Balinsky, B. I. 1981. *An Introduction to Embryology*. 5th ed. Saunders College/Holt, Rinehart and Winston.

Browder, L. W. 1980. *Developmental Biology*. Saunders College/Holt, Rinehart and Winston.

Costello, D. P., M. E. Davidson, A. Eggers, M. H. Fox, and C. Henley. 1957. *Methods for Obtaining and Handling Marine Eggs*. Marine Biological Laboratory, Woods Hole, Massachusetts.

Davenport, R. 1979. *Outline of Animal Development*. Addison-Wesley.

Harvey, E. B. 1954. Electrical Method of Determining the Sex of Sea Urchins. *Nature* (London) 176:86.

Harvey, E. B. 1956. *The American Arbacia and Other Sea Urchins*. Princeton University Press.

Karp, G., and N. J. Berrill. 1981. *Development*. 2nd ed. McGraw-Hill.

Lehman, H. E. 1977. *Chordate Development*. Hunter.

Saunders, J. W., Jr. 1970. *Patterns and Principles of Animal Development*. Macmillan.

Torrey, T. W., and A. Feduccia. 1979. *Morphogenesis of the Vertebrates*. 4th ed. Wiley.

Fertilization and Early Development of the Frog

The eggs of most frogs form in the summer months when the frogs are feeding heavily. By fall the eggs are fully developed, but they are usually retained in the ovaries until spring, at which time they are all released en masse. The release of the eggs from the ovaries is called **ovulation**. The eggs subsequently pass into the oviducts and are then passed out of the body.

Ovulation normally occurs as a result of stimulation of the ovaries by gonadotropic hormones produced in the pituitary gland. A mature female frog can be induced to ovulate earlier than usual by injecting whole pituitary glands into the body cavity. The number of glands needed varies with the time of year and with the sex of the frog supplying the glands. Because male pituitaries are about one-half as potent as female pituitaries, twice the number of glands must be used. Table 20-1 outlines the number of female pituitaries needed at various times of the year to induce ovulation.

In this exercise, you will induce ovulation in mature female frogs and prepare a frog sperm suspension. You will use the sperm suspension to fertilize the eggs and will then examine and become familiar with the patterns of cleavage and early development in the frog embryo.

TABLE 20-1
Number of female pituitaries needed to induce ovulation in frogs.

September–December	January–February	March–April
5–6	3–5	1–3

Your instructor will demonstrate how to remove and inject the pituitary glands. To have frogs that are ovulating at the time of the laboratory meeting, the female frogs should be injected 48 hours ahead of time.

A. ARTIFICIAL INDUCTION OF OVULATION

1. Anesthetize the number of frogs necessary to obtain the quantity of pituitaries shown in Table 20-1 by placing them in a sealed container in which a wad of cotton saturated (but not dripping) with ether has been suspended. Use a hood or a well-ventilated room to perform this operation. Shake the container and, when the frogs fail to move, remove them and dissect out the glands as illus-

Tympanic membrane

FIG. 20-2
Method of injecting pituitary preparation.

Foramen
magnum

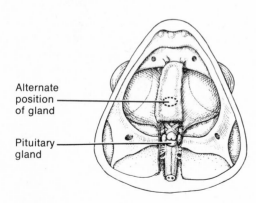

Alternate
position
of gland

Pituitary
gland

FIG. 20-1
Procedure for obtaining pituitaries.

trated in Fig. 20-1. Place the glands in a dish containing Holtfreter's solution (an optimal chemical solution for the maintenance of amphibian eggs and embryos).

2. When the required number of pituitaries has been collected, remove the needle from a 2-ml syringe and draw the glands into the barrel. Bring the volume to 1 ml, and attach an 18-gauge needle. Hold the syringe with the needle down, so that the glands settle into the mouth of the needle. If any pituitaries stick to the sides of the barrel, tap the syringe until all of them collect on the bottom.

3. Select the female to be injected and, holding her as shown in Fig. 20-2, insert the needle into the body cavity. Keep the needle parallel to the body wall so as not to injure any internal organs. When the needle is deeply inserted (check to see if the pituitaries are at the needle end of the syringe), quickly inject the pituitary glands. Leave the needle in position for a minute and then slowly remove it, pinching the skin to prevent any loss of fluid or glands.

4. Draw more Holtfreter's solution into the syringe to determine if any pituitary material is lodged in the needle. If so, eject all but about 0.5 ml of solution and then inject the preparation containing the pituitary material.

5. Place the frog in a covered container with about 10 mm of water, and put in a cool room at about 68°F (20°C). Check for ovulation after 24 hours by gently squeezing the abdomen, as shown in Figure 20-3.

FIG. 20-3
Method of holding frog to test for ovulation.

If eggs come out of the cloaca, ovulation has occurred. The frog may then be placed in a container of fresh water and kept in a refrigerator until needed. Eggs will remain viable in the oviduct from 3 to 4 days if the animal is kept at a temperature ranging from 10° to 15°C. If ovulation has not occurred, put the frog in fresh water and try again 24 hours later.

B. PREPARATION OF SPERM SUSPENSION

This should be done about 30 minutes before the laboratory meeting so that active sperm will be available at the time the eggs are stripped from the female.

1. Prepare a petri dish containing 20 ml of 10% Holtfreter's solution.

2. Pith a mature male frog (see Appendix D for this procedure) and remove the paired testes (Fig. 20-4). Clean away any adhering blood and tissue, and, using the blunt end of a clean probe, thoroughly macerate the testes in the Holtfreter's solution until a milky suspension is obtained.

3. Set the sperm suspension aside for 15 to 20 minutes to allow the sperm to become motile.

4. Pipet a drop of the sperm suspension onto a glass slide and examine under the high power of your microscope. Describe the shape of the sperm.

_____

What is the physical basis for the motility of the sperm?

_____

_____

Cut body wall from A to B and then laterally at X and Y.

Testis

FIG. 20-4
Procedure for removing testes.

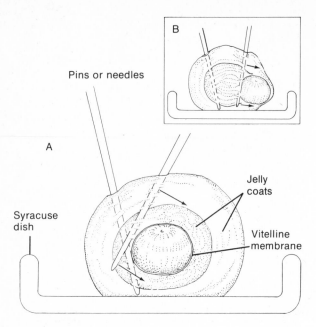

FIG. 20-5
Procedure for stripping jelly coats from frog eggs.

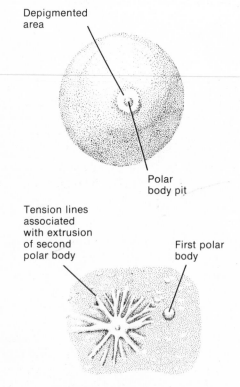

FIG. 20-6
Location of second polar body.

C. FERTILIZATION

Divide the motile sperm suspension prepared earlier among two or three *clean* petri dishes so that the bottom of each dish is just covered. Holding the female frog as shown in Fig. 20-3, strip the eggs directly into the sperm suspension. Line the egg masses in rows or in a spiral, so that all the eggs are in contact with the sperm. *Do not place them in a heaping pile in the sperm*. Shake the dishes gently. Why?

_____

Note the random orientation of the eggs. Some will have the pigmented animal pole uppermost; in others the light-colored vegetal pole will face up.

When the eggs are shed, the first polar body has been formed. The formation of the second polar body can be observed shortly after fertilization. To see this process, remove two or three eggs after they have been in the sperm suspension for several minutes. Remove the jelly coats (Fig. 20-5), place them in a Syracuse dish, and cover completely with Holtfreter's solution. Examine the eggs with a dissecting microscope. Adjust the light so that it strikes the egg surface at an oblique angle. With careful focusing, you will see a lighter, circular area in the animal pole. By adjusting the light, you may observe a pit in this light area (Fig. 20-6). This is where the second polar body will be expelled. Carefully observe the formation of this polar body. It may sometimes be seen more readily if the egg is rotated so that the pit area is at right angles to your field of vision.

After the remaining eggs have been in the sperm suspension for 10 minutes, flood them with 10% Holtfreter's solution. Rinse and completely cover the eggs with fresh Holtfreter's solution. The first cleavage will occur in about 2 hours. During this interval, go on to Part D or E as directed by your instructor.

D. UNFERTILIZED FROG EGGS

From the injected female frog, gently squeeze about a dozen eggs into a petri dish containing Holtfreter's solution. The solution should completely cover the eggs. Note that the eggs are clustered together when they first leave the cloaca but tend to separate from each other in the water. The eggs separate because the jelly that surrounds each egg swells considerably as the protein in the jelly absorbs water. Why is the swelling important in the development of the eggs?

_____

_____

Place one or two eggs on a glass slide, cover with water, and examine them with the low power of your microscope. How many jelly layers are present?

_____

Examine the remaining eggs, using a dissecting microscope. Adjust the spot lamp so the light is striking the eggs at about a 45° angle. How does the pigmentation of the frog egg differ from that of the sea urchin egg?

Remove as much jelly as possible from two or three eggs (Fig. 20-5). Place them in a Syracuse dish animal pole up, completely cover with Holtfreter's solution, and examine with the highest power available on your dissecting microscope. Adjust the spot lamp for maximum light. The dark color of the egg is due to granules of melanin pigment. Although the egg may seem to be inactive, close observation of the cytoplasm will reveal a great deal of movement of the pigment granules. What might be causing this activity?

_____

_____

_____

E. CLEAVAGE STAGES

Examine the fertilized eggs in your dish. When an egg is fertilized, it secretes a proteinaceous material. As a result, a **vitelline membrane** which has been tightly bound to the egg surface, is forced away when this proteinaceous material begins to absorb water. The yolk-laden vegetal pole, being heavier, shifts downward, so that the animal pole is oriented upward. How many of the eggs in your dish have been fertilized (one-third, one-half, all)?

_____

In nature, why is it advantageous to the development of the egg to have the pigmented area uppermost?

_____

Examine the eggs with a dissecting microscope for the appearance of the first cleavage, resulting in two cells. The phenomenon of cleavage is the partitioning of the egg cell into a large number of smaller cells with no increase in the size of the mass. (Be careful not to confuse degenerating eggs with normally dividing eggs; a broken, mottled surface is a sign that the egg is dead.) If your eggs have not reached the first cleavage stage, obtain eggs that were fertilized before the class meeting. Continue to examine the eggs periodically. Where does the first cleavage furrow begin?

_____

_____

Note: Continued reference to Fig. 20-7 (on the next two pages) will help you in identifying stages of normal development. The stages were originally numbered by Waldo Shumway in 1940. If embryos are allowed to grow at either of the temperatures indicated, various developmental stages can be made available when needed.

F. LATER STAGES OF DEVELOPMENT

1. Blastula

The process of cleavage terminates with the formation of the blastula (Fig. 20-7), although the organism is still undergoing cellular division. Different regions of the blastula have different prospective fates: that is, the cells of different areas will ultimately contribute to the skin, skeleton, nervous tissue, and so on (Fig. 20-8). How could you follow the movement of various cells as they proceed through subsequent developmental stages in the living embryo?

_____

_____

In commercially prepared models, these presumptive areas (called *ectoderm, mesoderm,* and *endoderm*) are arbitrarily colored blue, red, and yellow, respectively. A specialized region of mesoderm, called *chordamesoderm,* is colored green. From your readings and the instructor's

242

 1. Unfertilized

 2. Gray crescent

 3. Two cells

 4. Four cells

 5. Eight cells

 6. Sixteen cells

 7. Thirty-two cells

 8. Early blastula

 9. Late blastula

9A. Cross section of blastula

 10. Dorsal lip

11. Mid-gastrula

 12. Late gastrula

12A. Cross section of gastrula

 12B. Half gastrula

 13. Neural plate

 14. Neural folds

 15. Rotation

FIG. 20-7
Normal embryonic developmental stages of the frog from unfertilized egg through tadpole (after Shumway, 1940).

Shumway stage	Description	Age in hours	
		18°C	25°C
1	Unfertilized	0.0	0.0
2	Gray crescent	1.0	0.5
3	Two cells	3.5	2.5
4	Four cells	4.5	3.5
5	Eight cells	5.5	4.5
6	Sixteen cells	6.5	5.5
7	Thirty-two cells	7.5	6.5
8	Early blastula	16.0	11.0
9	Late blastula	21.0	14.0
10	Dorsal lip	26.0	17.0
11	Mid-gastrula	34.0	20.0
12	Late gastrula	42.0	32.0
13	Neural plate	50	40
14	Neural folds	62	48
15	Rotation	67	52
16	Neural tube	72	56
17	Tail bud	84	66
18	Muscular response	96	76
19	Heart beat	118	96
20	Gill circulation	140	120
21	Mouth open	162	138
22	Tail fin circulation	192	156
23	Opercular fold	216	180
24	Operculum closed on right	240	210
25	Operculum complete	284	240

16. Neural tube

17. Tail bud

18. Muscular response

19. Heart beat

20. Gill circulation and hatching

21. Mouth open and cornea transparent

22. Tail fin circulation

23. Opercular fold and teeth

24. Operculum closed on right

25. Operculum complete

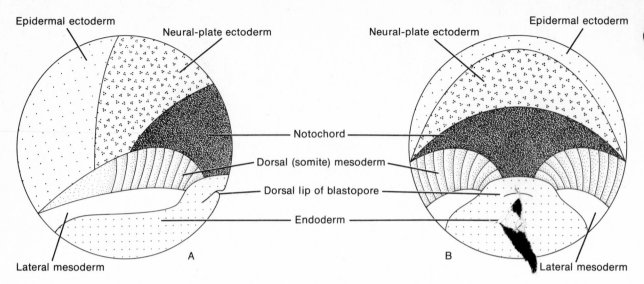

FIG. 20-8
Fate map of the frog embryo: (A) lateral view and (B) frontal
view of the blastula.

discussion, give examples of tissues that have their origin
in the following:

Presumptive mesoderm: _____

Presumptive endoderm: _____

Presumptive ectoderm: _____

Chordamesoderm: _____

At this stage of development, the presumptive areas
are associated with the *outside* of the embryo. However,
in the mature animal the muscles, alimentary tract, nervous tissue, and other tissues and organs that arise from
the areas are situated *inside*. The process of getting these
areas of cells to the interior is called *gastrulation*.

2. Gastrulation

Patterns of gastrulation vary. In the sea urchin, one side
of hollow blastula invaginates, forming a two-layer cup;
later a third tissue layer, the mesoderm, arises between
the inner and outer layers. In the frog, gastrulation is
accomplished in a quite different manner. From the use
of models, Fig. 20-9, and your instructor's discussion,
answer the following questions.

What is epiboly?

_____

_____

What is the first visible indication that gastrulation has
started?

_____

_____

_____

What is the blastopore?

_____

By what morphogenetic movement is the blastopore
formed?

_____

What role in development does the dorsal lip of the
blastopore play?

_____

_____

_____

What new cavity is formed during gastrulation?

_____

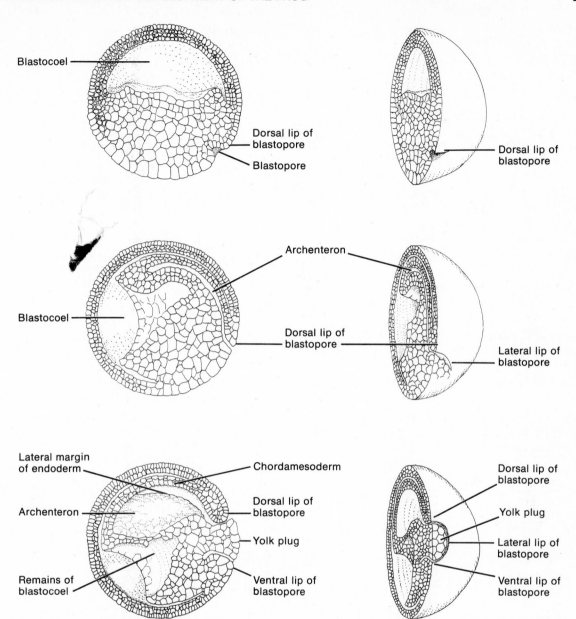

FIG. 20-9
Gastrulation in the frog. (After *An Introduction to Embryology,* 2nd ed., by B. I. Balinsky. Saunders, 1965.)

What does this cavity ultimately become in the adult?

_____

_____

_____

The chordamesoderm, which will form the notochord, plays what other important role in the development of the frog?

_____

_____

3. Formation of the Neural Tube

When gastrulation is completed, the embryo is completely covered, except for the yolk plug, by ectoderm. The endoderm and mesoderm have been moved inside. Soon, two ectodermal ridges will form on the dorsal surface of the gastrula. These grow upward and toward each other, eventually fusing in the midline. When the edges fuse, a tube of ectoderm will be formed, running from the anterior to the posterior end of the embryo. This tube, covered by an outer ectoderm layer, will develop into the brain and spinal cord. Follow these events, using Fig. 20-7 (Stages 13–16) and models. If available, examine living embryos at this stage of development.

4. Development of the Tadpole

The neural tube is formed as a result of the outfolding and fusion of the ectoderm. Most other tissue-forming processes occurring in later development consist of foldings, invaginations, evaginations, or cell movements of the various germ layers. For example, the digestive glands and lungs develop as evaginations of the endoderm at various stages. The eye develops, in part, from an evagination of the brain. Examine these morphogenetic movements on the models. List any others you find.

_____

_____

_____

_____

_____

REFERENCES

Balinsky, B. I. 1981. *An Introduction to Embryology.* 5th ed. Saunders College/Holt, Rinehart and Winston.

Browder, L. W. 1980. *Developmental Biology.* Saunders College/Holt, Rinehart and Winston.

Bryant, P. J., S. V. Bryant, and V. French. 1977. Biological Regeneration and Pattern Formation. *Scientific American* 237:66–81 (Offprint 1363). *Scientific American* Offprints are available from W. H. Freeman and Company, 660 Market Street, San Francisco 94104, and 58 Kings Road, Reading RG1 3AA, England. Please order by number.

Davenport, R. 1979. *Outline of Animal Development.* Addison-Wesley.

Ebert, J. D., and I. M. Sussex. 1970. *Interacting Systems in Development.* 2nd ed. Holt, Rinehart and Winston.

Epel, D. 1977. The Program of Fertilization. *Scientific American* 237:128–138 (Offprint 1372).

Ham, R. G. 1979. *Mechanisms of Development.* Mosby.

Johnson, L. G., and E. P. Volpe. 1973. *Patterns and Experiments in Developmental Biology.* Brown.

Karp, G., and N. J. Berrill. 1981. *Development.* 2nd ed. McGraw-Hill.

Lehman, H. E. 1977. *Chordate Development.* Hunter.

Rugh, R. 1951. *The Frog: Its Reproduction and Development.* McGraw-Hill.

Saunders, J. W., Jr. 1970. *Patterns and Principles of Animal Development.* Macmillan.

Shumway, W. 1940. Stages in the Normal Development of *Rana pipiens.* I. External Form. *Anatomical Record* 78:139–147.

Torrey, T. W., and A. Feduccia. 1979. *Morphogenesis of the Vertebrates.* 4th ed. Wiley.

Wolpert, L. 1978. Pattern Formation in Biological Development. *Scientific American* 239:154–164 (Offprint 1409).

Early Development
of the Chick

The chick embryo has been used so extensively in developmental studies that it is considered to be one of the most intensely studied of all organisms. The interest in the chick embryo is due to its ready availability and its marked similarity in early embryonic development to the mammalian embryo.

In this exercise, you will become familiar with the early developmental features of the chick embryo. However, many of the very early events (i.e., cleavage, formation of blastula, and gastrulation) are not as readily observed as are similar stages in the frog embryo. One reason for this lies in the unique organization of the chick "egg." The egg (popularly called the *yolk*) is surrounded by various secretory products from the female reproductive tract, called *accessory coverings*.

A. FERTILIZATION AND EGG LAYING

Direct observations of fertilization are very difficult in birds and mammals because the process takes place inside the body of the female. It is known that when the ovum

is liberated from the ovary it begins to undergo certain changes that can be characterized as aging. These changes progress rapidly to a point at which the ovum, although technically still alive, can no longer be fertilized. If, however, the ovum is fertilized soon after liberation, these aging processes are checked. Fertilization in the chicken takes place just as the ovum is entering the oviduct (Fig. 21-1).

The accessory coverings are secreted around the ovum in the course of its subsequent passage toward the cloaca. In the part of the oviduct adjacent to the ovary, a mass of stringy **albumen** is produced. This adheres to the **vitelline membrane** and projects beyond it in two masses extending in both directions along the oviduct. Because of the spirally arranged folds in the oviduct wall, the ovum rotates as it moves toward the cloaca. This rotation twists the albumen to form spiral strands at either end of the yolk, known as the **chalazae**. Additional albumen is added in concentric rings as the ovum moves down the first half of the oviduct. These layers of albumen can readily be seen in boiled eggs, because the heat causes the albumen to coagulate.

247

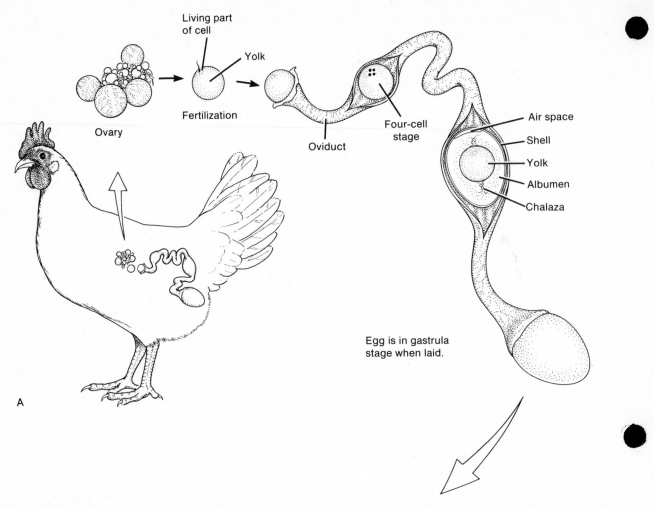

Living part of cell

Yolk

Fertilization

Ovary

Oviduct

Four-cell stage

Air space

Shell

Yolk

Albumen

Chalaza

Egg is in gastrula stage when laid.

A

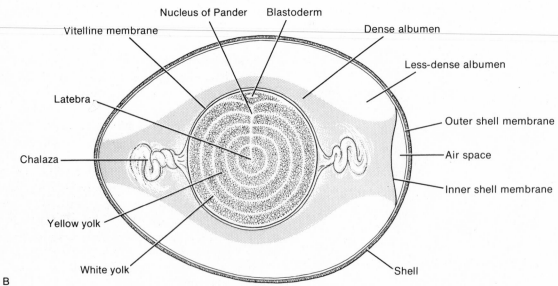

Nucleus of Pander   Blastoderm

Vitelline membrane

Dense albumen

Less-dense albumen

Latebra

Chalaza

Outer shell membrane

Air space

Inner shell membrane

Yellow yolk

White yolk

Shell

B

FIG. 21-1
(A) Stages of fertilization and early development in the hen oviduct.
(B) Structure of the egg when it is laid.

The **shell membranes**, which consist of matted organic fibers, are added farther along in the oviduct. The **shell** is secreted as the egg passes through the part of the oviduct containing the shell gland (the uterus). The entire passage of the ovum—from its discharge from the ovary until it reaches the end of the oviduct and is ready for laying—takes about 22 hours.

To examine the internal organization of the chicken egg, remove the shell from a hard-boiled egg, and then carefully remove the coagulated egg white surrounding the yolk. On the surface of the yolk, locate a small, lighter circular area. With a sharp razor blade, cut the yolk into two equal parts through this area. Close examination of the yolk will reveal that it consists of **white yolk** and **yellow yolk**, which differ in the size and shape of their granules, thus giving this difference in color (Fig. 21-1). The granules and globules in white yolk are generally smaller and less uniform in appearance than those in the yellow yolk. These concentric layers of yolk are believed to indicate the daily accumulations of cytoplasm in the final stages of the formation of the ovum. The principal accumulation of white yolk lies in a central flask-shaped area, the **latebra**, which extends toward the blastoderm and flares out under it into a mass known as the **nucleus of Pander**.

The albumen, except for the chalazae, is nearly homogeneous in appearance. Two layers of shell membranes lie in contact with the albumen everywhere except at the large end of the egg, where the inner and outer membranes are separated to form an air space. This space is believed to form after the egg has been laid because the egg contracts due to evaporation as the egg becomes cooler than it was inside the hen. In eggs that have been kept for any length of time, the size of the air space increases, owing to continued evaporation of water from the egg. This fact is used in the familiar method of testing the freshness of eggs by "floating" them.

The egg shell is composed largely of calcareous salts and is porous, which allows the exchange of gases between the embryo and the outside air.

On the surface of the yolk, locate a small, whitish spot—the **blastoderm**. This is the living part of the egg. The remainder is composed of inert food material and water. Normally the blastoderm faces up.

After the egg has been fertilized (as it passes through the upper region of the oviduct), cleavage of the blastoderm quickly occurs. The mitotic divisions of cleavage proceed as the egg passes through the oviduct, including the part that contains the shell gland. Cleavage in the chick is termed *partial,* or *discoidal,* because the highly irregular cleavage divisions are restricted to the blastoderm (Fig. 21-2), whereas the huge mass of yolk does not divide. As cleavage continues, the blastoderm

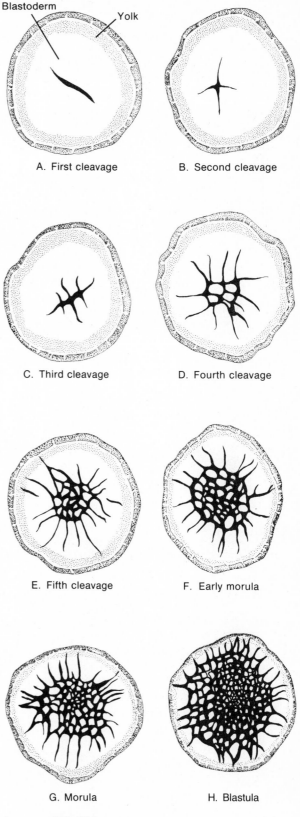

A. First cleavage

B. Second cleavage

C. Third cleavage

D. Fourth cleavage

E. Fifth cleavage

F. Early morula

G. Morula

H. Blastula

FIG. 21-2
Successive cleavages of the blastoderm.

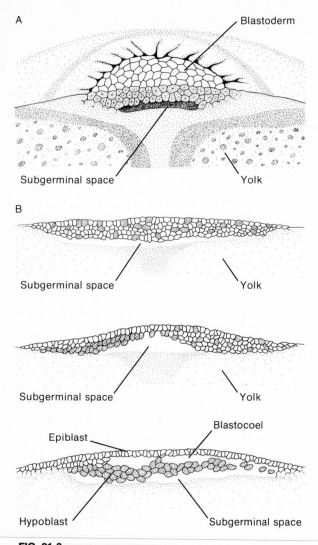

FIG. 21-3
(A) Cross section of the blastoderm. (B) Delamination of the blastoderm to form the epiblast and hypoblast.

becomes several cell layers thick and a fluid-filled **subgerminal space** develops beneath it (Fig. 21-3A).

B. BLASTULATION

The blastula begins to form when some of the cells of the blastoderm separate and move toward the subgerminal space (Fig. 21-3B). This movement leads to the formation of a two-layered structure, the two layers being separated by a space—the **blastocoel**. The newly formed and rather loosely organized lower layer is called the **hypoblast**. The upper **epiblast** contains cells that are arranged in an orderly epithelial (sheetlike) fashion. The developmental process of separation, by which the hypoblast and epiblast are formed is called **delamination**.

C. GASTRULATION

Following delamination (which is arrested when the egg is laid and only resumes when the egg is incubated), the cells of the epiblast reorganize themselves and move to new positions where they have different developmental fates; that is, the cells will ultimately contribute to the skin, skeleton, nervous system, and other tissues. The developmental roles of these cells are summarized in the **fate map** shown in Fig. 21-4.

At this time, a thickening of the blastoderm occurs that results in the formation of a narrow groove—the **primitive streak**. This groove traverses the surface of the pear-shaped blastoderm from approximately the center to the tapered edge (Fig. 21-5). Cells of the epiblast then begin moving toward, down, into, and then away from the primitive streak (Fig. 21-5B, C) to form a mesodermal layer

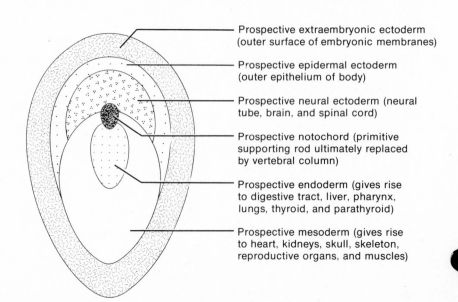

FIG. 21-4
Fate map of chick embryo epiblast.

and an embryonic endodermal layer. The remaining surface layer becomes the ectoderm.

When the mesoderm is fully established, gastrulation is complete. Eventually, the surface ectoderm will be folded under the embryo. When this is completed (Fig. 21-5D), the ectoderm will no longer be a single sheet of cells, but a complete outer covering.

D. LATER STAGES OF DEVELOPMENT

Like the frog embryo, the chick embryo passes through a number of recognizable morphological stages of development. These are usually identified by the number of hours of incubation (at 38°C) required to reach that stage of development. Stages after the appearance of blocklike cell masses of mesoderm, called **somites**, at about 21 hours are also often identified by the number of somites present.

In this exercise you will study two stages of chick development, the 33-hour stage (12–15 somites) and the 72-hour stage (36 somites). Your study will include examination both of living embryos at these two stages and of demonstration slides with cross sections cut through various regions of the 33-hour chick embryo.

1. The Living 33-Hour (12–15 Somites) Chick Embryo

Approximately 33 hours before the laboratory meeting, fertilized eggs were placed in an incubator by your instructor.

For observation of the living embryo, crack an egg, carefully remove the shell, and place the egg in a finger bowl containing warm chick Ringer's solution; the unbroken yolk with its developing embryo will float in the saline solution (Fig. 21-6A–C). (If only a white spot is found on the surface of the yolk, the egg has failed to develop. If this is the case, use another egg.) Remove the blastoderm from the yolk mass as shown in Fig. 21-6D–F. Examine the embryo, using a dissecting microscope. Supplement your observations of the living embryo with prepared slides and models available in the laboratory (Fig. 21-7).

At this stage of development, the blastoderm has become a thin disc about 20 mm across. Surrounding the embryo is a transparent region—the **area pellucida**. Outside of this is the **area opaca**, in which the blood vessels are beginning to develop. One of the most striking features of this stage is the presence of the "heart," which can be seen on the right side of the embryo. The heart originates as separate masses of cells on either side of the embryonic axis. These heart-forming regions move to the midline and eventually fuse (Fig. 21-8). If extra unin-

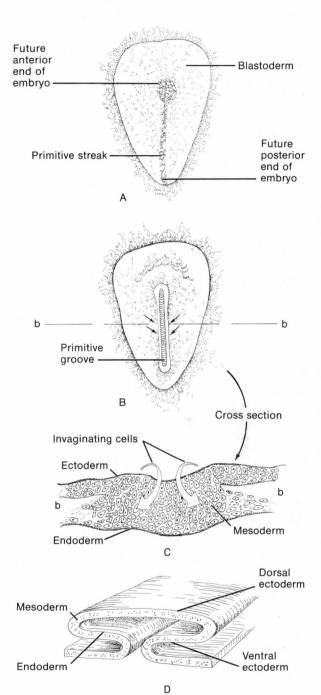

FIG. 21-5
Gastrulation in the chick.

FIG. 21-6
Procedure for opening egg and cutting blastoderm from yolk.

cubated fertilized eggs are available, you might incubate them for 26 hours and then remove the embryo as shown in Fig. 21-6. After about 26 hours, the heart mass can be seen to beat, even though it has not yet formed a heart.

A pair of **vitelline veins** enters the heart at its posterior end. What is the function of these veins?

_____

_____

_____

A single artery, the **ventral aorta**, leaves the heart anteriorly.

The brain region is divided into three parts: the anterior **prosencephalon (forebrain)**; the **mesencephalon (midbrain)**; and the **rhombencephalon (hindbrain)**, which continues for the length of the embryo as the **neural tube**. The lateral evaginations of the forebrain are the **optic vesicles**.

The **notochord**, which is ventral to the neural tube, can be seen in the midline of the embryo, extending anteriorly to the forebrain as a solid rod. Lying on either side of the neural tube are from 12 to 15 **somites.** These somites will form the vertebral column and the musculature on the dorsal side, and they may contribute to the ribs and musculature of the body wall.

2. Serial Sections of the 33-Hour Embryo

Study demonstration slides with cross sections cut through various regions of the 33-hour embryo and refer to Fig. 21-9. The approximate region from which each section shown in this figure was taken is indicated by the letters A through H in Fig. 21-7. The relationships of various body layers to one another and their differentiation into specific organs and tissues of the embryo can be reconstructed through a study of these sections.

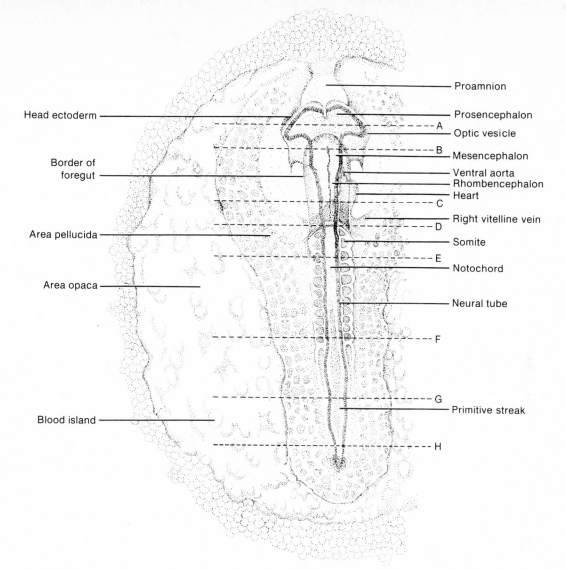

FIG. 21-7
Dorsal view of 33-hour chick embryo. (The letters A through H refer to the sections shown in Fig. 21-9.)

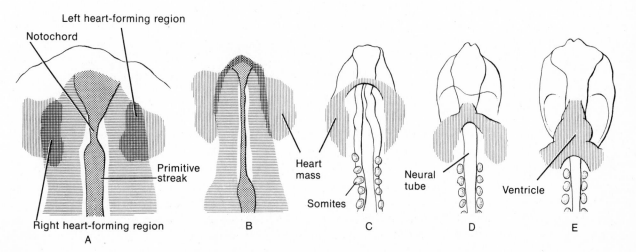

FIG. 21-8
Formation of the heart in the developing chick embryo (ventral view).

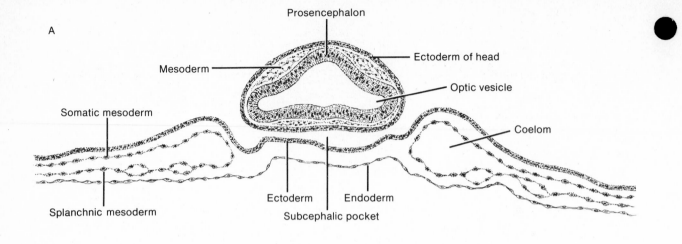

A

Prosencephalon

Ectoderm of head

Mesoderm

Optic vesicle

Somatic mesoderm

Coelom

Splanchnic mesoderm

Ectoderm

Endoderm

Subcephalic pocket

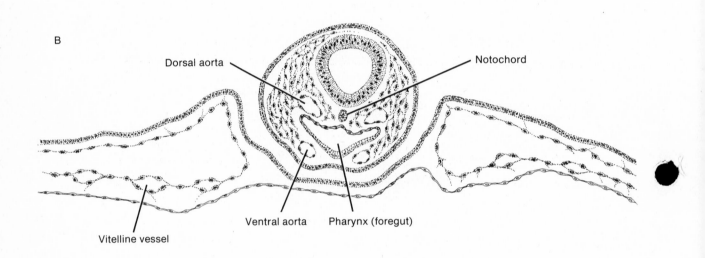

B

Dorsal aorta

Notochord

Vitelline vessel

Ventral aorta

Pharynx (foregut)

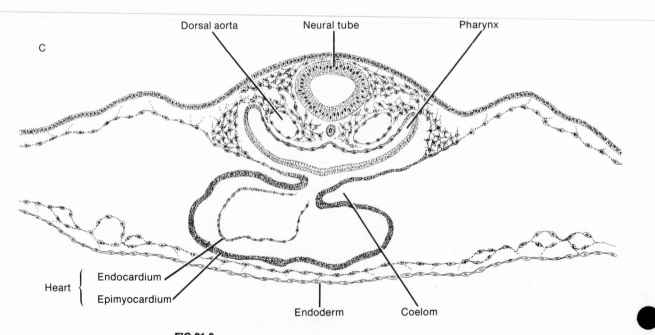

C

Dorsal aorta

Neural tube

Pharynx

Heart {
Endocardium

Epimyocardium

Endoderm

Coelom

FIG. 21-9
Serial sections through selected regions of a 33-hour (12–15 somite) chick embryo.
(After *General Zoology Laboratory Guide*, by J. E. Wodsedalek and C. F. Lytle. W. C. Brown, 1971.)

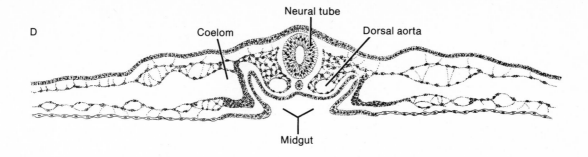

D

Coelom — Neural tube — Dorsal aorta

Midgut

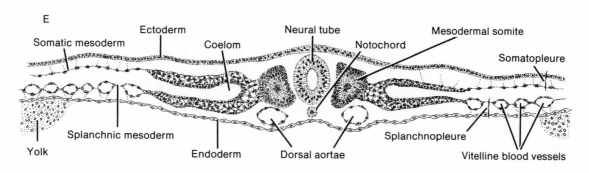

E

Somatic mesoderm — Ectoderm — Coelom — Neural tube — Notochord — Mesodermal somite — Somatopleure

Yolk — Splanchnic mesoderm — Endoderm — Dorsal aortae — Splanchnopleure — Vitelline blood vessels

F

Somite — Neural groove — Neural fold

Coelom — Notochord

G

Neural plate

H

Primitive groove — Primitive ridge

Mesoderm

Primitive streak

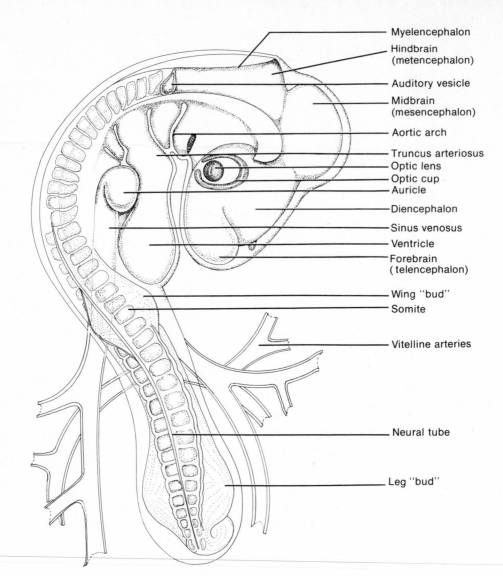

FIG. 21-10
Dorsal view of 72-hour chick embryo.

Section A is through the prosencephalon and optic vesicles, which will produce major parts of the eyes. The head region is free and is separated from the rest of the blastoderm by a definite space, called the **subcephalic pocket**. Note that the blastoderm immediately under the free head region consists of only ectoderm and endoderm.

Section B is through the head posterior to the optic cups. You can see the notochord, the dorsal and ventral aortas, and the pharynx (foregut).

Section C is through the region of the heart. Note the **epimyocardium**, the thick outer wall of the heart, and the **endocardium**, the thin inner lining. In this region, the embryo is no longer physically separated from the rest of the flat blastoderm.

Section D is through a region a short distance posterior to the heart. Observe the **midgut**, which is that part of the digestive tract just below the pharynx. Note the paired dorsal aortae, which will later fuse into a single dorsal aorta.

Section E is through a region that includes the third mesodermal somite. Note the absence of the digestive tract.

Sections F and G are through regions near the posterior end of the embryo and show the origin of the **neural tube**, which forms by a folding of the neural plate (Section G).

Section H is through the region of the primitive streak. Note the three germ layers that meet and fuse along the longitudinal axis of the embryo. A depression of the ectoderm forms the primitive groove bounded by two primitive ridges.

3. The 72-Hour Embryo

Remove the embryo from the yolk as shown in Fig. 21-6, and locate the various regions described below. At this stage, the anterior part of the embryo has turned to lie on its left side, whereas the posterior half remains dorsal side up (Fig. 21-10). Note the three pairs of **gill slits** and the blood vessels—the **aortic arches**—that pass through the gill arches. What is the significance of the appearance of these structures in the embryos of all higher vertebrates?

The central nervous system and the sense organs have now advanced considerably beyond their development in the 33-hour stage. The neural tube has developed into a five-part brain anteriorly and the spinal cord posteriorly. The optic vesicles have greatly enlarged and, by invaginating, have given rise to the double-walled **optic cups**. Concurrently, the surface ectoderm of the head immediately over the optic cups invaginates, thickens, and detaches to form the optic lens. Dorsal to the gill slits on each side is an invaginated thickening of the ectoderm forming the **auditory vesicle** ("ear").

The heart, which was tubular and single-chambered in the earlier stage, has become twisted and transformed into a two-chambered structure in this stage. The part of the heart next to the body is the **auricle** (atrium), and the part that dips ventrally is the **ventricle**. Note the **truncus arteriosus**; it arises from the ventricle and branches out into the aortic arches, which unite to form the **dorsal aortae**. Locate the **vitelline arteries**, a pair of large transverse blood vessels that leave the embryo about one-third of the distance from the posterior end and branch out into the **yolk sac,** and the **vitelline veins** that enter the auricle.

REFERENCES

Balinsky, B. I. 1981. *An Introduction to Embryology.* 5th ed. Saunders College/Holt, Rinehart and Winston.

Browder, L. W. 1980. *Developmental Biology.* Saunders College/Holt, Rinehart and Winston.

Davenport, R. 1979. *Outline of Animal Development.* Addison-Wesley.

Ebert, J. D., and I. M. Sussex. 1970. *Interacting Systems in Development.* 2nd ed. Holt, Rinehart and Winston.

Hamburger, V. 1960. *A Manual of Experimental Embryology.* University of Chicago Press.

Karp, G., and N. J. Berrill. 1981. *Development.* 2nd ed. McGraw-Hill.

Lehman, H. E. 1977. *Chordate Development.* Hunter.

Patten, B. M. 1971. *Early Embryology of the Chick.* 5th ed. McGraw-Hill.

Patten, B. M., and B. M. Carlson. 1974. *Foundations of Embryology.* 3rd ed. McGraw-Hill.

Rugh, R. 1962. *Experimental Embryology: Techniques and Procedures.* 3rd ed. Burgess.

Torrey, T. W., and A. Feduccia. 1979. *Morphogenesis of the Vertebrates.* 4th ed. Wiley.

Wolpert, L. 1978. Pattern Formation in Biological Development. *Scientific American* 239:154–164 (Offprint 1409). *Scientific American* Offprints are available from W. H. Freeman and Company, 660 Market Street, San Francisco 94104, and 58 Kings Road, Reading RGI 3AA, England. Please order by number.

Plant Growth and Development

A higher plant proceeds through a continuous series of changes during its life cycle. The outward expression of this activity begins with the embryo in the seed and proceeds, sequentially, through germination, the appearance and subsequent enlargement of stems, leaves, and roots, to the production of flowers, fruits and seeds. The location of these organs and their size and shape are the visible manifestations of the correlated activities of those cells produced by meristems. This complex and highly ordered series of events is called *development*.

Development may be divided into separate phases called growth, cell differentiation, and organogenesis. **Growth** may be defined as an irreversible increase in volume, which is usually—though not always—paralleled by an increase in weight. **Cell differentiation** includes all those events involved in the specialization of structure and function. **Organogenesis** is the development of the various plant organs.

A. COMPARATIVE STUDY OF SEEDS

The process of development in the higher plants begins with the seed. You will begin the study of plant growth and development by investigating the structure and function of seeds.

Seeds develop from ovules and are formed following the sexual union of the sperm and egg, an event that occurs in the ovary of the flower. If you are not familiar with floral anatomy, refer to Fig. 22-1 and a flower model or living flowers. The ovary and, in some cases, other parts of the flower become the fruit. Within the seed is the embryo, which consists of three parts: the **cotyledons** (sometimes called *seed leaves*), the **epicotyl**, which is located above the point of attachment of the cotyledons, and the **hypocotyl**, found below the cotyledons. The mature seed also may have an **endosperm**, which functions as a nutritive tissue for the developing embryo.

Obtain previously soaked bean, pea, and corn seeds. (The so-called seed of corn is really a fruit. The seed coat is intimately fused with a hard outer tissue called the **pericarp**, which is part of the fruit.) Carefully remove the outer seed coats from each seed. Then separate the other parts of each seed, comparing them with each other and with Fig. 22-2.

1. Cotyledons

Scrape the surface of the cotyledons of the bean and pea, and add a drop of iodine. On the basis of your observa-

tions, what appears to be the role of the cotyledons in the development of these seeds?

_____

_____

2. Epicotyl

This part of the embryo gives rise to the shoot system of the mature plant. What indication is there, if any, that this region will produce stem and leaf tissues?

_____

3. Hypocotyl

This region will primarily give rise to all root tissues and, in some cases, to the lower part of the stem.

4. Endosperm

The endosperm (although found in many seeds) is present only in the corn "seed" of the group you are examining. Depending on whether the endosperm is composed of starches or sugars, corn is "starchy" or "sweet." Remove the endosperm from several corn "seeds," and cut it up into fine pieces. Then add it to 5 ml of Benedict's solution in a test tube, and heat in a hot water bath for several minutes. If a reducing sugar is present, the solution will change in color (from blue to green to orange to red to brown), depending on the amount of sugar present. Cut through a kernel of corn, as shown in Fig. 22-2. Scrape the surface of the endosperm with a razor blade, and add a drop of iodine. The appearance of a blue color indicates the presence of starch. What commercial value does this starchy corn have?

_____

_____

B. GERMINATION

The seed is a resting stage in the development of a plant, serving to carry the plant over periods of unfavorable environmental conditions. When provided with optimal growing conditions, the seed, if living, will germinate

FIG. 22-1
Diagram of a flower. (Adapted from *Biology, Its Principles and Implications*, 3rd ed., by Garrett Hardin and Carl Bajema. W. H. Freeman and Company. Copyright © 1978.)

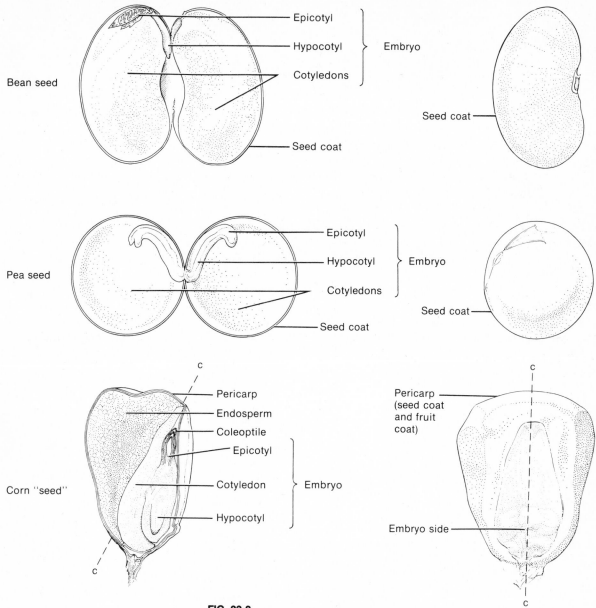

FIG. 22-2
Comparative anatomy of various seeds.

and produce another plant. The production of viable seeds is required for maintaining the existence of any plant species in nature. It is also commercially important to seed growers that they be able to judge the viability of the seed from any given crop. For biologists who grow research plants from seed, it is important that they be assured that the percentage of germination will be high. In this part of the exercise, you will determine the degree of viability of a batch of seeds. One way of doing this is to germinate sample batches of seed under standardized conditions. This **germination test** has one major drawback—it takes from 7 to 10 days for many seeds to germinate. A quicker and easier method is to use the fact

that embryos in viable seeds respire and are able to change colorless dyes, such as tetrazolium, into highly colored forms.

1. Germination Test

Obtain 100 bean seeds that have been soaked in water. Boil 50 of these seeds for 10 minutes to kill them. Plant 25 living seeds and 25 killed seeds about 15 mm deep in separate rows in the planting tray. The remaining boiled and unboiled seeds will be used for the tetrazolium test. Label each row as to section number, team number, date,

TABLE 22-1
Germination and tetrazolium data.

Data	Germination test				Tetrazolium test	
	Unboiled seeds		Boiled seeds		Unboiled seeds	Boiled seeds
	Week 1	Week 2	Week 1	Week 2		
Total number of seeds	( )	( )	( )	( )	( )	( )
Number of seeds germinated	( )	( )	( )	( )	( )	( )
Germination (%)	( )	( )	( )	( )	( )	( )

number of seeds, and treatment (boiled or unboiled). After a week, determine the total number of seeds in each treatment that have germinated and are growing, and record these data in Table 22-1. Record your team results and (in parentheses) those of the combined class.

Examine the tray again after 2 weeks, and determine the percentage of germination. Record your data in Table 22-1. How do you account for the difference, if any, between the results obtained after 1 week and that after 2 weeks?

2. Tetrazolium Test

Take the boiled and unboiled seeds not used in the germination test, and cut them longitudinally through the embryo, as shown in Fig. 22-3. Place each unboiled seed in a petri dish, with the cut surface up. Pour in enough tetrazolium chloride solution to cover the seeds. Repeat this procedure with seeds that have been boiled. *Make*

FIG. 22-3
Procedure for cutting bean seeds for tetrazolium test.

sure each dish is labeled as to contents. Set the seeds aside in a dark place for 30–45 minutes and then examine them. If the seed is viable, a red or pink color will be evident on the cut surface. Determine the percentage of viability, and record your data in Table 22-1. Record your results and (in parentheses) those of the combined class.

How does the percentage of viability obtained by the germination test compare with that obtained by the tetrazolium test?

_____

_____

_____

_____

If results obtained by your team were different from those of the class, account for the difference.

_____

_____

3. Factors Affecting Germination

The seeds used in the first part of this exercise germinated in a short period of time when placed under conditions suitable for germination. Viable seeds of many plants, however, fail to germinate even when provided with ample water and oxygen and a suitable temperature. Such seeds are in an arrested state of development called **dormancy**. In this part of the exercise, you will study one factor involved in the dormancy of seeds.

Place moistened filter paper in the bottoms of three petri dishes. Obtain 40 dry honey locust seeds (other possible seeds are sweet clover, okra, and alfalfa) and 20 honey locust seeds that have been soaking for 2–3 hours

TABLE 22-2
Factors affecting the germination of seeds.

Data	Seed treatment		
	Untreated	Seed coat cut	Treated with H_2SO_4
Total number of seeds	( )	( )	( )
Number of seeds germinated	( )	( )	( )
Germination (%)	( )	( )	( )

in a 70% sulfuric acid (H_2SO_4) solution. Carefully pour off the acid into a sink containing running water. With a rubber band, fasten cheesecloth over the beaker and wash the seeds in running water for 5 minutes.

Place the 20 acid-treated seeds in one petri dish. Put 20 of the untreated seeds into a second petri dish. With a sharp razor blade, remove a small chip from the 20 untreated seeds, exposing the inner tissues. Place these seeds with their cut surface down in the third dish. Cover all dishes, tape them shut (to retard evaporation), and label each as to contents. Put the dishes in the dark at room temperature (or wrap them in aluminum foil and take them home for observation). Periodically examine the seeds over the next 3–5 days, and determine the percentage of germination for each group of seeds. Record your team data and (in parentheses) those of the class in Table 22-2. What is the "factor" that controls dormancy in these seeds?

_____

_____

Of what advantage is dormancy to seeds?

_____

_____

C. MEASUREMENT OF PLANT GROWTH

Growth may be defined as an irreversible increase in volume generally accompanied by an increase in weight. Growth, therefore, is quantitative and can be measured. In these experiments you will determine the locus of growth, and plot a growth curve for a specific plant organ.

1. Localization of Plant Growth

Prepare a moist chamber as shown in Fig. 22-4A. Cover a glass plate (9 × 10 cm) with moist toweling, and place it in the chamber. Cover the container to prevent drying.

From the germinating seeds provided by the instructor, select one having a fairly straight root about 1.5–2 cm long. Blot the root to remove any excess moisture, and then lay it against a millimeter ruler. Carefully mark 10 lines, each 1 mm apart, *starting from the tip of the root* (Fig. 22-4D). Make sure you wipe the excess ink from the thread, or the mark will become smudged, making accurate observations difficult. Repeat the marking operation until five roots have been marked. Avoid drying the roots during marking. Lay the seedlings on the paper-covered glass plate, and hold them lightly in place with a rubber band so that the whole length of each root is touching the moist paper (Fig. 22-4F). Place the plate and seedlings in the moist chamber, and then cover and keep in a dark place.

After 48 hours, measure the distance between the ink marks on each root. Average the lengths for each interval. Record your data in Table 22-3, and plot your data in Fig. 22-5.

Where does most of the growth occur?

_____

If the ink lines were initially sharp and clear, how do you account for the smudging of the first, and possibly the second, line?

_____

If you were to cut a longitudinal section through a young root and examine it microscopically, what would you expect to see in the first millimeter or so that would account for the results you have observed?

_____

_____

Examine a prepared slide of a longitudinal section through an onion root tip (compare with Fig. 22-6). Locate a cone-shaped mass of loosely arranged cells covering the tip of the root. This is a root cap, which serves to protect the meristematic region of the root. Closely examine the cells of the meristematic region. What

264

A. Prepare a moist chamber lined with wet paper towel.

B. Select a germinating seed with a fairly straight root $1\frac{1}{2}$ to 2 cm long.

C. Blot the root with a paper towel to remove excess moisture.

D. Lay the root against a millimeter ruler. Wipe excess ink from thread and carefully mark 10 lines, 1 mm apart, starting from the tip of the root.

E. As each root is marked, place the seedling between moist towels to prevent drying.

Rubber band

Moist paper towel

Glass plate

F. Lay the seedlings on a glass plate and hold them in place with a rubber band.

G. Place the plate into your moist chamber, cover, and set in a dark place for 48 hours.

FIG. 22-4
Procedure for determining locus of growth in roots.

TABLE 22-3
Data for locus of root growth.

Root tip No.	Interval									
	1	2	3	4	5	6	7	8	9	10
1										
2										
3										
4										
5										
Total										
Average										
Control										

FIG. 22-5
Localization of root growth.

FG. 22-6
Logitudinal section of onion root tip.

occurred in this region when the tissue was living to account for the results obtained in the growth measurement experiment?

_____

_____

_____

_____

_____

Locate the region of the root in which cell differentiation is occurring. Approximately how far back from the tip does this region occur? (The diameter of your low-power field, 10× objective, is approximately 2 mm.)

_____

_____

_____

What is the consequence of cell division and the subsequent enlargement of cells at the root tip?

_____

_____

_____

_____

_____

_____

_____

_____

2. Growth Curve of Leaves

Select three bean seeds that have been soaking in water for several hours. Split them open and, with a millimeter ruler, measure the length of the embryonic foliage leaves (Fig. 22-7A). Determine the average length and record this figure under Date "0" in Table 22-4. This is the first in a series of measurements to be made of the growth of the first two foliage leaves.

Plant 25 of the soaked bean seeds about 7 mm deep in the container provided. Water thoroughly, and place them in the greenhouse. In two or three days, dig up 3 of the seeds and measure the length of the leaves, including the petiole (Fig. 22-7B). Enter the average length in Table 22-4, and discard the young plants.

TABLE 22-4
Growth curve data.

	Date of measurement					
	0					
Average length (mm)						

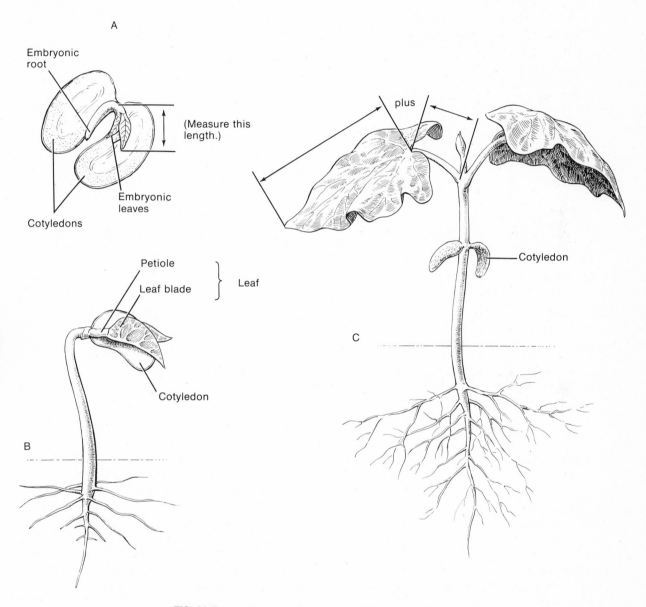

FIG. 22-7
Measuring the growth of a bean seedling. (Adapted from *Plants in Action*, by Leonard Machlis and John G. Torrey. W. H. Freeman and Company. Copyright © 1956.)

In succeeding laboratory periods, select three plants and measure the leaves as above (Fig. 22-7C). *Do not remove these plants from the container. Use the same three plants for all measurements beginning with the third measurement.*

Plot your data in Fig. 22-8. List several other organisms (or organs) that would show a similar growth curve.

Day of measurement

FIG. 22-8
Growth curve of bean plant leaves.

REFERENCES

Cutter, E. G. 1981. *Plant Anatomy: Experiment and Interpretation*. Part 1. 2nd ed. Addison-Wesley.

Cutter, E. G. 1971. *Plant Anatomy: Experiment and Interpretation*. Part 2. Addison-Wesley.

Esau, K. 1977. *Anatomy of Seed Plants*. 2nd ed. Wiley.

Foster, A. S., and E. M. Gifford, Jr. 1974. *Comparative Morphology of Vascular Plants*. W. H. Freeman and Company.

Galston, A. W. 1970. *The Life of the Green Plant*. 3rd ed. Prentice-Hall.

Leopold, A. C., and P. E. Kriedemann. 1975. *Plant Growth and Development*. 2nd ed. McGraw-Hill.

Levitt, J. 1969. *Introduction to Plant Physiology*. Mosby.

Sinnott, E. W. 1960. *Plant Morphogenesis*. McGraw-Hill.

Steward, F. C. 1968. *Growth and Organization in Plants*. Addison-Wesley.

Wareing, P. F., and I. D. J. Phillips. 1978. *The Control of Growth and Differentiation in Plants*. 2nd ed. Pergamon Press.

Plant Development: Hormonal Regulation

One of the challenging problems facing biologists is that of understanding the basic mechanisms that regulate the development of plants and animals. The systematic differentiation of millions of cells into various tissues and organs, and the development of specific form and shape, requires precise coordination between the individual parts of the organism during each stage of growth.

The development of a seed into a mature plant is one aspect of this remarkable process. It consists of growth by cell division and cell elongation, differentiation of new organs such as roots, stems, leaves, and flowers, and a complex series of chemical changes. The final form of the plant is a blend of the plant's genetic "blueprint" and modifying effects of the environment. When the seed begins to germinate, it absorbs large amounts of water, and cells at the meristems of the plant embryo begin to divide. For reasons not yet understood, the root almost always begins to develop before the shoot. At both root and shoot ends of the embryo, new cells are formed by the meristematic (dividing) areas of the growing points, followed by elongation and differentiation of these cells.

Ultimately, the control of growth and differentiation is in the DNA of the nucleus, which controls the production of hormones and other regulatory chemicals. Our present knowledge of the mechanisms of regulation of the various patterns of growth and differentiation, although somewhat limited, is expanding rapidly as new experimental evidence is reported.

Some of the growth-regulating substances in plants are auxins, gibberellic acids, cytokinins, and various growth inhibitors.

Auxins are produced in meristematic tissues. They influence cell elongation, inhibit the growth of lateral buds, promote the initiation of roots, and, in a few plants, regulate the differentiation of flower buds.

Gibberellic acids, also apparently synthesized in meristems, are highly complex substances that affect cell elongation, cell division, and flowering responses in some plants.

Cytokinins, which have been suggested to be related to a component of RNA, promote cell division, and, in the presence of auxin, induce the differentiation of roots and shoots.

270

A. Select 40 seeds that have been soaking for several hours. Plant 20 seeds in vermiculite and label "Gibberellic Acid." Plant remaining 20 seeds and label "Control."

B. After 7–10 days, select 10 plants that are about the same size. Tag them with a number (1, 2, 3, etc.) and the date. Discard remaining 10 plants.

Shoot tip

Measure this distance.

C. Apply a drop of gibberellic acid solution to shoot tip.

D. Measure each plant (in millimeters) in the experimental and control groups.

FIG. 23-1
Procedure for determining effect of gibberellic acid on plant growth.

Inhibitors of different types regulate such responses in plants as flowering, dormancy of buds and seeds, and rates of growth.

In the following parts of the exercise, the effects of certain environmental and chemical factors on the patterns of growth and differentiation in plants will be studied.

A. GIBBERELLIC ACID

Gibberellic acids, first discovered by Japanese scientists in the 1920s, went largely unnoticed until the early 1950s, when English and American biologists became interested in these compounds. They were first isolated from a fungus, *Gibberella*. To date, more than sixteen gibberellic acids have been isolated from higher plant tissues and appear to participate in normal plant development.

Before initiating your study, make a hypothesis (or prediction) as to what you expect the results to be. One way of doing this is to use the "If-Then" predictive approach. For example,

If gibberellic acids act to inhibit growth,
then plants treated with gibberellic acids should grow less than control plants that have not been treated with gibberellic acid.

Make a prediction as to what you expect the results to be in this study.

_____

_____

_____

_____

In this part of the exercise, you will determine some of the more obvious effects of gibberellic acid on plant development.

1. Working on teams of three, obtain 40 bean seeds that have been soaking in water for several hours.

2. Plant 20 seeds (about 15 mm deep) in moist vermiculite in a tray. Label the tray "Gibberellic Acid" (Fig. 23-1A). Plant the remaining 20 seeds in a second tray labeled "Control."

3. When the plants are 7 to 8 centimeters tall (about 3 inches), select 10 plants in each tray that are about the

same size. Label each individual plant with a number, along with the date. Cut the remaining plants at the ground level and discard the parts you have cut off (Fig. 23-1B).

4. Measure the height of each plant (in millimeters) from the cotyledons to the tip of the shoot apex. Can you think of other measurements you might take? If so, use these in place of the one suggested.

5. Record the date, height, and appearance of the plants in Table 23-1 under Day "0."

6. Apply a drop of gibberellic acid to the shoot apex of each plant in the tray labeled "Gibberellic Acid." What will you apply to the control plants?

_____

7. Apply gibberellic acid to the plants weekly, and record the height of each plant and the general appearance of all plants in Table 23-1. As the plants continue to grow, it may be advisable to "stake" the plants using thin bamboo sticks and twine. Be careful not to crush the stems when tying them to the sticks.

8. At the conclusion of the experiment (as determined by your instructor), plot the data in Fig. 23-2. Analyze the data, and determine whether the growth response obtained with gibberellic acid is significantly different from that of the controls. (See Appdneix E for a method of statistical analysis of the data.)

Given the results of your statistical analysis, do the data you obtained support your hypothesis? Explain.

_____

_____

_____

_____

B. PLANT GROWTH INHIBITORS

The idea that inhibitors were important in the regulation of plant growth first gained importance when it was discovered that dormant buds of ash trees contained large amounts of inhibitors. When dormancy ended, the inhibitor concentration declined. More recently, a substance called **dormin** has been isolated. It is believed to cause plants to stop growing and enter into their dormant state.

TABLE 23-1
Effect of gibberellic acid on plant growth.

Day	Date	Treated with gibberellic acid		Controls	
		Height of plants	Appearance of plants	Height of Plants	Appearance of plants
0		1.___ 6.___ 2.___ 7.___ 3.___ 8.___ 4.___ 9.___ 5.___ 10.___ Avg.___		1.___ 6.___ 2.___ 7.___ 3.___ 8.___ 4.___ 9.___ 5.___ 10.___ Avg.___	
		1.___ 6.___ 2.___ 7.___ 3.___ 8.___ 4.___ 9.___ 5.___ 10.___ Avg.___		1.___ 6.___ 2.___ 7.___ 3.___ 8.___ 4.___ 9.___ 5.___ 10.___ Avg.___	
		1.___ 6.___ 2.___ 7.___ 3.___ 8.___ 4.___ 9.___ 5.___ 10.___ Avg.___		1.___ 6.___ 2.___ 7.___ 3.___ 8.___ 4.___ 9.___ 5.___ 10.___ Avg.___	
		1.___ 6.___ 2.___ 7.___ 3.___ 8.___ 4.___ 9.___ 5.___ 10.___ Avg.___		1.___ 6.___ 2.___ 7.___ 3.___ 8.___ 4.___ 9.___ 5.___ 10.___ Avg.___	
		1.___ 6.___ 2.___ 7.___ 3.___ 8.___ 4.___ 9.___ 5.___ 10.___ Avg.___		1.___ 6.___ 2.___ 7.___ 3.___ 8.___ 4.___ 9.___ 5.___ 10.___ Avg.___	
		1.___ 6.___ 2.___ 7.___ 3.___ 8.___ 4.___ 9.___ 5.___ 10.___ Avg.___		1.___ 6.___ 2.___ 7.___ 3.___ 8.___ 4.___ 9.___ 5.___ 10.___ Avg.___	
		1.___ 6.___ 2.___ 7.___ 3.___ 8.___ 4.___ 9.___ 5.___ 10.___ Avg.___		1.___ 6.___ 2.___ 7.___ 3.___ 8.___ 4.___ 9.___ 5.___ 10.___ Avg.___	

Dormin has also been called **abscissin** because it is responsible for causing leaves to fall off (absciss) plants late in the growing season. (Both dormin and abscissin have now been shown to be **abscisic acid.**) Thus a single substance isolated from different plants not only controls leaf fall but also regulates dormancy and many other growth processes.

Before initiating this study, hypothesize on what you expect the results to be. Use the "If-Then" format given as an example in Part A.

_____

_____

_____

_____

_____

_____

Select three bean or sunflower plants that are in about the same stage of development (only the first two leaves should have expanded). Tag them (1) "Phosfon," (2) "Gibberellic Acid," and (3) "Control," along with your name and the date (Fig. 23-3B). Record the average beginning height of the plants in Table 23-2. In Fig. 23-4, draw the plants as they appear before treatment.

Using a wooden match or similar applicator, apply a ring of phosfon-lanolin paste around the stem of the plant

FIG. 23-2
Effect of gibberellic acid on plant growth.

TABLE 23-2
Effect of phosfon and gibberellic acid on plant growth.

Date	Phosfon			Gibberellin			Control		
	Average height (mm)	Color of leaves	Other	Average height (mm)	Color of leaves	Other	Average height (mm)	Color of leaves	Other
0									

D. Examine the plants every 2 to 3 days for the next 3 weeks.

FIG. 23-3
Effect of growth inhibitors on plant development.

labeled "Phosfon" about 15 mm below the first pair of leaves (Fig. 23-3C). Then place the plant in bright sunlight. *Note:* The phosphon (and gibberellic acid) is mixed with lanolin, an inert paste, which allows for even application of the growth substances to the treated part of the plant.

Using a different applicator, apply gibberellic-acid lanolin paste to the pot labeled "Gibberellic Acid." What should be applied to the control plants and why?

_____

_____

Examine your plants and those of other students every 2 to 3 days for the next 3 weeks. Record the average height of the plants, and other information in Table 23-2.

At the conclusion of the study, plot your data in Fig. 23-5. In Fig. 23-4, draw the plants as they appear at the end of the study.

C. DETECTION OF PLANT GROWTH

Hormonal regulation of growth in animals has been known for a number of years. By 1930, it was commonly accepted that plant growth was also under the regulation of special hormonal substances, now called **auxins**. The principal naturally occurring auxin is called **indoleacetic acid**, or **IAA** (Fig. 23-6).

Before indoleacetic acid was discovered, the term auxin was used when referring to the natural growth hormone. The term now is used to describe any of a large number of compounds having physiological activity similar to indoleacetic acid. IAA does have, or is suggested to have, several effects on growth. A critical effect is the ability to induce the elongation of cells.

The isolation and identification of auxins was simplified by the use of a biological testing procedure called a **bioassay**. There are numerous biologically active compounds present in living organisms in amounts so minute that they cannot be detected by the usual chemical procedures. In a bioassay, the whole organism, or some part of it, is used to detect the presence of, and to measure the amounts of, biologically active substances.

The most sensitive bioassay for auxins is the *Avena* **curvature test**. This test makes use of the coleoptile of the *Avena* (oat) seedling (Fig. 23-7). The **coleoptile** is a cellular sheath that surrounds the embryonic leaves of the developing seedling. If oat seeds are germinated in the dark, cells of the coleoptile continue to divide until the coleoptile is approximately 1 cm long. For the next 3 or

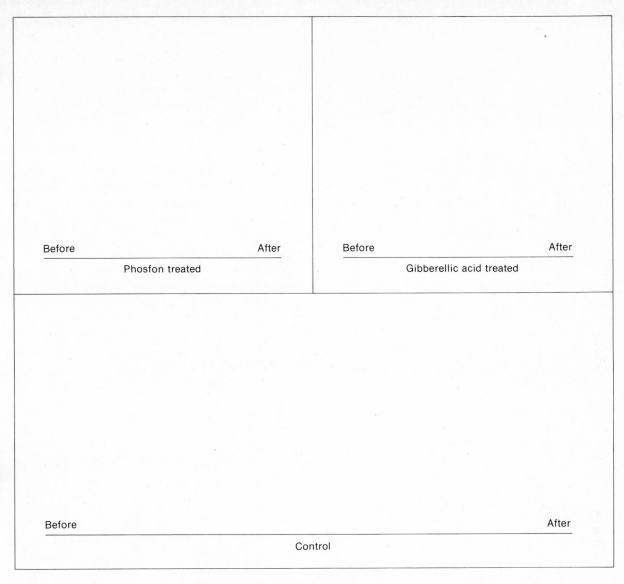

Before   After   Before   After
          Phosfon treated   Gibberellic acid treated

Before   After
                                        Control

FIG. 23-4
Effect of phosfon and gibberellic acid on plant growth.

FIG. 23-5
Effect of phosfon and gibberellic acid on plant growth.

Height of plants (cm)

Time (days)

4 days, when the coleoptile reaches its maximum length of 5–6 cm, extension of the coleoptile is by cell elongation only. This elongation is brought about by auxin produced in the tip of the coleoptile. When grown in the dark, the auxin is directed downward, causing the embryonic cells of the coleoptile to elongate. If the tip is removed, no cellular enlargement occurs. If the decapitated tip is replaced by an agar block containing auxin, growth of the coleoptile resumes. If the block of agar is displaced to one side, the cells on that side elongate more rapidly than the cells on the opposite side with the result that the coleoptile curves. This is the basis for the cur-

FIG. 23-6
Structure of indoleacetic acid.

FIG. 23-7
Avena seedling. (From *Plants in Action*, by Leonard Machlis and John G. Torrey. W. H. Freeman and Company. Copyright © 1956.)

vature test. It has been shown that the degree of curvature is, within limits, proportional to the concentration of auxin in the agar block. This test is a highly reliable and sensitive quantitative test for the detection of substances having auxin activity.

Although the *Avena* curvature test is very sensitive, it also requires rigidly controlled conditions of temperature and humidity and accurate measurements of curvature. For these reasons, it is difficult to conduct such a test in most introductory laboratory courses. There is a simpler bioassay using oat coleoptiles, which is less sensitive in terms of the concentration of auxin measurable. It is called the *Avena* **straight-growth test**. The test measures straight growth as reflected in an increase in length of coleoptile sections. To save time, the preliminary steps of soaking and planting the oat seeds will be carried out before the laboratory meeting.

1. The *Avena* Coleoptile Straight-Growth Test

1. For each laboratory section, soak 600–700 Brighton hull-less oat seeds for 2 hours in a liter of distilled water. After soaking, rinse the seeds two or three times with distilled water. Plant the oats on moist germinating paper (or Kleenex) in a tray; cover and pack tightly with about 15 mm of moist vermiculite; cover and place in the dark at room temperature. Germinate for 70–72 hours, exposing the seeds to 1 hour of red light out of each 24.

2. Label six test tubes and fill them as indicated in Table 23-3. The IAA dilutions and incubating medium (a buffered nutrient solution containing sucrose) will be provided.

3. Using the information given in the note at the bottom of Table 23-3, describe how you would prepare the various dilutions used in this experiment. (*Hint:* Notice that 1 ml of each dilution series is further diluted with 1 ml of incubating solution.)

4. Approximately 70 hours after planting, the coleoptiles will be 20–30 mm in length. Working in a room illuminated with red light (or use a room darkened as much as possible—but work quickly) select 60 coleoptiles measuring 25–30 mm in length. Cut off the root and seed and place the coleoptiles on moistened filter paper in a petri dish.

5. Place four or five coleoptiles at a time on a paraffin block and cut them with the special cutter, as shown in Fig. 23-8. This cutter will divide each coleoptile into three parts: a 3-mm tip portion, a 5-mm section, and a base of about 20 mm. Discard the 3-mm tips and the bases. Place 10 of the 5-mm sections in each of the six test tubes.

Base
(discard)

5–mm section
(place 10 in
each tube)

3–mm tip
(discard)

Paraffin
block

Razor
blades

Tubing cut to
correct length

FIG. 23-8
Method of cutting coleoptiles for *Avena* straight-growth test.

6. Stopper the test tubes with cotton or styrofoam plugs and place in the dark for 24 hours at 25°C. After 24 hours, remove the sections from the tubes and measure them with a millimeter ruler to the nearest 0.5 mm. Record the average length in Table 23-4.

7. Plot your data in Fig. 23-9 to obtain the standard curve for these concentrations. Does the curve show a proportional increase in growth with increasing IAA concentration? Explain.

_____

_____

_____

_____

_____

_____

TABLE 23-3
Protocol for the *Avena* straight-growth test.

Tube contents	Tube No.					
	1	2	3	4	5	6
Incubation solution (ml)	1	1	1	1	1	1
Distilled H_2O (ml)	1	—	—	—	—	—
10^{-7} M IAA solution (ml)	—	1	—	—	—	—
10^{-6} M IAA solution (ml)	—	—	1	—	—	—
10^{-5} M IAA solution (ml)	—	—	—	1	—	—
10^{-4} M IAA solution (ml)	—	—	—	—	1	—
Unknown IAA solution (ml)	—	—	—	—	—	1

Note: The dilution series uses solutions of varying molar *(M)* concentration. A molar solution is made by dissolving the molecular weight of a compound, in grams, in a liter of solvent. Thus, the molecular weight of IAA is 175.2. A 1.0 *M* solution of IAA contains 175.2 g/1000 ml of water. In a similar manner:

$$
\begin{array}{llll}
1/10\ M & = 10^{-1}\ M = & 17.52000000\ \text{g/liter} = & 17520.00000\ \text{mg/liter} \\
1/100\ M & = 10^{-2}\ M = & 1.75200000\ \text{g/liter} = & 1752.00000\ \text{mg/liter} \\
1/1000\ M & = 10^{-3}\ M = & 0.17520000\ \text{g/liter} = & 175.20000\ \text{mg/liter} \\
1/10{,}000\ M & = 10^{-4}\ M = & 0.01752000\ \text{g/liter} = & 17.52000\ \text{mg/liter} \\
1/100{,}000\ M & = 10^{-5}\ M = & 0.00175200\ \text{g/liter} = & 1.75200\ \text{mg/liter} \\
1/1{,}000{,}000\ M & = 10^{-6}\ M = & 0.00017520\ \text{g/liter} = & 0.17520\ \text{mg/liter} \\
1/10{,}000{,}000\ M & = 10^{-7}\ M = & 0.00001752\ \text{g/liter} = & 0.01752\ \text{mg/liter} \\
\end{array}
$$

TABLE 23-4
Data for *Avena* straight-growth test.

	IAA (moles)					
	0 Incubating medium	$10^{-7}\,M$	$10^{-6}\,M$	$10^{-5}\,M$	$10^{-4}\,M$	Unknown
Average coleoptile length (mm)						

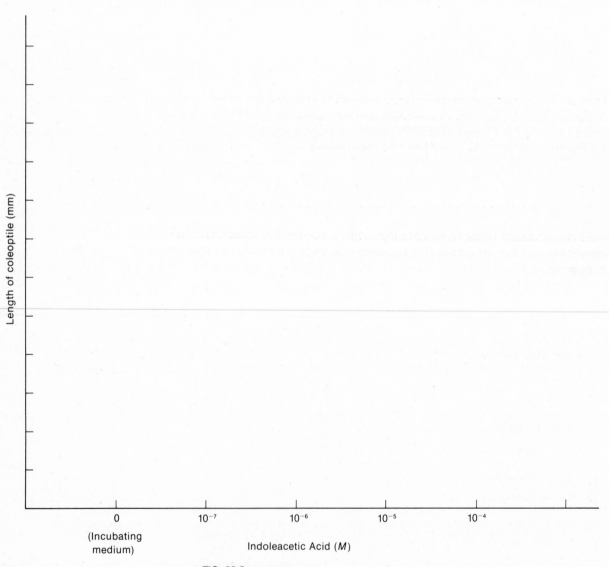

FIG. 23-9
Standard curve for *Avena* straight-growth test.

8. Plot the unknown IAA concentration on the graph. On the basis of the position of the unknown, estimate the concentration of the IAA in the unknown solution.

_____

9. What is the reason for having Tube 1?

_____

_____

_____

2. Colormetric Test for IAA

There is a simpler chemical test for detecting one of the natural auxins (such as IAA), much less sensitive than either of the bioassays, but useful for in vitro (test tube) studies of auxin concentrations well above those normally found in plant tissue. For example, an enzyme found in plant tissues, called _indoleacetic acid oxidase,_ breaks down IAA. This test would be useful for studying the action of such an enzyme.

The color test you will perform makes use of the fact that IAA, in the presence of iron chloride in Salkowski reagent, forms a red color complex that may be quantitatively measured with a colorimeter (see Appendix B for a discussion of colorimetry).

You will be provided with a stock solution of IAA at a concentration of 100 mg/liter. Make 10-ml samples of the following concentrations: 40, 20, 10, 1, and 0 mg/ liter. This is done as follows. Collect 10 ml of the stock solution in a test tube. Pipet 4 ml of this solution into a test tube and dilute with distilled water to 10 ml. Label this tube "40 mg/1." Repeat this procedure using 2 ml, 1 ml, and 0.1 ml of the stock solution, diluting each to 10 ml. Mark these tubes "20 mg/1," "10/mg1," and "1 mg/1," respectively. For the 0 mg/liter concentration, merely pipet 10 ml of distilled water into a tube. This dilution series will be used to establish a standard curve. In addition, you will be given a solution containing an unknown concentration of IAA.

To conduct the color test, add 2 ml of the solution being tested to a test tube containing 8 ml of Salkowski reagent. (_Note:_ because full color development is a function of time, stagger your tests to allow time for each colorimetric measurement.) Shake the mixture thoroughly (_and carefully,_ as the reagent contains sulfuric

acid!) and set aside for exactly 30 minutes to allow the color to develop. While waiting for the color reaction, warm up the colorimeter and adjust the wavelength to read 510 nm (see Appendix A for instructions on the use of the Bausch & Lomb Spectronic 20 colorimeter).

Standardize the colorimeter, using a solution consisting of 2 ml of distilled water and 8 ml of Salkowski reagent. Immediately transfer about 3 ml of this mixture to a colorimeter tube and place in the Spectronic 20. Adjust the instrument to read 100% transmittance. Why is this step required?

_____

_____

_____

At the end of 30 minutes, record the percent transmittance for each of the IAA concentrations and the unknown, and record the data in Table 23-5. Plot your data in Fig. 23-10. What is the concentration of the unknown IAA solution?

_____

Of the three methods discussed in this exercise, which would you use if you had to assay accurately for the total amount of auxin in 500 mg of plant tissue? Explain.

_____

_____

_____

_____

_____

_____

_____

_____

_____

TABLE 23-5
Data for colorimetric determination of IAA

	Tube contents (mg/liter)					
	0 Control	1	10	20	40	Unknown
Transmittance (%)						

FIG. 23-10
Colorimetric determination of IAA.

REFERENCES

Cutter, E. G. 1971. *Plant Anatomy: Experiment and Interpretation*. Part 2. Addison-Wesley.

Ebert, J. D., and I. M. Sussex. 1970. *Interacting Systems in Development*. 2nd ed. Holt, Rinehart and Winston.

Leopold, A. C., and P. E. Kriedemann. 1975. *Plant Growth and Development*. 2nd ed. McGraw-Hill.

Salisbury, F. B., and C. Ross. 1978. *Plant Physiology*. 2nd ed. Wadsworth.

Sinnott, E. W. 1960. *Plant Morphogenesis*. McGraw-Hill.

Steward, F. C. 1968. *Plant Physiology*. Addison-Wesley.

Steward, F. C., and A. D. Krikorian. 1971. *Plants, Chemicals and Growth*. Academic Press.

Torrey, J. C. 1967. *Development in Flowering Plants*. Macmillan.

Van Overbeek, J. 1968. The Control of Plant Growth. *Scientific American* 219:75–81 (Offprint 1111). *Scientific American* Offprints are available from W. H. Freeman and Company, 660 Market Street, San Francisco 94104, and 58 Kings Road, Reading RG1 3AA, England. Please order by number.

Wareing, P. F., and I. D. J. Phillips. 1978. *The Control of Growth and Differentiation in Plants*. 2nd ed. Pergamon Press.

Plant Development: Effect of Light

The morphogenetic effects of light on plants have been known since the latter part of the nineteenth century. As early as 1880, experiments conducted with carbon arc lamps showed that artificially prolonged days promoted plant growth. After the invention of the electric light bulb, a large amount of data began to accumulate on the morphogenetic effects of light on plants. These observations ranged from such anatomical effects as variations in fiber and vascular tissue development to establishing the presence of a pigment called **phytochrome**, which may regulate many of the responses of plants or plant parts to light.

In this exercise, you will study the effects of light on development and the effect of day length on flowering and dormancy of plants.

A. PLANT GROWTH IN THE ABSENCE OF LIGHT

Obtain two pots or trays that contain vermiculite. Label one "Dark" and the other "Light." Include your name, the date, and section number on each label. Plant 10 bean seeds about 15 mm deep in each container. Water thoroughly, and then place one of the pots in the sunlight and the other in the dark (Fig. 24-1). *(Note: Water plants daily throughout the period of the study.)*

After about 4 or 5 days, examine the plants that have been growing in the dark. Compare them with those growing in the light. Record your observations in Table 24-1.

Reverse the conditions under which the plants have

A. Plant 10 bean seeds about 15mm
   deep in each of 2 containers
   labeled "light" and "dark" (include
   your name and the date).

B. Place the "dark" plants in a
   cabinet and the "light" plants
   where they will get sunlight.

FIG. 24-1
Effect of darkness on plant growth.

TABLE 24-1
Effect of darkness on plant growth.

Observations and measurement	Treatment	
	Plants grown in dark	Plants grown in light
Color of shoot		
Average number of leaves		
Average length of first pair of leaves		
Average length of shoot between cotyledons and first leaves		

been growing (that is, place the "dark" plants in the light and the "light" plants in the dark). Examine the plants after 4 or 5 days. Describe the appearance of the plants.

_____

_____

Record your observations in Table 24-2.

The growth response observed in the plants grown in the dark is called **etiolation**. What advantage does such a response have for plant survival?

_____

_____

B. EFFECT OF DAY LENGTH ON PLANT GROWTH

Day length varies with the seasons. In the Northern Hemisphere, the day length increases during spring to a maximum on June 21, and thereafter it decreases to a minimum on December 21. This day length is called the **photoperiod**, and the response of plants to photoperiods of varying lengths is called **photoperiodism** or a **photoperiodic response**. In this part of the exercise, you will examine the effects of the photoperiod on two aspects of plant development.

1. Regulation of Flowering

There are basically two types of photoperiodic flowering responses. These are called **long-day** and **short-day responses**. Plants that exhibit these responses are called long-day (L-D) and short-day (S-D) plants. L-D plants flower when the photoperiod *exceeds* some critical value, which is generally in excess of 14 hours (Table 24-3). At day lengths less than the critical value the plant usually grows only vegetatively. An S-D plant (really a long-night plant) will flower when the photoperiod is *less* than some critical value, usually about 10 hours, and grows vegetatively when this critical day length is exceeded. Other plants, not responsive to day length, are called **day-neutral** plants.

The photoperiodic control of flowering involves a complex mechanism about which few facts are known. These responses appear to be under the control of the light-sensitive proteinaceous pigment called *phytochrome*.

This bluish green pigment has been extracted and isolated with a high degree of purity.

The effect of phytochrome on flowering appears to be related to its having two forms in the plant. One form, called P_{660}, absorbs red light (with maximum absorption at 660 nm) and is converted into a second form, called P_{730}. The P_{730} form of the pigment strongly absorbs far-red radiation (maximally at 730 nm) and may then be reconverted to the P_{660} form. The photoperiod responses in various plants may be a result of differences in the rate of conversion of one form of phytochrome to another. There is also some evidence for a second photomorphogenic receptor involving a system of pigments absorbing blue and far-red radiation. These appear to operate independently of the red, far-red phytochrome system.

In this study, you will be given two different species of plants and will attempt to determine whether they are L-D or S-D plants.

The L-D and S-D conditions are shown in Fig. 24-2.

1. Obtain two trays of plants provided by your instructor. Label one of the trays "L-D," along with your name, section number, and the date. Label the other tray "S-D" (Fig. 24-2A).

2. Place the trays under light conditions so that the L-D plants receive 16 hours of light and 8 hours of darkness (Fig. 24-2B). The S-D plants should receive 8 hours of light and 16 hours of darkness (Fig. 24-2C).

3. Examine the plants weekly, and watch for the appearance of flower buds. The detection of flowers is difficult in the early stages of formation, so close inspection may be necessary. However, avoid excessive handling of the plants.

4. If, at the conclusion of the experiment (as determined by your instructor), no flowers are visible, remove the buds from each plant and place them in separate, labeled petri dishes containing moistened filter paper.

5. Using a dissecting microscope, dissect the buds and determine if flower primordia are present or if the buds are still producing leaves. Your instructor will have floral buds and vegetative buds on demonstration to help you distinguish between the two.

6. Determine the photoperiod response of the plants, and confirm your results with your instructor. What economic use can be made of the photoperiodic response?

_____

_____

_____

_____

TABLE 24-2
Effect of placing "light-grown" plants in the dark and "dark-grown" plants in the light.

Observations	Plants grown in dark ⟶ light	Plants grown in light ⟶ dark
Color of shoot		
Other observations		

TABLE 24-3
Flowering responses of long-day, short-day, and day-neutral plants.

Plant	24-hour period		Flowers
	Light	Dark	
Long-day	⟶		no
	⟶	⟶	yes
Short-day	⟶		yes
	⟶	⟶	no
Day-neutral	⟶		yes
	⟶	⟶	yes

(Critical day length)

287

A. Label "L-D" (long-day) or "S-D" (short-day), along with your name, date, and section number.

B. Place one group of plants under L-D conditions.

C. Place the second group under S-D conditions.

L-D (short-night) conditions

S-D (long-night) conditions

8 hours of sunlight   8 hours of artificial light   8 hours of darkness

8 hours of sunlight   16 hours of darkness

D. Examine the plants weekly for the appearance of flowers. After 3 to 4 weeks (if no flowers are visible) dissect the buds to determine if they have flowers or leaves in them.

FIG. 24-2
Effect of photoperiod on flowering.

TABLE 24-4
Observations of plant response to photoperiod.

Day	Date	L-D treatment		S-D treatment	
		Length of shoot (cm)	Other observations	Length of shoot (cm)	Other observations
0					

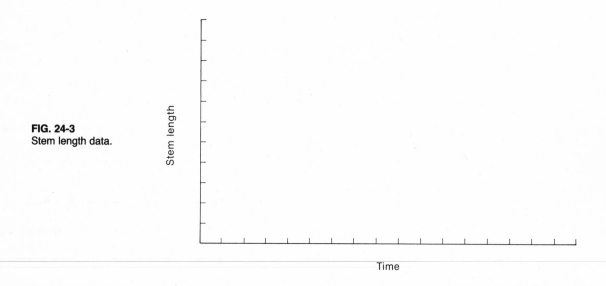

FIG. 24-3
Stem length data.

Many other aspects of plant growth are under photoperiodic control. Basing your answer on your reading, list several of these here.

_____

_____

_____

_____

2. Dormancy

In the broadest sense, and without reference to the factors involved, dormancy can be defined as a temporary suspension of visible growth and development. In this study,

you will determine the effects of the photoperiod in regulating the initiation of the dormant, winter bud in a woody plant. If you are unfamiliar with the appearance of a winter bud, examine the demonstration of dormant buds set up by the instructor.

1. Working in teams, obtain two potted seedlings that are approximately the same height. Label each with your name, section number, the date, and treatment (L-D or S-D).

2. Place the plants on the L-D and S-D benches in the greenhouse. Measure the length of the main shoot on each plant and record this and any other observations that seem appropriate under Day 0 in Table 24-4.

3. Examine the plants during succeeding laboratory periods and record the date and stem length. What evidence is there that the plant (under one treatment or the other) is forming a dormant bud? Examine the plants of other students, but do not handle them excessively. Make

similar measurements and observations over the next several weeks, or until your instructor concludes the experiment.

4. At the conclusion of the experiment, plot the "stem length" data in Fig. 24-3. Suggest reasons for the differences in stem length, if any, between the plants given the L-D and S-D treatments.

_____

_____

_____

Under which photoperiod has a dormant bud been formed?

_____

In view of your knowledge of growth regulators, suggest a mechanism by which the photoperiod is inducing a state of dormancy in these plants.

_____

5. Remove all the leaves of the dormant plants, and return the plants to the same photoperiod that induced dormancy. Examine the plant weekly for 2–3 weeks. List your observations below, and discuss how the plant may receive the light stimulus.

_____

_____

_____

_____

_____

_____

_____

_____

_____

_____

REFERENCES

Galston, A. W., and P. F. Davies. 1970. *Control Mechanisms in Plant Development*. Prentice-Hall.

Leopold, A. C., and P. E. Kriedemann. 1975. *Plant Growth and Development*. 2nd ed. McGraw-Hill.

Sinnott, E. W. 1960. *Plant Morphogenesis*. McGraw-Hill.

Smith, H. 1975. *Phytochrome and Photomorphogenesis*. McGraw-Hill.

Vince-Prue, D. 1975. *Photoperiodism in Plants*. McGraw-Hill.

Wareing, P. F., and I. D. J. Phillips. 1978. *The Control of Growth and Differentiation in Plants*. 2nd ed. Pergamon Press.

Kingdom Monera: Phyla Schizophyta and Cyanophyta

In this manual, we will use the Whittaker five-kingdom system of classification shown in Fig. 25-1. The kingdom Monera comprises the simplest known organisms and includes all of those that lack true nuclei in their cells: the **procaryotes**. The organisms in the other four kingdoms possess nuclei and therefore are collectively referred to as the **eucaryotes**. The three "higher" kingdoms (Plantae, Fungi, Animalia) have in common the property of being multicellular but differ in their modes of acquiring nutrients. Plants acquire their nutrients by photosynthesis, fungi by absorption, and animals by ingestion. The remaining kingdom, Protista, includes all the lower organisms that do not fit into one of the other four kingdoms. Thus it contains a diverse group of organisms, some of which are less closely related to each other than to certain members of the other four kingdoms. Organisms in the kingdom Monera are unicellular but

sometimes aggregate into filaments or other loose collections of cells. These procaryotes lack mitochondria, plastids, lysosomes, Golgi apparatus, and endoplasmic reticulum. Their mode of nutrition is predominantly by absorption, although some groups are photosynthetic or chemosynthetic. Reproduction is primarily asexual, by budding or fission, but conjugation, a mechanism of sexual reproduction, occurs in some species.

In this exercise, you will study examples of the following phyla:

Phylum Schizophyta (bacteria): unicellular, reproduction usually asexual by cell division, nutrition usually heterotrophic.

Phylum Cyanophyta (blue-green algae): unicellular or colonial, have chlorophyll but no plastids, reproduction by fission, nutrition usually autotropic.

292

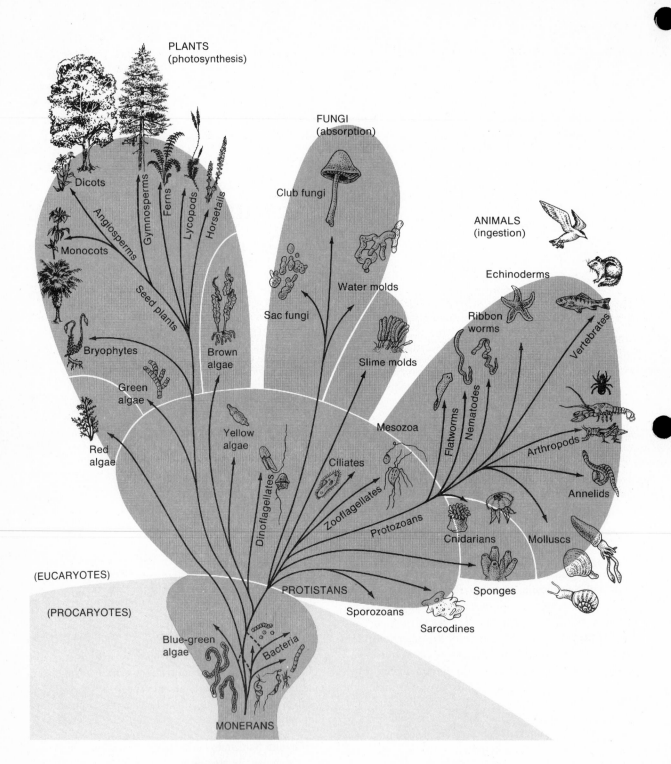

FIG. 25-1
The Whittaker five-kingdom system of classification. (After *Biology Today,* 3rd ed., by David L. Kirk. CRM Books, a division of Random House, Inc. © 1980.)

A. PHYLUM SCHIZOPHYTA (BACTERIA)

Despite their minute size and apparently simple structure, bacteria have become adapted to a wide variety of environments. In fact, they are more widely distributed in nature than any other group or organisms.

Bacteria are especially abundant in the soil. Some species play an important role in the nitrogen cycle—where nitrogen gas in the atmosphere is converted into nitrogenous salts that are used by plants for growth.

Bacteria are also responsible for the decay of organic matter, such as dead plants and animals. During the breakdown of this material, carbon dioxide is released and may then be reused in photosynthesis. Although most bacteria are **heterotrophs**, some are **autotrophs** and can make their own sugars, fats, amino acids, and so forth. One group of bacteria has the ability to obtain energy for their synthetic activities by converting light energy into chemical energy by a process similar to photosynthesis. Photosynthesis in bacteria, however, differs from that in eucaryotic organisms in that water (H_2O) is not used as the reductant for carbon dioxide. Rather, hydrogen sulfide (H_2S) may be used. Thus, in bacterial photosynthesis sulfur is evolved rather than oxygen. They obtain their nitrogen from ammonia or nitrate, and their carbon from carbon dioxide in the air.

A second group of autotrophic bacteria produces its own organic materials from carbon dioxide, ammonia, or nitrate by obtaining the energy for these syntheses from the oxidation of inorganic substances. For example, a bacterium present in the soil is capable of oxidizing ammonia to nitrate, thus generating useful energy. This organism is a typical **chemosynthetic** autotroph. Because these bacteria contain carbohydrates, fats, proteins, nucleic acids, and vitamins, they represent magnificent synthetic factories for making protoplasm.

Other bacteria are widely used in the commercial production of bakery goods, alcohol, vinegar, chemicals, enzymes, antibiotics, and many other products. These microorganisms are also responsible for food spoilage, food poisoning, and for many plant and animal diseases, including tuberculosis, scarlet fever, pneumonia, and diphtheria. Bacteria, therefore, directly or indirectly influence the survival of humanity.

The functional unit of these organisms is a single cell, the smallest of which is barely visible with the light microscope. For many years, bacteria were thought to reproduce asexually by a process called *fission*, during which the cell pinches in two. It is now known that bacterial cells also exchange genetic material through sexual reproduction. Although sexual mechanisms have been found in only a few species, future research in this area may reveal that sexual reproduction is actually widespread among bacteria.

1. Bacterial Identification

Bacterial cells generally assume three basic shapes: rods (**bacilli**), minute spheres (**cocci**), and corkscrews (**spirilla**). The cells of many species tend to adhere to each other and form relatively simple colonies. However, each cell in the colony still functions as an independent unit and maintains the ability to carry out all of the processes necessary for survival.

In this exercise, you will examine some bacteria and stain them to identify the three cell types just listed.

1. Using the wide end of a clean toothpick that has been dipped in alcohol, scrape your teeth near the gums. Spread the scrapings in a thin film on a clean glass slide (Fig. 25-2A and B).

2. Allow the smear to dry, then heat it gently by quickly passing the slide back and forth several times over the flame of an alcohol lamp or Bunsen burner (Fig. 25-2C). Support the slide over a beaker or other small dish, and apply several drops of crystal violet—a dye that stains bacteria (Fig. 25-2D).

3. Leave the dye on the smear for 1 minute. Wash off the dye under a gentle stream of tap water or water squirted from an eyedropper (Fig. 25-2E). Using a paper towel, wipe off any dye that may be sticking to the bottom of the slide. Blot the excess water from the upper surface, avoiding only the smear (Fig. 25-2F).

4. Place a drop of water on the stained smear, add a cover slip and examine your slide with the high power of your microscope.

In Fig. 25-3 draw the different types of bacteria you observed. Which bacterial type is most common?

2. Control of Bacterial Growth

The control of bacterial infections is a major medical problem. The use of antibiotics is an effective method of controlling infectious bacteria and other disease-causing organisms. The story of antibiotics began in 1929 when the British biologist Alexander Fleming found that a petri dish containing a bacterial culture had become contaminated by a mold called *Penicillium*. Noticing that the growth of the bacteria around the mold colony was inhibited, he concluded that the mold produced a diffusable chemical agent capable of inhibiting bacterial growth. Fleming later isolated this antibacterial chemical, calling it *penicillin*. Such chemicals, which are produced by living organisms and have the ability to retard the growth of certain other organisms, are called **antibiotics**. Among the wide variety of such antibiotics are streptomycin,

294

A. Using a clean tooth-pick, scrape the teeth near the gums.

B. Spread the scrapings, using a circular motion, on a clean slide.

C. Allow the smear to dry and then quickly pass the slide through a flame several times to "fix" the bacteria to the slide.

D. Support the slide over a beaker, and cover the smear with several drops of crystal violet, a dye that stains bacteria.

E. Leave the dye on the smear for 1/2 minute; then rinse it off with water.

Paper toweling

F. Blot, do not wipe, excess water, add water and cover slip, and examine the slide with a microscope.

FIG. 25-2
Procedure for staining bacteria.

FIG. 25-3
Types of bacteria.

chloromycin, and terramycin. The use of such antibiotics has significantly lowered the occurrence of a number of infections.

In this part of the exercise, you will examine the effect of different antibiotics on the growth of one of the more common bacteria.

1. Obtain a petri dish containing nutrient agar—a mixture of chemicals that is optimal for the growth of the bacterium you are to study. Divide each plate into four sections labeled "1," "2," "3," and "Control" by marking the bottom of the dish with black pencil (Fig. 25-4A).

2. Lift the cover of the petri dish slightly, and add 10 drops of the bacterial suspension (provided by your instructor) to the plate (Fig. 25-4B, C). Holding the plate at eye level, tilt the plate, allowing the suspension to run to the far edge (Fig. 25-4D). Then, holding the plate level, jerk it toward you. Repeat this several more times, rotating the plate partway between each jerk (Fig. 25-4E). In this way, the bacterial suspension will cover the entire surface of the agar.

3. Incubate the plate for 24 hours at 37°C (or 48 hours at room temperature) before proceeding with the next step. After incubation, partially lift the cover. Then, using flamed forceps place three antibiotic discs in the numbered sections of the plate (Fig. 25-4G). Use a different antibiotic in each section.

What should be placed in the control section of the plate?

_____

Incubate the plate. Examine daily for the next 3 or 4 days. Record the effects of the antibiotics in Fig. 25-5. Why might incubation for a period of time be desirable before adding the antibiotic discs?

_____

_____

_____

_____

Some bacteria have an enzyme called *penicillinase*. Would the growth of such bacteria be inhibited by penicillin? Explain.

_____

_____

_____

_____

_____

3. Bacteria in Milk

Milk is an excellent medium for the growth of bacteria. Therefore, great care must be used in its processing.

296

A. Mark the bottom of the dish with black marking pencil.

B. Shake bacterial suspension.

C. Add 10 drops of bacterial suspension to the surface of agar.

D. Holding the plate at eye level, tilt the plate, allowing the suspension to run to the edge.

E. Holding the plate level, jerk several times while rotating plate.

F. Incubate plate for 24 hours at 37° C or for 48 hours at room temperature.

G. Add a different antibiotic disc to sections 1, 2, and 3. What will you place in the "control"?

H. Incubate at 37° C or room temperature. Examine daily for the next 3–4 days.

FIG. 25-4
Procedure for determining effect of antibiotics on bacterial growth.

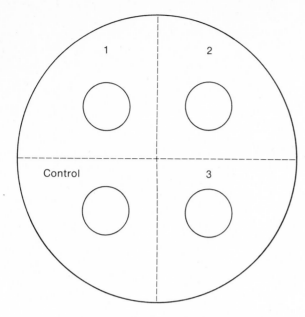

FIG. 25-5
Effect of antibiotics on bacterial growth.

A. Fill the test tubes ⅓ full with different samples of milk of various ages or from different sources. Label each tube for its contents.

B. Add 1 ml (20 drops) of methylene blue solution to each tube. Mix by shaking.

C. Plug the tubes with cotton and incubate (or place them in a hot water bath) at 37°C.

D. Examine each tube periodically. Rate the quality of the milk according to its bacterial population as described in the procedure.

FIG. 25-6
Procedure for estimating bacterial contamination of milk.

Harmful bacteria in milk are killed by the process of **pasteurization**. In this exercise, you will examine milk from different sources and determine the quality of the milk in terms of its bacterial population.

1. Bring to class three to four samples of milk of varying age or from different sources (fresh milk from a dairy farm, milk in an unopened carton or bottle, milk in a carton or bottle that has been opened and in the refrigerator for one to three or more days, powdered milk, canned milk, etc.).

2. Fill separate test tubes one-third full with each of these milk samples (Fig. 25-6A). Label each tube, and then add 1 ml (20 drops) of methylene blue solution (Fig. 25-6B). Mix by shaking.

3. Plug each tube with sterile cotton, and incubate or place the tubes into a water bath at 37°C (Fig. 25-6C). Record the time in Table 25-1.

When bacteria are actively growing in milk, they consume oxygen. The reduction of oxygen can be detected by using methylene blue, which becomes colorless as the oxygen content of the milk diminishes. If the number of bacteria present is high, the methylene blue-milk mixture will rapidly lose its color. If the bacterial population is low, more time will be required for decolorization.

For the purposes of this study, the quality of the milk with respect to the number of bacteria present can be rated by the time it takes to decolorize the methylene blue solution. Periodically examine the milk samples. In Table 25-1, record the time it takes to decolorize each sample. Rate each sample according to the description given in

TABLE 25-1
Rating of milk samples of different ages or different sources.

Contents of tube	Time methylene blue added	Length of time to decolorize methylene blue	Rating
1			
2			
3			
4			

TABLE 25-2
Decolorization times.

Time to decolorize methylene blue	Rating
Less than 20 minutes	Highly contaminated
20 minutes to 2 hours	Poor
2–5½ hours	Fair
5½–8 hours	Good
More than 8 hours	Excellent

Table 25-2. Which sample rated the highest in bacterial contamination?

_____

Which rated the lowest?

_____

From your results, what appears to lead to the contamination of milk?

_____

What appears to reduce contamination?

_____

B. PHYLUM CYANOPHYTA (BLUE-GREEN ALGAE)

The group of organisms known as cyanophyta (blue-green algae) exhibits two types of plant body structure—unicellular and colonial. The unicellular condition is considered to be more primitive. In addition, blue-green algae, although considered to be procaryotic organisms on the basis of their cellular structure, use water in photosynthesis as the reducing agent for CO_2 and therefore evolve oxygen as a by-product of photosynthesis. In this respect, they are biochemically similar to photosynthetic eucaryotic organisms. In this study, you will examine blue-green algae to become familiar with their morphology, cytology, and range of complexity.

1. Unicellular Forms

Prepare a wet mount of *Chroococcus* and *Gloeocapsa*. To see the characteristic gelatinous sheath that surrounds the cells of blue-green algae, add a drop of India ink to the slide. The sheath will stand out against the dark background. Where several cells are clustered together, do they share a common sheath?

_____

Although these are unicellular forms, they frequently form small clusters of cells. Would you consider these clusters as representing multicellular organisms? Explain.

_____

_____

_____

2. Colonial Forms

In colonial forms, the shape of the colony is largely determined by the plane of cell division and may result in filaments, plates, or spheres. Examine the following algae and classify each as to body form (e.g., filamentous) and plane of cell division (single, double, or irregular) that resulted in the form of the colony.

1. *Merismopedia:* Locate the gelatinous sheath. Frequently cells within the colony may be seen in cytokinesis.

2. *Oscillatoria:* What evidence is there of cellular differentiation within this colony?

_____

_____

Describe any motility you observe.

_____

_____

How does this organism reproduce?

_____

_____

_____

3. *Rivularia:* How does this alga differ from *Oscillatoria?*

_____

_____

_____

Locate the heterocyst. What is its function?

_____

_____

4. *Gloeotrichia:* How does this alga differ from *Rivularia?*

_____

_____

_____

5. *Anabaena:* Crush the cells of the water fern *Azolla* to release this alga. What function might this alga carry out in the cells of *Azolla?*

_____

_____

_____

C. BLUE-GREEN ALGAE IN WATER SUPPLIES

The increasing human population and rapid development of industry and agriculture has resulted in a phenomenal increase in the use of water. This need for water has produced many difficult problems in procuring an adequate and suitable water supply.

As population and industrial demands increase, villages and cities are turning from groundwater sources to surface waters, such as lakes, streams, and reservoirs, for their water supplies. Ground waters are essentially free from contaminating organisms. Surface waters, on the other hand, contain many organisms that in one way or another contribute to the unpalatability of the water supply. Such organisms affect the odor and taste of water, clog filters, grow in pipes, cooling towers, or on reservoir walls, form mats or blooms on the surface of the water, produce toxic materials, and so forth. Furthermore, the present methods of waste disposal are intensifying the problems of such nuisance organisms in water. Materials such as sewage and organic wastes from paper mills, fish-processing factories, slaughterhouses, and milk plants, to name a few, greatly increase the growth of algae and other organisms. Many of these cause problems when they become abundant.

Blue-green algae are among the common nuisance inhabitants of surface waters. Collect surface water samples from different sources—for example, lakes, streams, reservoirs (including the walls), swimming pool filters, or water treatment plants. Table 25-3 characterizes some of the more common problems associated with an over-

Anabaena circinalis   Anabaena constricta   Anabaena planctonica   Anabaena flos-aquae

Anacystis cyanea

Anacystis dimidiata

Anacystis montana

Aphanizomenon flos-aquae

Cylindrospermum muscicola   Arthrospira jenneri   Calothrix braunii

FIG. 25-7
Blue-green algae that contaminate water supplies.

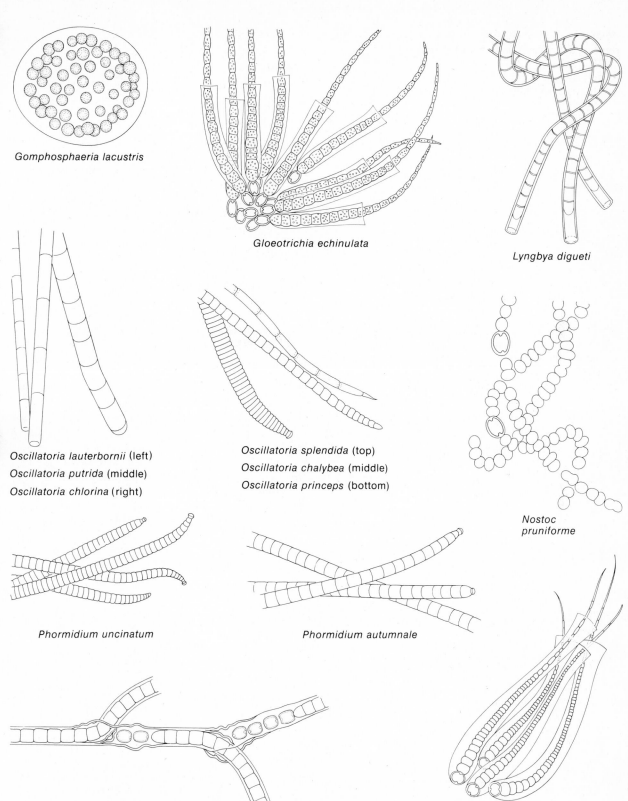

Gomphosphaeria lacustris

Gloeotrichia echinulata

Lyngbya digueti

Oscillatoria lauterbornii (left)
Oscillatoria putrida (middle)
Oscillatoria chlorina (right)

Oscillatoria splendida (top)
Oscillatoria chalybea (middle)
Oscillatoria princeps (bottom)

Nostoc pruniforme

Phormidium uncinatum

Phormidium autumnale

Tolypothrix tenuis

Rivularia dura

abundance of blue-green algae. Use Fig. 25-7 to identify some of the algae in your water samples.

TABLE 25-3
Problems caused by blue-green algae in water supplies.

Problem	Organism
Taste and odor	Anabaena circinalis Anacystis cyanea Aphanizomenon flos-aque Cylindrospermum muscicola Gomphosphaeria lacustris
Filter clogging	Anabaena flos-aque Anacystis dimidiata Gloeotrichia eschinulata Oscillatoria princeps Oscillatoria chalybea Oscillatoria splendida Rivularia duro
Reservoir wall growth	Calothrix braunii Nostoc pruniforme Phormidium uncinatum Tolypothrix tenuis
Polluted water	Anabaena constricta Anacystis montana Arthrospira jenneri Lyngbya digireti Oscillatoria chlorina Oscillatoria putrida Oscillatoria lauterbornii Phormidium autumnale

REFERENCES

Bold, H. C. 1977. *The Plant Kingdom.* 4th ed. Prentice-Hall.

Brock, T. 1979. *Biology of Microorganisms.* 3rd ed. Prentice-Hall.

Cairns, J. 1966. The Bacterial Chromosome. *Scientific American* 214(1):36–44 (Offprint 1030). *Scientific American Offprints* are available from W. H. Freeman and Company, 660 Market Street, San Francisco 94104, and 58 Kings Road, Reading RG1 3AA, England. Please order by number.

Davis, B. D., R. Dulbecco, H. N. Eisen, H. S. Ginsburg, and W. B. Wood, Jr. 1968. *Principles of Microbiology and Immunology.* Harper & Row.

Delevoryas, T. 1977. *Plant Classification.* 2nd ed. Holt, Rinehart and Winston.

Palmer, C. M. 1959. *Algae in Water Supplies.* U.S. Public Health Service Publication No. 657.

Pringsheim, E. G. 1949. *Pure Cultures of Algae: Their Preparation and Maintenance.* Cambridge University Press.

Sharon, N. 1969. The Bacterial Cell Wall. *Scientific American* 220(5):92–98 (Offprint 1142).

Smith, G. M. 1950. *The Freshwater Algae of the United States.* 2nd ed. McGraw-Hill.

Stanier, R. Y., E. A. Adelberg, and J. L. Ingraham. 1976. *The Microbial World.* 4th ed. Prentice-Hall.

Volk, W. A., and M. F. Wheeler. 1980. *Basic Morphology.* 4th ed. Lippincott.

Walsby, A. E. 1977. The Gas Vacuoles of Blue-Green Algae. *Scientific American* 237(2):90–97 (Offprint 1367).

Whitaker, R. H. 1969. New Concepts of Kingdoms of Organisms. *Science* 163:150–160.

Wollman, E. L., and F. Jacob. 1956. Sexuality in Bacteria. *Scientific American* 195(1):109–118 (Offprint 50).

Kingdom Protista: Phyla Euglenophyta, Flagellata, Ciliata, Sarcodina, Sporozoa, and Gymnomycota

In this exercise, representatives of the kingdom Protista will be studied in terms of their structure and reproduction.

The characteristic feature of protists is that they are typically unicellular, although some members form simple colonies of similar cells. It is of interest that, although protists are frequently called "simple," "lowly," or "primitive," they possess a tremendous degree of specialization at the cellular level. This has resulted in their having become adapted to a wide range of highly diverse habitats. These organisms are found in brackish, fresh, and marine waters and exhibit a variety of symbiotic and parasitic relationships.

This kingdom is divided into a number of phyla, but only the following six will be studied in this exercise:

Phylum Euglenophyta: plantlike, autotrophic organisms

Phylum Flagellata (Mastigophora): unicellular, mostly heterotrophic organisms that move by means of long, whiplike flagellae

Phylum Ciliata (Ciliophora): unicellular, heterotrophic organisms that move by cilia, typically having macro- and micronuclei and unique reproductive patterns

Phylum Sarcodina: heterotrophic organisms that lack cilia or flagella and move by irregular cytoplasmic extensions, called *pseudopodia*

Phylum Sporozoa: parasitic organisms that live for a part of their life cycle in cells of other organisms, most having very complex reproductive cycles

Phylum Gymnomycota: the slime molds, heterotrophic amoeboid organisms that mostly lack a cell wall but form sporangia at some stage in their life cycles

A. PHYLUM EUGLENOPHYTA

The euglenoids seem to be protists that, in the long course of evolution, have acquired chloroplasts similar in biochemical properties to those of the green algae. The phy-

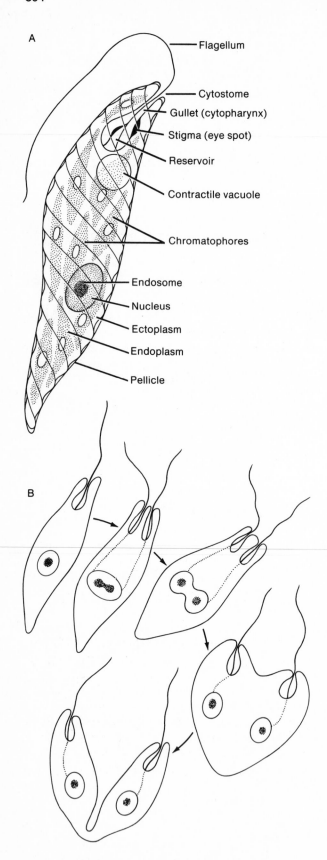

A

— Flagellum

— Cytostome

— Gullet (cytopharynx)

— Stigma (eye spot)

— Reservoir

— Contractile vacuole

— Chromatophores

— Endosome

— Nucleus

— Ectoplasm

— Endoplasm

— Pellicle

B

FIG. 26-1
Morphology (A) and reproduction (B) in *Euglena*.

lum takes its name from *Euglena*, a photosynthetic auto-troph.

1. Euglena

a. Morphology and Reproduction

Euglena is a green, unicellular organism commonly found in the surface scum of standing or very slowly moving waters.

Place a drop of culture of living *Euglena* on a slide. Add a drop of 10% methyl cellulose, which will slow down the rapid movement of the organism. Add a cover slip and examine microscopically. Observe the method of locomotion of an actively moving specimen. The motility of the organism is due to the movement of a long **flagellum**, which pulls the organism through the water. Does the beating of the flagellum move from the base toward the tip, or in the opposite direction?

_____

_____

Euglena also exhibits a wormlike movement in which a series of contractions pass along the body. This type of movement is peculiar to *Euglena* and consequently has been termed **euglenoid movement**.

With the help of Fig. 26-1A, locate the following morphological features of *Euglena*. You may find it useful to supplement your observations by studying a commercially prepared slide of this organism. Using high power, identify the **pellicle**, a thin, elastic membrane that may be striated because of spiral thickenings; the **ectoplasm**, the peripherally located cytoplasm; the **endoplasm**, the denser, internal cytoplasm; the **chromatophores (chloroplasts)**, organelles containing the green pigment chlorophyll; and the **nucleus**, which is centrally located. More readily seen in prepared slides is a dense staining body in the nucleus, called the **endosome**, and the **cytostome** (cell "mouth"), a funnel-shaped depression near the anterior end that leads to the **cytopharynx** (cell "gullet"), which is enlarged at the base to form the **reservoir**. *Euglena* does not ingest solid food. However, adjacent to the reservoir is a **water-expulsion vesicle** (contractile vacuole) that periodically collects excess cell water and discharges it into the reservoir and then out through the cytopharynx. The **stigma**, a reddish orange eye spot located near the anterior end of the animal and adjacent to the cytopharynx, is a light-sensitive organelle. What function might it serve?

When you have finished making your observations of the living organism, add a drop of Lugol's iodine solution to the edge of the cover slip and let it be drawn under by capillary action. The iodine will kill *Euglena* but will also stain the flagellum so that it is more easily seen.

Nutrition of *Euglena* is normally **autotrophic** (Greek *autos,* "self"; *trophe,* "nourishment"); that is, the organism is able to synthesize its organic needs using inorganic molecules from its surroundings and sunlight in a process called **photosynthesis**. Some species of *Euglena*, however, even in the absence of any visible chloroplasts or chlorophyll, are able to grow and reproduce. They exhibit **heterotrophic** (Greek *heteros,* "other"; *trophe,* "nourishment") nutrition. Suggest ways in which these organisms obtain their food requirements.

Reproduction in *Euglena* is by **binary fission** (Fig. 26-1B). The nucleus first divides by mitotic division. Then the anterior organelles (e.g., reservoir, flagella, and stigma) are duplicated. This is followed by a longitudinal splitting of the animal beginning at the anterior end. If available, examine demonstration slides showing this type of reproduction.

Wood particles

A. *Trichonympha*

B. *Trypanosoma*

FIG. 26-2
Other flagellates: (A) *Trichonympha* and (B) *Trypanosoma*.

B. PHYLUM FLAGELLATA (MASTIGOPHORA)

The members of this group move by means of long whip-like **flagellae**. A few of the flagellates exist as free-living organisms in fresh or salt waters. However, most live as symbionts in the bodies of higher plants or animals. The genus *Trypanosoma* lives as a parasite in the blood of humans or domestic animals.

1. Trichonympha

Trichonympha is a flagellate that inhabits the intestine of wood-eating termites. Although termites ingest bits of

wood, they are unable to digest cellulose, the chief constituent of wood. *Trichonympha* forms pseudopodia that engulf the wood fragments ingested by the termite, digesting the cellulose and transforming it into soluble carbohydrates that can then be used by the termite (Fig. 26-2A). Neither the termite nor *Trichonympha* can live without the other. Examine slides of this organism. Note the large number of flagella that cover the upper part of the organism and the small fragments of wood in the cytoplasm.

2. Trypanosoma

Trypanosoma (Fig. 26-2B) is a slender flagellate that inhabits the blood of vertebrates and is carried from one

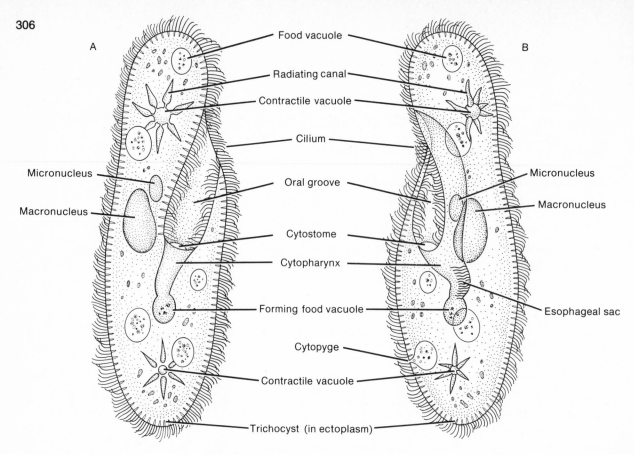

FIG. 26-3
Paramecium: (A) ventral view and (B) lateral view.

host to another by bloodsucking invertebrates. The trypanosomes that cause human sleeping sickness in Africa are transmitted by the bloodsucking tsetse fly. Examine stained slides of human blood showing these parasitic flagellates.

C. PHYLUM CILIATA (CILIOPHORA)

The ciliates, compared with other protists, are relatively large and complex. They are distinguished from other protists by having **cilia**, two types of nuclei (**micro**, small; and **macro**, large), and a unique type of reproduction. Most of the ciliates are free-living (nonparasites) and are commonly found in fresh and salt waters. A few are parasitic in human beings. These organisms also play an important role in the aquatic food chain, serving as food for small multicellular animals, which, in turn, are eaten by larger animal forms.

1. Paramecium Caudatum

a. Morphology

Paramecium caudatum, one of several species of paramecia, is often selected as a typical ciliate to study because it is easy to obtain and, owing to its size, is easy

to observe. In nature, this ciliate is frequently found in pond water that contains large amounts of decaying vegetation. Because it can be easily grown in large numbers under controlled laboratory conditions, it is used extensively in studies of nutrition, cancer, behavior, genetics, and ecology.

Place a small drop of *Paramecium* culture on a clean slide. Then add a small drop of methyl cellulose to slow down the movements of this ciliate. Add a cover slip and examine microscopically using the low-power objective. You may have to adjust the iris diaphragm to increase contrast.

Paramecium caudatum somewhat resembles a twisted slipper. With the aid of Fig. 26-3 and commercially prepared slides, locate the following structures on the living organism.

The **oral groove** begins at the anterior end, runs diagonally toward the posterior end, and leads to the **cytostome** (cell mouth) and then to the **cytopharynx**. Food is carried into the oral groove by beating **cilia**, which may be seen by using the high-power objective and reducing the illumination.

A **contractile vacuole** is located at each end of the organism. Do these vacuoles move or are they stationary?

Do they contract at the same time, or alternately?

_____

Locate the canals that radiate outward from each vacuole. Suggest a function for these structures.

_____

_____

_____

What is the function of contractile vacuoles?

_____

_____

_____

The **macronucleus** can be seen as a relatively large, clear area in the central part of the cell (**endoplasm**). A **micronucleus** is located adjacent to the macronucleus. Because these nuclei are difficult to observe in living material, add a drop of acetocarmine or methyl green stain to one side of the cover slip, and draw it under by applying a piece of paper toweling to the other side. (Supplement these observations using commercially prepared slides of *Paramecium* specifically stained to show the nuclei.) The macronucleus is associated with vegetative functions (i.e., feeding and digestion), whereas that of the micronucleus is reproductive.

Trichocysts are located in the peripheral layer of cytoplasm (**ectoplasm**). They are carrot-shaped structures, in some cases containing coiled, barbed threads. The function of trichocysts in *Paramecium* is not known; however, in other animals that have them, they serve to capture and hold smaller organisms that the animals feed on.

Add a small drop of iodine or acetic acid at the edge of the cover slip. Allow it to run underneath and observe the discharge of the trichocysts.

b. Nutrition and Feeding

The majority of protists, including *Paramecium*, are **holozoic**; that is, they ingest solid food such as other protists, bacteria, or organic **detritus** (decaying material) from the environment. These food particles must be digested before they can be used for growth, repair, or reproduction.

Place a drop of *Paramecium* culture on a slide and add a *small* drop of congo red-stained yeast (*Note: The result-

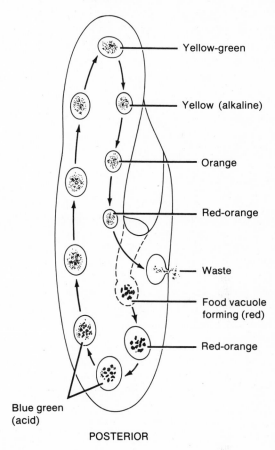

ANTERIOR

- Yellow-green
- Yellow (alkaline)
- Orange
- Red-orange
- Waste
- Food vacuole forming (red)
- Red-orange

Blue green (acid)

POSTERIOR

FIG. 26-4
Digestion in *Paramecium*. Arrows indicate pathway of food vacuoles.

ing color should be pink, not red.) Add a cover slip, and locate a *Paramecium* under high magnification. Observe the vortex of water produced by the cilia in the vicinity of the oral groove. This carries the yeast into the oral groove and then to the mouth and cytopharynx. The cytopharynx leads to an **esophageal sac** where the food vacuole is then formed. A food vacuole is a membrane-bound sac containing water and suspended food particles. As soon as one is formed, it is carried away by a rotary movement of the cytoplasm (cyclosis) and the formation of another vacuole begins. Food vacuoles travel in a defined route through the organism (Fig. 26-4). They first pass posteriorly, then forward, and finally in a posterior direction to the region of the oral groove where the undigestible contents are eliminated through the **anal pore**.

Locate a food vacuole. You should note that, when first formed, the vacuole is bright red-orange. Closely observe the vacuole as it moves through the animal. You will see that its contents changes color in the course of digestion from red-orange to blue-green to yellow and finally back to red-orange (Fig. 26-4). The reason for this is that congo red is an indicator dye that changes color with pH: it is blue-green under acidic conditions and red-orange under alkaline conditions. What does this indicate about the content of the food vacuoles?

_____

_____

_____

_____

What similarity is there between the acidity and alkalinity of the food vacuoles as they pass through this animal and that of the mouth, stomach, and intestines in human beings?

_____

_____

_____

_____

FIG. 26-5
Asexual reproduction (binary fission) in *Paramecium*.

c. Reproduction

Asexual Reproduction

Binary fission is the most common type of reproduction in protists. In this kind of asexual reproduction, the cell divides into two roughly equal parts, giving rise to daughter cells that are genetically identical. In sarcodines, there is no specific plane of division; in flagellates, the plane of division is longitudinal; and in ciliates, the cell divides transversely.

Examine demonstration slides of *Paramecium* showing the various stages in binary fission (Fig. 26-5).

Sexual Reproduction

Ordinarily, paramecia divide by binary fission. Occasionally, however, these organisms reproduce sexually by a process called **conjugation** in which micronuclei are exchanged. The process of conjugation is diagrammed in Fig. 26-6. Conjugation in living *Paramecium* can be observed by following the directions outlined below. For this study, mating strains of *Paramecium bursaria*, which is symbiotic with a green alga, will be used. You should supplement your observations by examining commercially prepared slides showing conjugation.

1. Into a depression or deep-well slide, add a *small* drop of one of the two mating strains.

2. While examining the slide with a dissecting microscope, add a drop of the *second* mating strain.

3. You should see, almost immediately, the **agglutination** (or clumping) of opposite mating strains, which brings the cells together for the subsequent transfer of nuclear material.

4. Place the slide in a covered petri dish containing moist filter paper to prevent dessication of the culture.

5. Examine periodically. Conjugating paramecia may be seen up to 48 hours, after which few or no conjugants will be found.

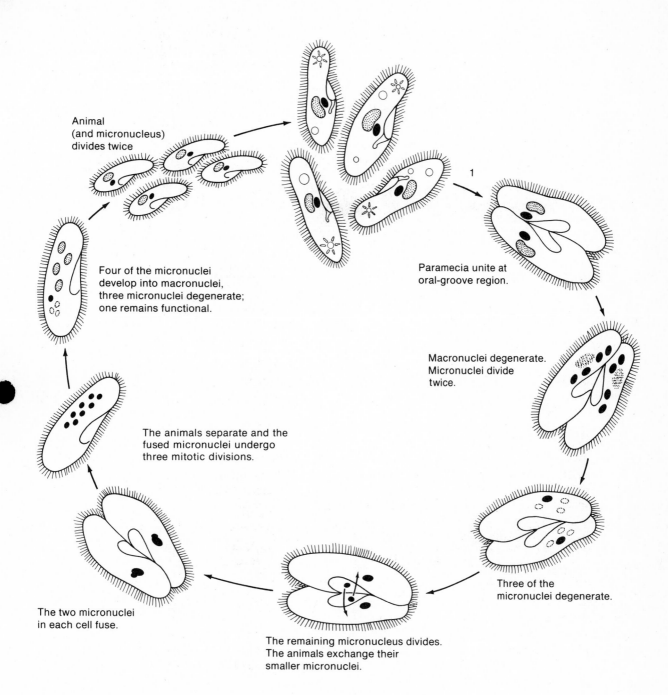

Animal
(and micronucleus)
divides twice

Four of the micronuclei
develop into macronuclei,
three micronuclei degenerate;
one remains functional.

1

Paramecia unite at
oral-groove region.

Macronuclei degenerate.
Micronuclei divide
twice.

The animals separate and the
fused micronuclei undergo
three mitotic divisions.

Three of the
micronuclei degenerate.

The two micronuclei
in each cell fuse.

The remaining micronucleus divides.
The animals exchange their
smaller micronuclei.

FIG. 26-6
Sexual reproduction (conjugation) in *Paramecium*.

310

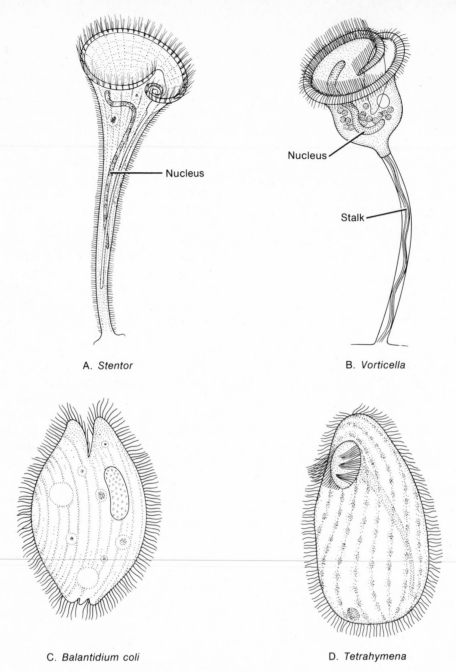

A. *Stentor*

Nucleus

B. *Vorticella*

Nucleus

Stalk

C. *Balantidium coli*

D. *Tetrahymena*

FIG. 26-7
Other ciliates.

2. Other Ciliata

Obtain samples of the following ciliates and examine microscopically.

a. Stentor

This organism is characteristically trumpet-shaped, blue in color if alive, and has a macronucleus in the shape of a string of beads (Fig. 26-7A). Food is brought into the organism through activity of cilia that surround the mouth.

b. Vorticella

This freshwater ciliate somewhat resembles an inverted bell attached to a stalk that anchors it to submerged vegetation and stones (Fig. 26-7B). Locate an organism in which the stalk is straight and extended. While watching the animal, gently tap the slide and describe what occurs.

_____

_____

c. Balantidium coli

This ciliate (Fig. 26-7C) is the only ciliate parasite found in human beings. It is found in the intestinal tract where it frequently burrows into the wall of the colon and causes ulcers. It is **pathogenic** (disease producing) and may cause symptoms similar to amoebic dysentery. The most common source of infection is the pig.

d. Tetrahymena

This small ciliate (Fig. 26-7D), which is relatively easy to grow in pure culture, has been widely used in physiological and genetic research.

D. PHYLUM SARCODINA

1. Amoeba

Amoebas (Greek *amoibe,* "change") are protists that are common in freshwater ponds and streams. Under the microscope, they look like gray, irregular masses that are continually changing shape owing to the extension and withdrawal of fingerlike protuberances called **pseudopodia** (Fig. 26-8).

Using a clean dropper pipet, obtain a sample of amoebas from the bottom of the culture dish. Place a few drops of the culture in a depression slide (alternatively, place a few drops on a clean glass slide, and add a few pieces of debris from the culture and a few grains of sand or some small pieces of broken cover slips to prevent the organism from being crushed when you place a clean cover slip over the preparation). Study your preparation under low power (10×). You will have to reduce the amount of light by closing the iris diaphragm, because the amoebas are nearly transparent and thus almost invisible under bright light. With the help of Fig. 26-8 and commercially prepared slides, locate the following: the **pseudopodia**; the **endoplasm**, the inner granular material that makes up most of the cytoplasm; the **ectoplasm**, a thin layer of cytoplasm surrounding the endoplasm; the **cell membrane (plasmalemma)**; the **plasmagel**, the gel-like outer layer of the endoplasm; the **plasmasol**, the fluid, central region of the endoplasm (streaming of the cytoplasm should be evident in this area); the **nucleus**, a somewhat transparent structure that is not fixed in position and sometimes has a wrinkled or folded appearance; and the **contractile vacuoles**, clear spherical vacuoles found in the endoplasm that collect water from the cell and discharge it to the outside. These vacuoles function to maintain water balance in the cell. Would you expect a marine (saltwater) form of amoeba to have contractile vacuoles? Explain.

FIG. 26-8
Amoeba.

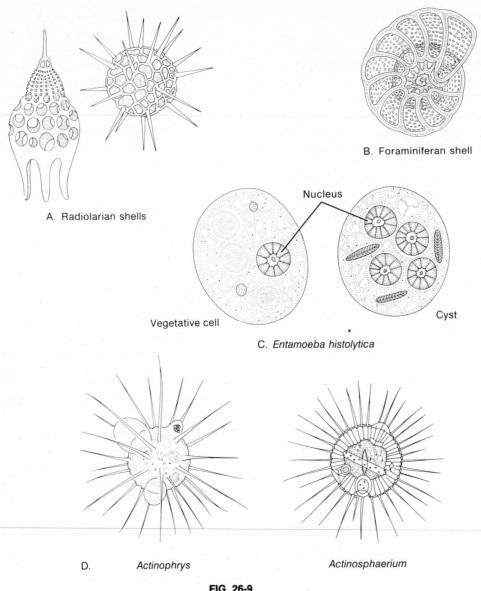

A. Radiolarian shells

B. Foraminiferan shell

Nucleus

Vegetative cell

Cyst

C. *Entamoeba histolytica*

D.   *Actinophrys*   *Actinosphaerium*

FIG. 26-9
Other Sarcodina.

Food vacuoles contain ingested food and enzymes for digestion. How are food vacuoles formed?

_____

_____

_____

_____

How are the products of digestion made available to the cell?

_____

_____

_____

Reproduction in *Amoeba* is by binary fission in which the cytoplasm and nucleus divide to form two genetically identical daughter amoebas.

2. Other Sarcodina

Radiolarians (Fig. 26-9A) are amoebas that have silicious skeletons secreted by the cytoplasm, usually taking the form of an intricate latticework, through which extend stiff radiating spines. Examine prepared slides of radiolarian skeletons.

Foraminiferans (Fig. 26-9B) are a large group of marine amoebas that secrete slimy, snaillike shells about themselves. Long, delicate feeding pseudopodia stream out of minute pores that perforate the surface of the shells. Examine prepared slides showing a variety of these foraminiferan shells.

Entamoeba histolytica (Fig. 26-9C) is the causative organism of amoebic dysentery. Examine prepared slides showing both the active (vegetative) stages and the cysts (resistant, infective stages of the organism). In its vegetative stage, the organism has a single nucleus; the cysts have four nuclei, as well as a heavy wall surrounding the entire cell.

Actinosphaerium and *Actinophrys* (Fig. 26-9D) are members of a group of spherical amoebas that have delicate pseudopodia that are supported by axial rods. Most species of this group live in fresh waters. Examine slides of *Actinosphaerium*. Note in particular the delicate pseudopodia, which have suggested the name "sun animalcules" for these organisms.

E. PHYLUM SPOROZOA

All members of this phylum are parasites and can be found infecting nearly all the major groups of the animal kingdom, ranging from simple invertebrates to human beings. In this exercise, you will become familiar with *Plasmodium vivax,* a sporozoan that causes one form of malaria in human beings.

Malaria is probably one of the most devastating diseases of humankind with respect to sickness, mortality (death), and economic loss. Although partly under control, it is not yet eliminated and indeed seems to be increasing in incidence once again.

There are four kinds of malaria. One, **benign tertian malaria**, caused by *Plasmodium vivax,* is characterized by attacks of fever every 48 hours. **Quartan malaria**, which usually produces fever every 72 hours, is caused by *Plasmodium malariae. Plasmodium ovale* causes fever every 48 hours. **Pernicious malaria**, in which the fever is virtually continuous, is produced by *Plasmodium falciparum;* this form has the highest mortality rate.

Because all four kinds have fairly similar life cycles, *Plasmodium vivax* will be the representative sporozoan studied in this exercise, with reference to Fig. 26-10 and commercially prepared slides of the life cycle.

Malaria is transmitted through the bite of female mosquitoes; male mosquitoes cannot infect because they lack the mouth parts for piercing the skin and sucking blood. Many animals can be infected with malaria that is transmitted by a variety of different mosquitoes; however, the malarial parasite is transmitted to human beings only by mosquitoes of the genus *Anopheles.*

When the mosquito's mouth parts enter the skin, saliva, containing anticoagulants, enters the wound. If the mosquito is a carrier, **sporozoites**, the form of the parasite in its infective stage, enter the bloodstream (Fig. 26-10A), but do not invade the erythrocytes. Instead, they first penetrate certain cells of the liver, where they grow and multiply. On release from the liver cells, the parasites enter the bloodstream and penetrate the erythrocytes, where they first become ring-shaped and then irregular in shape. At this stage, the parasite is called a **trophozoite** (Fig. 26-10B). The trophozoite undergoes maturation (the time required depending on the species) and then divides, by a type of fission called **schizogony**, to form another stage, called a **merozoite** (Fig. 26-10C). These merozoites are released from the red blood cells, where they reproduce asexually to form more merozoites. At regular intervals, depending on the species of *Plasmodium,* all infected red blood cells burst, releasing merozoites. Toxic substances that are released along with the merozoites account for the chills and fever that are typical of malarial attacks. Each merozoite in turn penetrates another erythrocyte and becomes a trophozoite. This cycle is repeated a number of times, with ever-increasing numbers of erythrocytes being affected.

Eventually, some merozoites, instead of becoming trophozoites, develop into **gametocytes** (Fig. 26-10C). As long as the gametocytes remain in the human host, they are of no significance. However, if they are sucked up by an *Anopheles* mosquito, they will pass into the insect stomach and become active (Fig. 26-10C). One female gametocyte develops into one egg; one male gametocyte gives rise to several sperm by a process termed *exflagellation.* Union of the egg and sperm produces a zygote called an **ookinete**, which migrates through the stomach epithelium and becomes embedded in the wall of the stomach. The nucleus undergoes successive mitotic divisions and produces large numbers of sporozoites within a structure now called an **oocyst**. When the oocyst ruptures, the sporozoites enter the body cavity of the mosquito and then migrate to the salivary glands. The next time a mosquito bites a host, sporozoites are injected into the human body and the life cycle is repeated.

F. PHYLUM GYMNOMYCOTA

Slime molds are divided into two groups based on the form of the feeding phase. The vegetative phase of the *cellular slime molds* consists of masses of single amoeboid cells. The acellular, or *plasmodial slime molds,* have a vegetative phase consisting of naked masses of protoplasm (**plasmodia**) of indefinite size and shape. Both types live predominantly on decaying plant material, primarily microorganisms (especially bacteria). In this part of the exercise, you will study the plasmodial slime molds

314

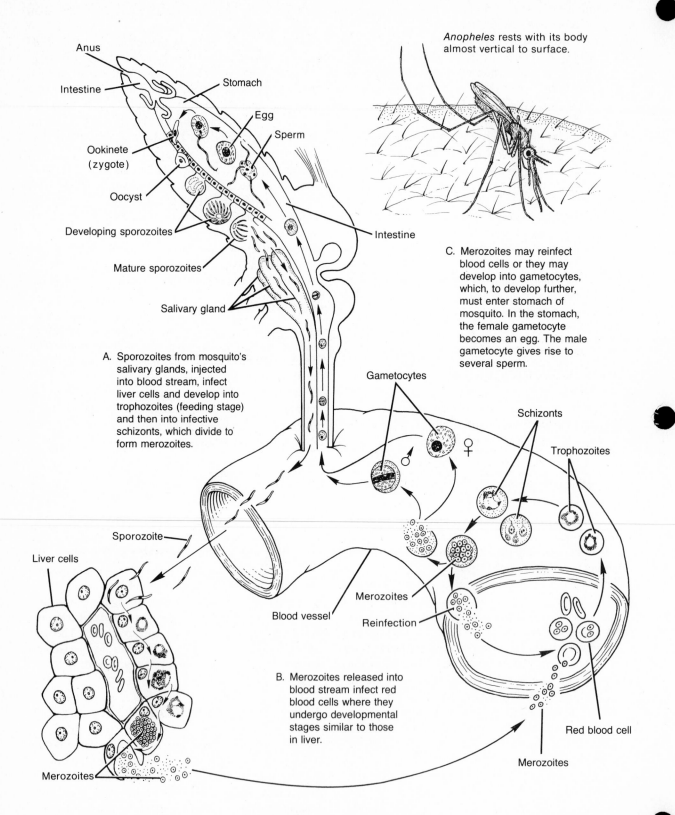

Anus

Intestine

Stomach

Egg

Sperm

Ookinete (zygote)

Oocyst

Developing sporozoites

Mature sporozoites

Salivary gland

Intestine

Anopheles rests with its body almost vertical to surface.

C. Merozoites may reinfect blood cells or they may develop into gametocytes, which, to develop further, must enter stomach of mosquito. In the stomach, the female gametocyte becomes an egg. The male gametocyte gives rise to several sperm.

A. Sporozoites from mosquito's salivary glands, injected into blood stream, infect liver cells and develop into trophozoites (feeding stage) and then into infective schizonts, which divide to form merozoites.

Gametocytes

Schizonts

Trophozoites

♂

♀

Sporozoite

Liver cells

Blood vessel

Merozoites

Reinfection

B. Merozoites released into blood stream infect red blood cells where they undergo developmental stages similar to those in liver.

Red blood cell

Merozoites

Merozoites

FIG. 26-10
Life cycle of *Plasmodium vivax*.

by observing their growth and production of fruiting structures.

Obtain a small piece of slime mold **sclerotia** (a dry, resting phase of the organism) and place it on the surface of the agar in the petri dish (Fig. 26-11).

Sprinkle a few oatmeal flakes over the sclerotium. Add 2 or 3 drops of water to moisten the oatmeal.

Replace the cover on the dish and set it aside in a dark place. After 24 hours, examine the plates for growth of the slime mold. Record your observation by drawing the growing organism in Fig. 26-12.

A. Place small piece of filter paper containing slime mold sclerotium in center of Petri dish containing agar.

B. Sprinkle some crushed oatmeal over the sclerotium.

C. Add 2–3 drops of water.

D. Cover and put in dark place.

Examine after 24 hours.

FIG. 26-11
Procedure for growing slime mold.

After 24 hours

After 48 hours

FIG. 26-12
Growth of slime molds.

Once growth has begun, examine the slime mold with a hand lens, a dissecting microscope, or the low power of your compound microscope. Describe the unique pattern of cytoplasmic movement observed in the plasmodium of the mold.

_____

_____

Puncture a branch of the slime mold with a needle and watch it for a few minutes.

After the dish becomes covered with the plasmodium of the slime mold, partially remove the cover. Under these conditions, the slime mold will begin to dry out and in the process will initiate the formation of fruiting bodies. Examine the culture during the next few days and describe the shape of the fruiting body that is formed.

_____

_____

REFERENCES

Bold, H. C. 1978. *Introduction to the Algae*. Prentice-Hall.

Chandler, A. C., and C. P. Read. 1961. *Introduction to Parasitology*. 10th ed. Wiley.

Grell, K. G. 1973. *Protozoology*. 2nd ed. Springer-Verlag.

Hyman, L. H. 1940. *The Invertebrates, Protozoa Through Ctenophora*. Vol. 1. McGraw-Hill.

Levine, N. D. 1973. *Protozoan Parasites of Domestic Animals and of Man*. 2nd ed. Burgess.

Sherman, I. W., and V. G. Sherman. 1976. *The Invertebrates: Function and Form: A Laboratory Guide*. 2nd ed. Macmillan.

Sleigh, M. A. 1973. *The Biology of the Protozoa*. Elsevier.

Kingdom Fungi

The fungi include a variety of organisms that are without chlorophyll and lack roots, stems, and leaves. Nutrition is by heterotrophic means; that is, complex, organic compounds are obtained from the environment. Among the fungi, there are two types of heterotrophs: parasites, which obtain food from living organisms, and saprophytes, which obtain their food from nonliving, organic materials.

There are several classes in this kingdom:

Class Oomycetes: Mostly aquatic organisms that have motile cells at specific stages of their life cycle. Cell walls composed of polymers of glucose, including cellulose.

Class Zygomycetes: Terrestrial fungi with hyphae that develop septa (cross walls) during formation of reproductive structures. Chitin is the predominant component of the cell walls (black bread mold).

Class Ascomycetes: Terrestrial and aquatic fungi. Hyphae have perforated septa; complete septa cut off reproductive structures. Chitin in cell walls. Sexual reproduction involves formation of saclike ascus in which meiosis precedes spore formation (yeasts, mildews, morels, and truffles).

Class Basidiomycetes: Terrestrial fungi. Hyphae have perforated septa; complete septa cut off reproductive structures. Sexual reproduction involves formation of basida in which meiosis takes place and on which the spores are borne (mushrooms and rusts).

Fungi Imperfecti: Consists mainly of fungi that have characteristics of the ascomycetes but where sexual reproduction has not been observed. These organisms are generally classified on the basis of their asexual spore-bearing structures. Includes fungi that cause athlete's foot and other skin diseases and many of the molds that flavor cheeses (e.g., Camembert and Roquefort).

In this exercise, we will only study the Zygomycetes, Ascomycetes, and Basidiomycetes.

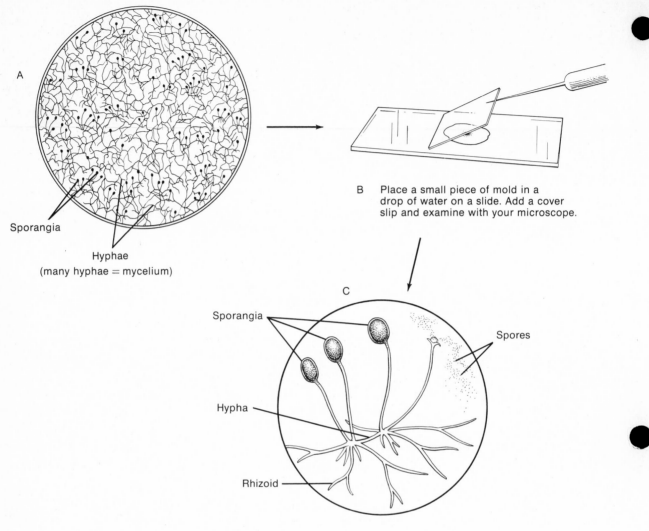

Sporangia

Hyphae
(many hyphae = mycelium)

B Place a small piece of mold in a
drop of water on a slide. Add a cover
slip and examine with your microscope.

C

Sporangia

Spores

Hypha

Rhizoid

FIG. 27-1
Structure of the black bread mold.

A. CLASS ZYGOMYCETES (THE BREAD MOLDS)

The black bread mold *(Rhizopus stolonifer)* is one of the most common fungi and can be found growing on many foods that contain starches.

1. Asexual Reproduction

Examine a petri dish containing black bread mold. Here, the mold is not growing on bread, but on agar containing various organic compounds needed for growth. If you wish, bring some bread from home (but remember that many mass-produced breads contain mold inhibitors) and place a piece in a petri dish. Moisten it with several drops of water, and then place a small piece of the mold from the agar on the bread. Cover the dish and set it aside for 1–2 days.)

Examine the mold with your dissecting microscope. *Do not remove the cover!* Note the whitish mass of filaments growing over the surface of the agar (Fig. 27-1A). Each filament is called a **hypha** (plural **hyphae**). The total mass of hyphae is a **mycelium**. Some hyphae grow upward and form small, black, globelike structures called **sporangia** (Fig. 27-1C). Inside the sporangia are cells called **spores**. They are released when the sporangia open. What is the function of the spores?

_____

_____

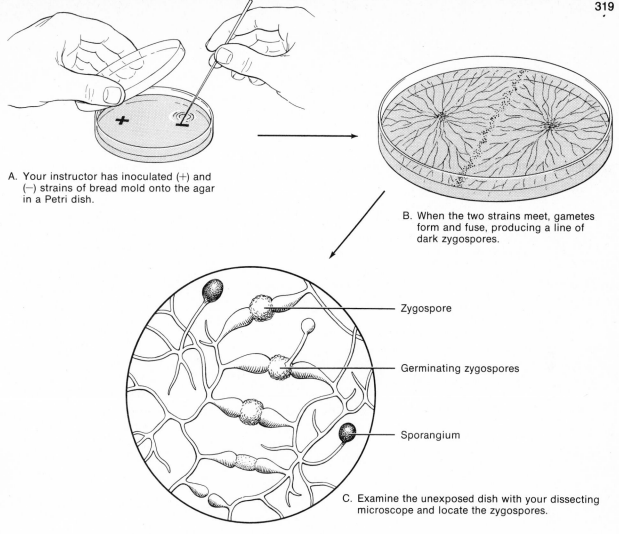

A. Your instructor has inoculated (+) and (−) strains of bread mold onto the agar in a Petri dish.

B. When the two strains meet, gametes form and fuse, producing a line of dark zygospores.

Zygospore

Germinating zygospores

Sporangium

C. Examine the unexposed dish with your dissecting microscope and locate the zygospores.

FIG. 27-2
Sexual reproduction in the black bread mold.

Many hyphae penetrate the agar. Turn the dish over, and focus downward through the agar to locate small, rootlike hyphae called **rhizoids** growing into the agar (Fig. 27-1C). Suggest a function for the rhizoids.

_____

_____

Remove a small piece of the mold, and place it in a drop of water on a slide (Fig. 27-1B). Add a cover slip and examine with your microscope. Locate sporangia, spores, hyphae, and rhizoids.

2. Sexual Reproduction

The black bread mold requires two different strains before sexual reproduction can occur. Your instructor has inoc-

ulated an agar plate with a plus (+) strain and a minus (−) strain. The growth of each strain has brought them into contact. At the points of contact, gametes are formed. Fusion of the gametes (fertilization) has resulted in the formation of a line of black, thick-walled **zygospores** (Fig. 27-2B, C) across the culture. Keeping the dish closed, locate the zygospores with your dissecting microscope. In what ways, if any, do the plus and minus strains look different?

_____

_____

Would you consider each strain to have a different sex? Explain.

_____

_____

_____

_____

B. CLASS ASCOMYCETES (SAC FUNGI)

The members of this group produce spores in a saclike structure called an **ascus**. These spores, usually eight in number, are called **ascospores**.

1. Yeasts

Yeasts are among the simpler ascomycetes. Mount some living yeast cells on a slide and examine microscopically. Look for nuclei and small glistening food granules. Note that some of the yeast cells may exhibit small, rounded projections called _buds_ (Fig. 27-3). What do these buds represent?

_____

_____

If none of the yeast cells are budding, examine a demonstration slide that shows this process.

Yeasts are classified as ascomycetes because at some period in their life cycle an ascus is formed. Examine a demonstration slide that shows the ascus of yeast and its contents. List several ways in which yeasts are economically important to human beings.

_____

_____

_____

_____

2. Powdery Mildew (_Microsphaera_)

Examine leaves of a lilac plant that are infected with this fungus. Why is this organism called _powdery mildew?_

_____

FIG. 27-3
Budding in yeast.

_____

_____

The mycelium that grows over the surface of the leaf occasionally penetrates the epidermal cells (Fig. 27-4). These hyphae are called **haustoria** (singular haustorium). What is their function?

Examine demonstration slides that show haustorial penetration of the epidermal cells of the host plant. What kind of nutrition does this fungus exhibit?

During late spring, large numbers of asexual spores (**conidia**) are produced and disseminated by the wind to spread the infection to the same or other lilac plants. Examine slides of powdery mildew, and locate the conidia.

Toward the end of summer, large numbers of spherical fruiting bodies are formed as a result of sexual reproduction. Examine an infected leaf with a dissecting microscope, and locate some of these fruiting bodies. Scrape the surface of the leaf, and mount the material in a drop of water on a slide. Examine microscopically. Locate a fruiting body, and note the elaborate appendages. How might these appendages be useful to the fungus?

_____

_____

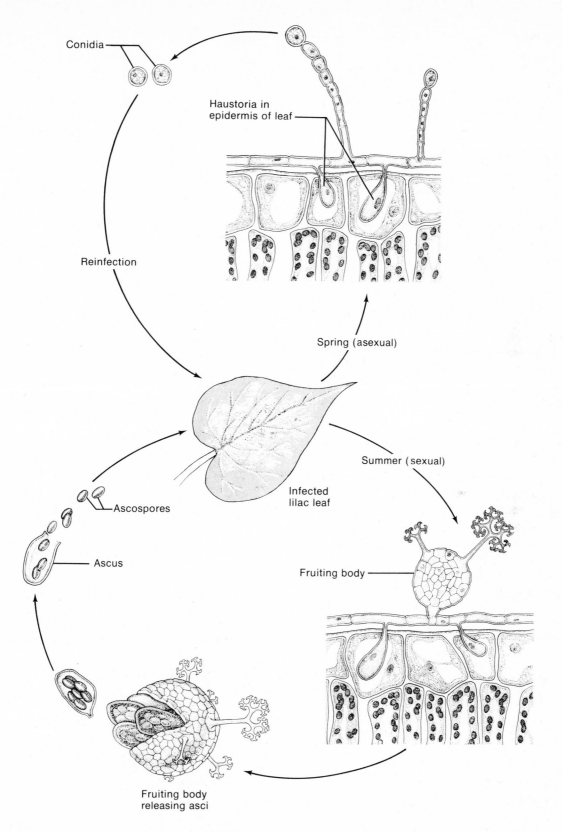

Conidia

Haustoria in
epidermis of leaf

Reinfection

Spring (asexual)

Infected
lilac leaf

Ascospores

Summer (sexual)

Ascus

Fruiting body

Fruiting body
releasing asci

FIG. 27-4
Life cycle of a powdery mildew.

While examining the fruiting body, gently apply pressure to the cover slip. Note the saclike asci that are extruded. Locate an ascus that contains ascospores. How many spores does each ascus contain?

_____

What becomes of the ascospore after it is released?

_____

_____

_____

3. *Penicillium*

Much spoilage of food, leather, and cloth occurs as a result of this fungus. Examine a living culture of *Penicillium*. Why is it sometimes referred to as a *blue-green mold?*

_____

Examine prepared slides showing the special hyphal branches that produce asexual spores or conidia (Fig. 27-5). How does *Penicillium* differ from *Rhizopus* in the way in which spores are produced?

_____

_____

_____

FIG. 27-5
Conidia of *Penicillium.*

How is it similar to *Microsphaera?*

_____

_____

_____

One species, *Penicillium notatum*, was found to produce a potent antibiotic, penicillin. It has proven to be one of the most effective antibiotics for combating bacterial infections.

C. CLASS BASIDIOMYCETES (CLUB FUNGI)

The basidiomycetes represent another large and varied group of fungi that have both saprophytic and parasitic members. They are characterized by having a **basidium** (a club-shaped structure on which are usually produced four spores—**basidiospores**) formed at some point in the life cycle.

1. Mushrooms

Mushrooms are characterized by plates or gills on the undersurface of a fruiting body. The basidia extend from the free surface of the gills (Fig. 27-6).

The mushroom mycelia grow beneath the surface of their substrate. When haploid mycelia of different strains unite, another mycelium is formed that is diploid. This mycelium may produce a fruiting body, commonly called a *mushroom*, which consists of a stalk and cap.

Examine the fruiting body of *Agaricus campestris,* the common commercial mushroom. Note the stalk and cap. Examine the undersurface of the cap and locate the gills. If the mushroom is young, the gills may be covered by a thin membrane that extends from the stalk to the outer margin of the cap.

Mount one of the gills in a drop of water on a slide and microscopically examine the edges of the gills. Locate basidia and basidiospores. If available, examine a prepared slide of *Coprinus,* showing a cross section through the cap. Identify gills, basidia, and basidiospores.

2. Bracket Fungi

These fungi are parasitic or saprophytic on various trees. The mycelium of the fungus may grow within the trunk several years before forming the characteristic woody

Gills

Mycelium

Cap

Basidium

Basidiospore

Haploid nuclei Nuclear fusion   Meiosis

Development of basidiospores

FIG. 27-6
Details in the life of a mushroom.

fruiting body on the outside of the tree. Examine several bracket fungi, and note the several growth layers that are evident. How could these growth layers be used to estimate the age of a bracket fungus?

_____

_____

_____

_____

Examine the undersurface of one of the fruiting bodies with a dissecting microscope. How does the undersurface of a bracket fungus differ from a mushroom?

_____

_____

Examine a prepared slide showing a cross section of the fruiting body of a bracket fungus. What do the circular openings in the cross section represent?

_____

Locate basidia and basidiospores.

3. Rusts

The rusts are a group of parasitic basidiomycetes that infect almost every living species of seed plants as well as some of the ferns. All species of rust produce at least two distinctly different types of spores; some have three, four, or five different kinds.

The most widely known rust, and one that causes perhaps the greatest economic loss, is the stem rust of wheat, _Puccinia graminis_. Infection by this parasite affects the wheat plant in several ways. First, many of the host's cells are killed as the fungus uses the content of the cells for its own growth. Second, the fungus is robbing the host of food that otherwise would be used for growth in parts of the plant not infected by the fungus. Third, due to the killing of cells that may contain chloroplasts, photosynthetic processes are greatly reduced. Thus, as a result of infection by *Puccinia,* the wheat plant becomes pale green, stunted in overall growth, and ripens prematurely, with its small, shrunken, kernals having very limited food reserves.

a. Phases of the Rust in the Wheat Plant

1. **Urediospores.** Examine stems and leaves of wheat showing reddish patches (hence the name "rust") on the surface. These masses (called **uredia**; singular, **uredium**) contain large numbers of reddish orange, binucleate **urediospores** (Fig. 27-7A). These are the first of several different types of spores produced and appear in late spring. They continue to be produced throughout the growing season until the plant is mature. Urediospores are transported by various means (but primarily by the wind) to other wheat plants where the spore germinates and sends out a hyphal branch that enters a stoma and penetrates the intercellular spaces of the leaf. The mycelium becomes highly branched. Haustoria penetrate and absorb food from the host cells. After a period of growth, the hyphal mass forms a layer of cells just beneath the epidermis, which then develops into the stalked urediospores, which are produced in such abundance that the epidermis ruptures.

With a razor blade, scrape a small amount of the uredia into a drop of water on a slide, and add a cover slip. Locate and examine some urediospores. Next examine a slide of a cross section through a uredium. Locate urediospores, mycelia, and haustoria.

2. **Teliospores.** As the wheat plant approaches maturity, the mycelium, which until this time was producing urediospores, now begins to produce **teliospores** (Fig. 27-7B) located in masses called **telia.** These spores have thicker walls than urediospores and generally do not germinate until the following spring.

Scrape a small amount of material from a wheat stem or leaf containing telia into a drop of water on a slide. Add a cover slip and examine microscopically. Locate and examine some teliospores. How many cells make up each teliospore?

_____

Next examine a slide of a cross section through a telium. Locate immature teliospores, which when first formed are binucleate, and mature spores, in which the nuclei have fused and the spores are uninucleate.

b. Phase of the Rust in the Barberry (Alternate Host)

In the spring, the nuclei of cells making up the teliospore undergo meiosis so that each cell contains four haploid nuclei. Each cell then forms a short mycelium called a **basidium.** The nuclei migrate into the basidium, which then is partitioned into four cells, each of which contains a haploid nucleus. Each cell of the basidium forms a small projection, into which will pass the nucleus. The swollen end of this projection becomes a **basidiospore.**

The wheat rust requires an alternate host to complete its life cycle. Basidiospores cannot reinfect wheat. They can only infect the alternate host—the common barberry (Fig. 27-7C, D).

When it lands on a fruit, branch, or leaf of the barberry, the basidiospore germinates and forms a hyphal branch that penetrates the tissue. In the tissue, the mycelium proliferates extensively. Ultimately, two types of structures are formed: **spermagonia** (singular, *spermagonium*) and **aecia** (singular, *aecium*)—see Fig. 27-7E. These are best observed by examining cross sections through them.

1. **Spermagonium.** The spermagonium is a flask-shaped structure just below the epidermis. It contains numerous hairlike hyphae at the ends of which are spore-like cells called **spermatia** (singular, *spermatium*).

Spermatia may be carried by insects to **receptive hyphae** protruding from other spermagonia where the nucleus from the spermatium enters the receptive hyphae. This initiates the development of another type of mycelium that ultimately produces cuplike structures called *aecia* that protrude from the lower surface of the barberry leaf (Fig. 27-7E).

2. **Acium.** Masses of **aeciospores** are formed within the aecia. If these spores are carried by air currents to the leaves or stems of wheat, they germinate and form an intercellular mycelium that then forms urediospores to complete the life cycle.

Examine infected leaves of barberry and locate spermagonia and aecia. Then examine slides showing cross sections through these structures. Locate spermatia, receptive hyphae, and aeciospores.

How do you control the spread of a fungus, such as wheat rust, whose infective spores can be carried by air currents to infect plants thousands of miles away?

_____

_____

_____

_____

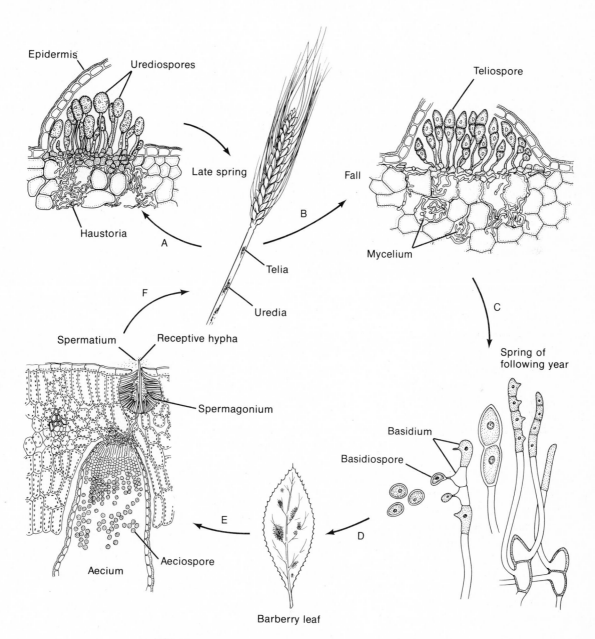

FIG. 27-7
Life cycle of wheat rust. (Adapted from *A Textbook of General Botany,* 5th ed, by G. M. Smith *et al.,* Macmillan, 1956.)

REFERENCES

Alexopoulos, C. J., and C. W. Mims. 1979. *Introductory Mycology.* 3rd ed. Wiley.

Benson, L. 1957. *Plant Classification.* Heath.

Bold, H. C. 1973. *Morphology of Plants.* 3rd ed. Harper & Row.

Bold, H. C. 1977. *The Plant Kingdom.* 4th ed. Prentice-Hall.

Delevoryas, T. 1977. *Plant Diversification.* 2nd ed. Holt, Rinehart and Winston.

Foster, A. S., and E. M. Gifford, Jr. 1974. *Comparative Morphology of Vascular Plants.* 2nd ed. W. H. Freeman and Company.

Smith, G. M. 1955. *Cryptogamic Botany* Vol. 2, 2nd ed. *Bryophytes and Pteridophytes.* McGraw-Hill.

Wallace, B., and A. M. Srb. 1964. *Adaptation.* 2nd ed. Prentice-Hall.

Webster, J. 1970. *Introduction to Fungi.* Cambridge University Press.

Kingdom Plantae: Phyla Chlorophyta, Phaeophyta, and Rhodophyta

There are more than 20,000 species of algae grouped into several phyla. All members of these phyla are (with few exceptions) photosynthetic. They have a relatively simple plant body, which may consist of a single cell, filaments of cells, plates of cells, or a structure somewhat comparable to that of some land plants. They do not have the complex organization of tissues found in the vascular plants.

Algae differ from each other in the type of flagella (if they consist of motile cells) and in several biochemical characteristics. While all contain chlorophyll, there is a wide variety of carotenoids distributed in the various groups. Indeed, the names given to the various divisions are derived from the various pigments that mask the green color of the chlorophylls. Great diversity exists in the type of food storage products found in the different groups.

Reproduction is accomplished asexually by fragmentation of the parent body or through the production of spores capable of developing into other individuals. In addition, new individuals may arise as a result of the union of two gametes. The zygote that is formed as a result of this union may develop directly into another alga or may produce spores.

There are several algal phyla:

Phylum Chlorophyta (green algae): Unicellular and multicellular organisms having chlorophylls *a* and *b*; various carotenoids, and food stored as starch. Motile cells have two flagella.

Phylum Phaeophyta (brown algae): Multicellular, marine organisms having chlorophylls *a* and *c* and the pigment fucoxanthin. Food stored as a carbohydrate called *laminarin*. Motile cells have two flagella, one anterior, the other trailing. Multicellular forms, unlike green algae, show considerable differentiation. Some have specialized conducting cells.

Phylum Rhodophyta (red algae): Mostly marine plants having chlorophyll *a* and phycobilins. Food stored as carbohydrate called *floridean starch*. No motile cells in life cycle. Lack specialized conducting cells found in brown algae.

In this exercise, you will study several members of the Chlorophyta and examples from the red and brown algae.

A. PHYLUM CHLOROPHYTA (GREEN ALGAE)

The green algae exhibit the greatest diversity, both in form and reproductive patterns, of all algae. Of the approximately 7,000 species, most are aquatic, although other habitats include the surface of snow, hot springs, trunks of trees, and (as symbionts) in lichens, protozoa, and hydra. Many of the green algae are microscopic, although some of the marine forms, called *kelps,* achieve lengths in excess of 25 meters.

1. The Volvocine Line of Evolution in Green Algae

In the volvocine line, a primitive, unicellular alga is thought to have given rise to increasingly complex colonial forms. In this study, you will examine *Chlamydomonas,* which could be considered the primitive form; *Gonium* and *Pandorina* as progressively complex forms; and *Volvox,* which could be considered the peak of the evolutionary line.

Two general trends are evident in the evolution of this group: (1) There is an increase in complexity of the plant body from a single cell to a colonial type. Unicellular forms are considered the most primitive. Colonial forms probably had their origin in an ancestral unicellular alga and achieved their complex forms through cell divisions occurring in different planes. (2) There is evidence of increasing differences between the type of gametes and/or reproductive organs with **isogamy** being the most primitive and **oogamy** being the most advanced.

Observe these differences as you examine various representatives of this group.

a. Chlamydomonas

Chlamydomonas is an isogamous, single-celled, motile alga commonly found in damp soil, lakes, and ditches. It is typically egg-shaped and has a large cup-shaped chloroplast containing a proteinaceous body, the **pyrenoid**, which functions in starch formation. The nucleus is difficult to observe in living material.

Prepare a slide of living *Chlamydomonas,* and examine microscopically (Fig. 28-1). Add a drop of methyl cellulose to slow the movement of this alga. Locate the conspicuous chloroplast and the pyrenoid. The activity of threadlike structures, **flagella**, located at the anterior end of the cells, enables the organism to move through water.

The flagella can be more easily observed by closing the iris diaphragm to reduce the light.

Locate a reddish pigment spot (**stigma**) near the flagellar end of the cell. Suggest a function for this structure.

_____

_____

At the start of **asexual reproduction**, the flagella are retracted and movement ceases. During this quiescent period, mitosis results in the formation of daughter protoplasts, which may divide a second and third time (Fig. 28-1). A cell wall is formed around each of the daughter protoplasts, resulting in the formation of temporary colonies that soon rupture and release individual daughter cells called **zoospores**. Locate nonmotile, vegetative colonies showing two, four, or eight daughter cells.

In **sexual reproduction**, haploid gametes are formed in the majority of the green algae. In *Chlamydomonas,* however, vegetative cells may function as gametes, one functioning as the male and another as the female gamete. The gametes are identical in size and appearance, although in some species the female gamete may be slightly larger. Gametes that are morphologically indistinguishable from each other are called **isogametes**.

Sexuality in *Chlamydomonas* can be demonstrated by using mating strains having separate sexes characterized as plus ($+$) and minus ($-$). Place a drop of each of the mating types next to each other on a slide. Do not mix. While examining them with the dissecting microscope, mix the drops together. Note the peculiar "clumping" phenomenon that precedes union of the gametes. Using a compound microscope, locate cells that have paired. At which end of the cell has union occurred?

_____

_____

As a result of sexual union, a diploid zygote is formed that secretes a thick, spiny wall and then enters a period of dormancy. Examine the preparation closely and observe zygotes. Under favorable conditions, the zygote nucleus undergoes meiotic division to form four haploid nuclei. The protoplast then divides and forms four uninucleate zoospores, which soon escape from the old zygote wall, develop flagella, and swim away.

b. Gonium

Gonium is an isogamous, but colonial, organism made up of *Chlamydomonas*-like cells that are loosely arranged

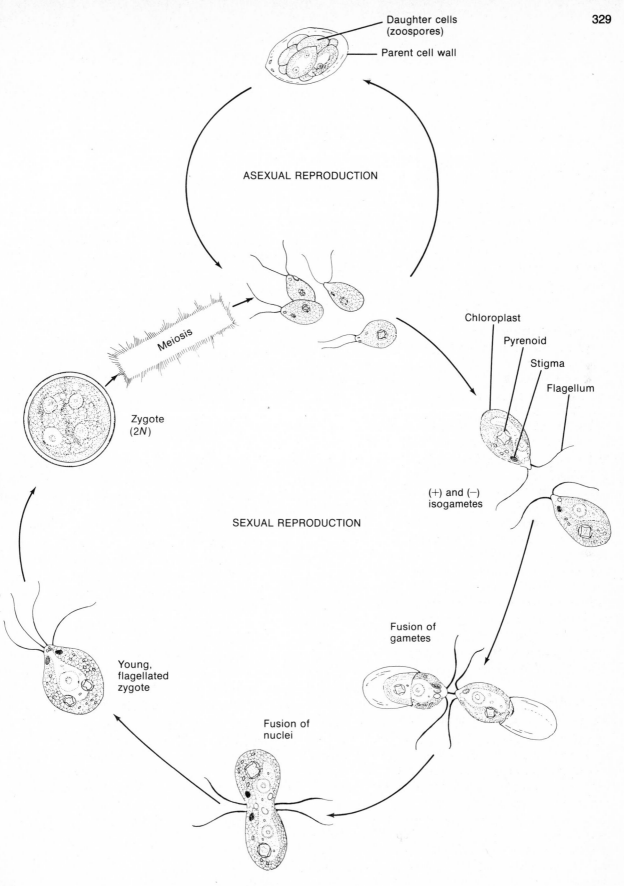

Daughter cells (zoospores)

Parent cell wall

ASEXUAL REPRODUCTION

Meiosis

Zygote (2N)

SEXUAL REPRODUCTION

Chloroplast

Pyrenoid

Stigma

Flagellum

(+) and (−) isogametes

Fusion of gametes

Young, flagellated zygote

Fusion of nuclei

FIG. 28-1
Life cycle of *Chlamydomonas.*

A

B

FIG. 28-2
Green algae: (A) *Gonium* and (B) *Pandorina*.

into a flat, platelike colony (Fig. 28-2A). The cells are held together by a gelantinous matrix.

Gonium represents a stage in evolution where the plant body has become larger by the assembly of a few cells exhibiting a relatively simple degree of coordination. The cells in this colony swim in unison so that the entire plate of cells moves as a unit.

Examine living colonies of *Gonium*. Is the number of cells in each colony constant?

_____

If not, describe the variability in cell number found in different colonies.

_____

_____

_____

_____

c. Pandorina

Examine living colonies of *Pandorina,* another colonial type composed of *Chlamydomonas*-like cells (Fig. 28-2B). This organism is also isogamous. How does the colony of *Pandorina* differ from *Gonium* in shape?

_____

_____

In number of cells?

_____

In *Pandorina,* as well as in *Gonium,* each cell of the colony, when mature, gives rise asexually to a new colony within the gelatinous envelope of the parent colony.

In sexual reproduction, isogametes fuse to form a zygote that undergoes meiosis to form zoospores. Each zoospore is capable of developing into a new colony.

d. Volvox

Volvox is a colonial alga in which the cells are bound together is a common matrix (Fig. 28-3A). Individually, the cells exhibit many of the features seen in *Chlamydomonas;* that is, they have a stigma, flagella, and large chloroplasts. However, in *Volvox* only specialized cells are able to function during reproduction.

Asexual reproduction is accomplished by the enlargement and subsequent division of certain of the cells within the colony. In early development, these cells form a flat plate, which soon rounds up into a sphere (**daughter colony**) having a small pore at the posterior end. The colony continues to increase in size, and then the sphere evaginates through the pore and turns itself inside out. The daughter colonies are released on disintegration of the parent colony.

Examine a sample of living *Volvox* with a dissecting microscope. Describe the motility of *Volvox*.

_____

_____

What is the shape of the colony?

_____

A

Adult colony

B

Sperm

Vegetative cell

Sperm

Zygote

Egg

FIG. 28-3
Sexual reproduction in *Volvox*.

Examine living material and prepared slides of *Volvox* for presence of daughter colonies.

The green algae studied thus far all produced isogametes. In contrast, *Volvox* produces gametes that are morphologically differentiated into sperm and eggs (Fig. 28-3B). These are developed from cells that become differentiated as the colony grows. In forming an ovum, a cell of the colony increases greatly in size, takes on a rounded form, and becomes filled with food materials, especially lipids. The male gametes are formed from other cells, which give rise to flat bundles of flagellated sperm. When mature, the eggs are fertilized by the sperm. They then develop heavy spiny walls and become zygotes. Germination of the zygote occurs in the spring and results in the formation of a new colony. Examine prepared slides of *Volvox,* and locate sperm, ova, and zygotes.

2. Filamentous Green Algae

a. Spirogyra

Spirogyra is a free-floating alga found in small freshwater pools in the spring. It is frequently referred to as "pond scum" (Fig. 28-4). Prepare a fresh mount and examine microscopically. Is any branching evident?

Examine a single cell under high power. What is the shape of the chloroplast?

Locate several small **pyrenoids** within the chloroplast. The nucleus, suspended in the center of the cell by cytoplasmic strands, is difficult to observe unless stained. Apply a drop of methylene blue to the edge of the cover glass. After a few minutes, reexamine and locate the nucleus, which will now appear as a bluish body in the central part of the cell.

In sexual reproductoin, filaments of opposite mating types come to lie adjacent to one another and small projections appear in opposing cells of each filament (Fig. 28-4). The projections increase in length and eventually contact each other. At the point of junction, the cell walls dissolve, forming a **conjugation tube**. The protoplasts of the conjugating cells become isogametes. One gamete functions as the male and migrates through the conjugation tube to unite with the nonmotile female gamete. Fusion of the gametes produces a zygote, which is released on disintegration of the filament. Before germination, the nucleus of the zygote undergoes meiosis, and three of the four haploid nuclei that are formed disintegrate. On germination of the zygote, a short protuberance is formed, which contains the fourth nucleus.

Mitosis, followed by cell division, results in a filament of cells similar to the parental filament. Examine your living material, and look for various stages in gametic union. If your preparation does not show any stages of conjugation or zygote formation, examine prepared slides showing this process.

No means of asexual reproduction is known to occur in *Spirogyra* other than fragmentation of the individual filaments.

b. Ulothrix

The plant body of *Ulothrix*, like *Spirogyra*, is a simple, unbranched filament of cells. Unlike *Spirogyra*, it is not

Asexual reproduction
by fragmentation

Filament of *Spirogyra*

Meiosis

Pairing of opposite
mating types

Zygote

Formation of
conjugation tube

Gametes

FIG. 28-4
Life cycle of *Spirogyra*.

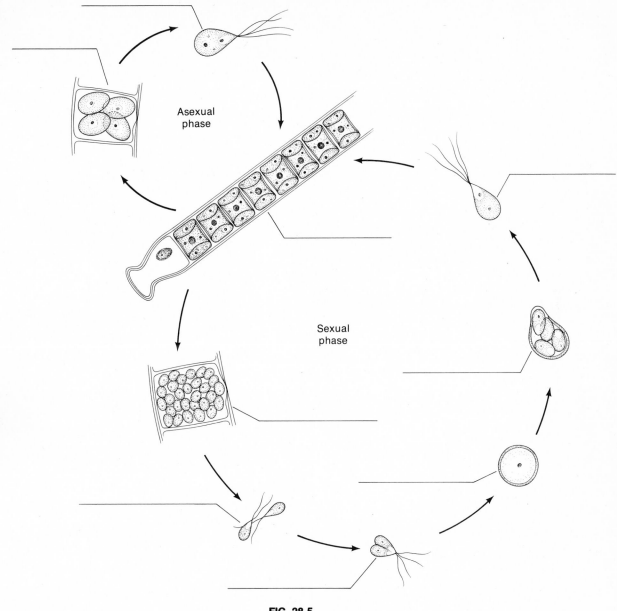

FIG. 28-5
Life cycle of *Ulothrix*.

free-floating, but has a basal **holdfast** cell used to attach it to rocks or other objects in fresh, and in some cases, salt water (Fig. 28-5).

Examine a prepared slide or living specimens of *Ulothrix*. Note that all cells, with the exception of the holdfast, are alike. The holdfast cell may not be present. Why?

_____

_____

_____

_____

The chloroplast is C-shaped and may have one or more pyrenoids. Is an eye spot (stigma) present?

_____

If not, would you expect this alga to have such a structure?

_____

_____

_____

With the exception of the holdfast, any cell is capable of reproducing the plant by asexual or sexual means. In the asexual phase, the protoplast of the parent cell undergoes mitosis and produces four to eight daughter cells that, when released from the parent cell (the **zoosporangium**), become flagellated **zoospores** (Fig. 28-5). Label this figure, and give the chromosome complement as you locate the various structures described. After swimming around for a short period of time, each spore loses its flagella, settles to the bottom, and, through a series of mitotic divisions, gives rises to a new filament.

In the sexual phase, the parent cell (called a **gametangium**) produces from 32 to 64 isogametes. These differ from zoospores in being smaller and having two rather than four flagella. Gametes from different filaments fuse to form a zygote that enters a dormant period. At this time it is called a **zygospore**. Under favorable conditions, this resting spore undergoes meiosis. The four haploid zoospores each then develop into a new filament of cells.

Is the plant body in *Ulothrix* haploid or diploid?

_____

Explain.

_____

_____

Which type of reproduction (asexual or sexual) is primarily responsible for increasing the number of individual in the population?

_____

Explain.

_____

_____

_____

Under what environmental conditions would you expect sexual reproduction to occur and why?

_____

_____

_____

_____

c. Oedogonium

Oedogonium, like *Spirogyra* and *Ulothrix*, has a simple, unbranched plant body consisting of a series of cells. It differs from the latter algae in that some of the cells have become specialized reproductive structures that produce distinctively different gametes.

Examine living specimens or prepared slides of *Oedogonium*. As you locate the following structures, label them on Fig. 28-6 and indicate whether they are haploid or diploid.

A holdfast cell is present in some species.

How does the shape of the chloroplast differ from those found in *Spirogyra* and *Ulothrix*?

_____

_____

Where are the pyrenoids found?

_____

_____

Describe any differences in the shape of the cells found in the plant body of *Oedogonium*.

_____

_____

_____

Asexual reproduction can take place in either of two ways. The plant body can simply fragment, with each fragment increasing in size through cell division, or the protoplast of any **vegetative cell** (i.e., nonreproductive cell or holdfast cell) can become a zoospore that, when released, actively swims for a while and then produces a new filament of cells (Fig. 28-6).

To study the sexual phase, examine a prepared slide or living material showing **antheridia** and **oogonia**, the specialized reproductive cells. The antheridia are shortened, disc-shaped cells in contrast to the elongated vegetative cells of the filament. Each antheridium gives rise to two male gametes called **antherozoids** (sperm). They are small, egg-shaped cells with a ring of flagella at the pointed end.

The *oogonium* is a large, spherical cell in which the protoplast rounds up to form a single gamete—the egg. As the egg matures, a small pore, or transverse crack, appears in the oogonial wall. Antherozoids swimming near the oogonium are attracted to the egg and enter the

FIG. 28-6
Life cycle of *Oedogonium*.

oogonium through the pore or crack. Fertilization results in a **zygote** that is retained in the oogonium. The zygote soon develops a thick wall and becomes dormant. At this time, it is called an **oospore**. Disintegration of the oogonial wall releases the oospore, which remains dormant for several months. When environmental conditions are conducive to growth, the oospore undergoes meiosis producing four haploid zoospores, which soon develop into new filamentous plants.

In what way is *Oedogonium* more advanced than *Spirogyra* or *Ulothrix?*

B. PHYLUM PHAEOPHYTA (BROWN ALGAE)

The brown algae are almost exclusively marine organisms ranging in size from microscopic forms to plants in excess of 50 meters in length. Economically, the brown algae provide us with several useful products, such as **alginic acid**, which is used as a stabilizer to impart the smooth body and texture to ice cream. It is also used in the manufacture of fire-resistant paints, cosmetics, and many pharmaceuticals.

In many parts of the world, the brown algae are an important food source. In oriental countries, *Laminaria* (Fig. 28-7A) is grown on ropes suspended between bamboo poles driven into the sea bottom along the coasts. A food product prepared from these algae, called "Kimbri," is a dietary staple in Japan.

Macrocystis, the giant Pacific kelp, is being cultivated on an experimental basis along the California coast to determine its potential as a source of methane fuel.

Examine specimens of brown algae, noting the variation in size and complexity of the plant body. Many of the "kelps" (Fig. 28-7B) are externally differentiated in parts looking like "roots" (the **holdfast**), "stems" (the **stipe**), and "leaves" (the **blade**). Also observe that many of the specimens have air-filled bladders. How are such "floats" advantageous to the organism?

_____

_____

_____

If available, examine **Sargassum**, a floating brown alga typically found in tropical waters (Fig. 28-7C). These plants occur in large numbers and may extend over thousands of acres of the ocean's surface. The Sargasso Sea takes its name from this alga.

Blade

Stipe

Holdfast

B. *Kelps*

Nereocystis

Potelsia

Macrocystis

A. *Laminaria*

C. *Sargassum*

FIG. 28-7
Brown algae: (A) *Laminaria*, (B) Kelps—*Macrocystis, Potelsia* and *Nereocytis*, (C) *Sargassum*.

C. PHYLUM RHODOPHYTA (RED ALGAE)

Red algae, like the browns, are primarily marine organisms. Although occasionally found in cooler regions, they are most abundant in tropical waters. Unlike brown algae, the red algae always grow attached to solid objects and usually grow below the tide level. In the warm waters they inhabit, they are typically found at depths of 100 to 200 meters.

The plant body of red algae is similar to that of the brown algae in that it is differentiated into a holdfast, stipe, and blade. In some, known as **corallines**, the plants are heavily impregnated with limestone and are considered to be just as important to the formation of coral reefs and atolls as are the coral animals.

Red algae provide several useful products. For example, a gelatinous cell wall material provides agar, which is used extensively in laboratories for the culture of bacteria and fungi and some higher plants. Carrageenan, another colloidal substance, is used as an emulsifying agent in dairy products such as chocolate milk, where it prevents the chocolate from settling out.

The red algae *Porphyra* is used as food in several oriental dishes. In one, called "sushi," various meats and rice are wrapped in sheets of the alga.

Examine various specimens of red algae on demonstration.

REFERENCES

Bold, H. C. 1973. *Morphology of Plants*. 3rd ed. Harper & Row.

Bold, H. C. 1977. *The Plant Kingdom*. 4th ed. Prentice-Hall.

Bold, H. C., and M. J. Wynne. 1978. *Introduction to the Algae*. Prentice-Hall.

Chapman, V. J. 1970. *Seaweeds and Their Uses*. Methune.

Delevoryas. T. 1977. *Plant Diversification*. 2nd ed. Holt, Rinehart and Winston.

Prescott, G. W. 1978. *How to Know the Freshwater Algae*. 3rd ed. Brown.

Scagel, R. F., R. J. Bandoni, G. E. Rouse, W. B. Schofield, J. B. Stein, and T. M. C. Taylor. 1965. *An Evolutionary Survey of the Plant Kingdom*. Wadsworth.

Smith, G. N. 1950. *The Freshwater Algae of the United States*. 2nd ed. McGraw-Hill.

Starr, R. G. 1964. Culture Collection of Algae. *American Journal of Botany* 51:1013–1044.

Trainor, F. R. 1978. *Introductory Phycology*. Wiley.

Kingdom Plantae: Phylum Bryophyta

Some botanists consider liverworts to be closely related to mosses and thus classify both in the phylum Bryophyta. Others consider them to be sufficiently different from each other to place them in separate phyla. In this exercise, we will follow the classification of placing the mosses and liverworts in the Bryophyta.

There are three classes in the Bryophyta:

Class Hepaticae (liverworts): Plant body (gametophyte) green and dorsoventrally flattened and bilaterally symmetrical, reproductive structures multicellular, water necessary for fertilization.

Class Musci (mosses): Plant body (gametophyte) erect and radially symmetrical; has stem and leaflike structures. Reproductive structures multicellular and require presence of water for fertilization. Lack true vascular tissues.

Class Anthocerotae (hornworts): Plant body (gametophyte) is multilobed thallus growing closely appressed to rocks and soil. Gametophytes may contain nitrogen-fixing blue-green algae. Reproductive structures are multicellular. Spores produced continuously over several months.

In this exercise, several representatives of the liverworts and mosses will be studied, with special emphasis on form, habitat, and reproductive processes. Algae and fungi plant bodies are reproduced by fragmentation, by production of asexual structures (spores), or by the union of isogamous or anisogamous gametes. The reproductive structure is single-celled in each case. In the liverworts and mosses, the gametes are produced in multicellular sex organs—the **archegonia** (female) and **antheridia** (male).

A. CLASS HEPATICAE (LIVERWORTS)

1. The Plant Body

Long ago liverworts were given their rather curious name because the lobing of the plant body in some species resembled the lobes of the liver. The term "wort" meant "plant," particularly a herbaceous (nonwoody) plant. Examine living gametophyte plants of *Marchantia*. Note the characteristic Y-shaped (**dichotomous**) branching of the thallus. Meristematic tissue found in the notch of the

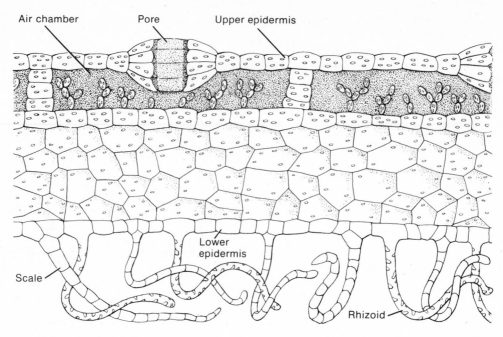

FIG. 29-1
Diagrammatic cross section of a *Marchantia* thallus.

Y produces the peculiar growth pattern seen here. Is the plant body diploid or haploid with respect to the chromosome number in the cells?

_____

Remove a small piece of the thallus, and examine the ventral (bottom) surface with a dissecting microscope. At the edges, locate slender, hairlike structures, the rhizoids. What is the function of the rhizoids?

_____

_____

Associated with the rhizoids are long, flattened structures, the scales. Locate these structures. Examine the dorsal surface. Observe the minute "pores" in the center of small, diamond-shaped areas. Because *Marchantia* is photosynthetic, what role might be ascribed to these openings?

_____

_____

_____

What structures in the higher plants appear to be morphologically and functionally similar to these openings?

_____

_____

_____

Examine prepared slides of a cross section of the thallus of *Marchantia* (Fig. 29-1). Locate the upper epidermis and the "pores" that were seen in the living material. Below the epidermis, find a series of small air chambers that are partitioned by branching filaments arising from the floor of the chambers. In living material, the filaments contain chloroplasts. Suggest a function for the air chambers.

_____

_____

_____

The tissue underlying the air chambers is several cells thick. Many of the cells contain leucoplasts. A few large cells contain mucilage, a gelantinous substance that tends to absorb water. What is the advantage of having this substance in the cells?

_____

_____

On the lower epidermis, locate the rhizoids and scales. How do scales differ morphologically from rhizoids?

_____

_____

2. Asexual Reproduction

The gametophyte of *Marchantia* reproduces asexually by means of small "plantlets" (**gemmae**), produced from cells located in the bottom of gemma cups. These are found on the dorsal surface of the thallus (Fig. 29-2). Examine a demonstration of the gemma cups using a dissecting microscope. Describe the appearance of any gemmae present in the cups.

_____

_____

If none are present, how could you account for their absence?

_____

_____

Are gemmae haploid or diploid?

_____

3. Sexual Reproduction

The reproductive (sex) organs of *Marchantia* are borne on special upright branches (Fig. 29-2). Each branch is composed of a stalk and terminal disc. Many species of *Marchantia* are **dioecious**; that is, there are separate male and female gametophytes and therefore two kinds of reproductive branches. Examine a male gametophyte,

which bears an **antheridial branch**. What is the shape of the terminal disc?

_____

_____

Compare the antheridial branch with the **archegonial branch** of the female gametophyte. Describe the female reproductive branch.

_____

_____

_____

What is the chromosomal condition (haploid or diploid) of the antheridial and archegonial branches?

_____

Examine slides showing cross sections of the antheridial branch. Locate the antheridia just below the upper surface of the disc (Fig. 29-2). Note that the antheridium is contained within a chamber that opens to the surface of the disc through a pore. Examine an antheridium closely, and note that it is attached to the base of the chamber by a stalk. The body of the antheridium consists of an outer layer of cells, the **jacket**. Within the jacket are found numerous small cells, which will develop into male gametes called *sperm*. If available, examine slides of *Marchantia* sperm.

Obtain a slide showing a cross section of an archegonial disc, on the ventral surface of which are located the archegonia. Locate an **archegonium** that shows the following parts: an elongated neck, an enlarged venter (containing the egg), and the stalk.

What type of division (mitosis or meiosis) is involved in the formation of the sperm and egg? Explain your answer.

_____

_____

_____

_____

342

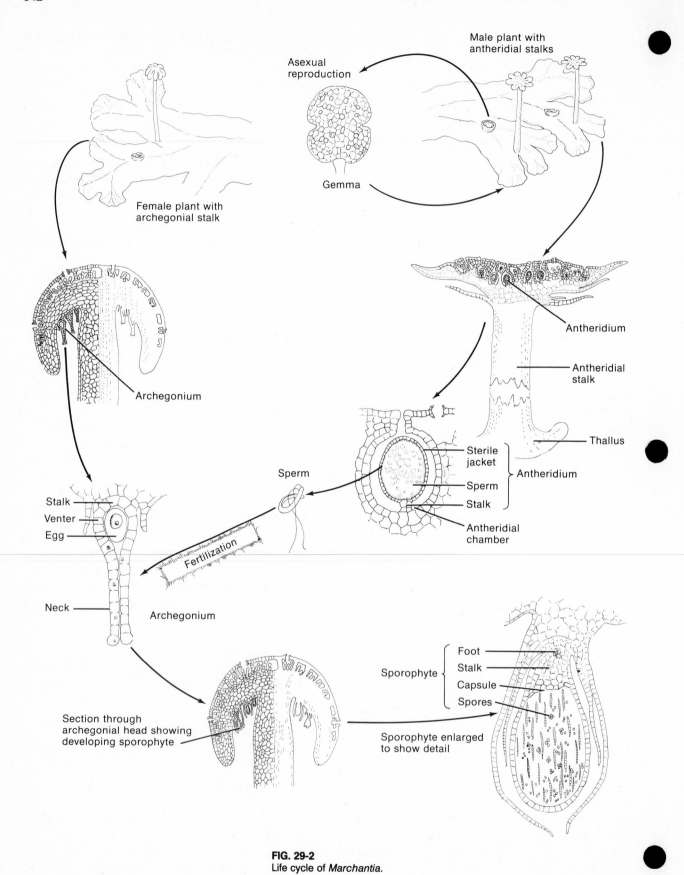

Asexual reproduction

Male plant with antheridial stalks

Gemma

Female plant with archegonial stalk

Archegonium

Antheridium

Antheridial stalk

Thallus

Sperm

Sterile jacket

Sperm

Stalk

Antheridium

Antheridial chamber

Stalk

Venter

Egg

Fertilization

Neck

Archegonium

Sporophyte

Foot

Stalk

Capsule

Spores

Section through archegonial head showing developing sporophyte

Sporophyte enlarged to show detail

FIG. 29-2
Life cycle of *Marchantia*.

4. Fertilization

When the antheridia are mature, the sperm are released and fertilize the egg. The zygote (Fig. 29-2), which remains within the **venter**, undergoes cell division and develops into a multicellular embryo (young **sporophyte**). The embryo differentiates into three distinct parts—the foot, stalk, and capsule. What is the chromosomal condition of the sporophyte?

_____

Examine a prepared slide of a developing sporophyte. Locate the foot embedded in gametophytic tissue. What are some functions of the foot?

_____

_____

Note the large, terminal capsule within which are found spores. By what type of division were the spores formed?

_____

What is the chromosomal conditions of these spores?

_____

_____

Into what structure will the spores develop?

_____

Among the spores, locate elongated cells with spirally thickened walls. These **elaters** help disperse the spores when the capsule breaks open. Note that the sporophyte matured within the archegonium. Before the release of the spores, the capsule is pushed free of the gametophyte by the elongation of the stalk.

Label the various structures in Fig. 29-2 with an _N_ or _2N_ to indicate whether they are haploid or diploid.

B. CLASS MUSCI (MOSSES)

Mosses differ from the liverworts in that the gametophyte of the moss begins as a filamentous, branching structure—a **protonema**—and is differentiated into "stems" and "leaves." In addition, the capsule of the sporophyte contains a central, sterile region of cells—the **colu-**

mella—which greatly reduces the amount of **sporogenous** (spore-producing) tissue. The capsule contains a highly complex series of "teeth," which regulate the dispersal of the spores.

1. Sporophyte of *Polytrichum*

Examine living specimens of the common moss, *Polytrichum,* or, if this is not available, study preserved specimens that consist of both the gametophytic and sporophytic generations. The sporophyte is readily distinguishable, because it consists of a terminal capsule (often covered by a hairy cap, the **calyptra**), a slender stalk (the **seta**), and a foot that is embedded in the top of the "leafy" gametophyte (Fig. 29-3). Carefully separate the sporophyte from the gametophyte. Remove the calyptra and save for later examination. Note that the capsule has a lid. Gently remove the lid, and examine the exposed surface of the capsule with a hand lens. Describe what you see.

_____

Suggest a function for these structures.

_____

_____

Crush the capsule in a drop of water on a slide. Examine microscopically. If the sporophyte is mature, numerous spores will be present. These spores represent the first cells of the gametophyte generation. What is the chromosomal condition of these spores?

_____

What type of division, meiosis or mitosis, is involved in the development of these spores?

_____

2. Gametophyte

After release from the capsule, if suitable environmental conditions exist the spore soon germinates and grows into the filamentous structure of the protonema. Note the similarity of the protonema to filamentous algae. What

344

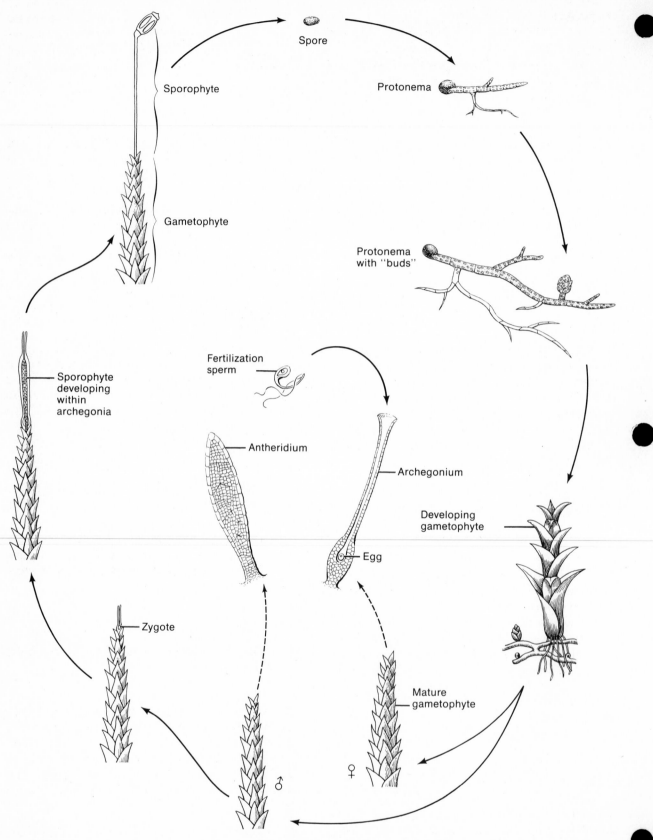

Spore

Sporophyte

Protonema

Gametophyte

Protonema
with "buds"

Sporophyte
developing
within
archegonia

Fertilization
sperm

Antheridium

Archegonium

Developing
gametophyte

Egg

Zygote

Mature
gametophyte

♂

♀

FIG. 29-3
Life cycle of *Polytrichum*.

TABLE 29-1
Advances in complexiity shown by the bryophytes over the algae.

Character	Algae	Liverworts	Mosses
Morphology			
Habitat			
Asexual reproduction			
Sexual reproduction			

evolutionary significance, if any, is indicated here?

_____

_____

Look for small, budlike structures along the length of the filament. These will later develop into mature, "leafy" gametophytes (Fig. 29-3).

Examine the leafy part of *Polytrichum* that remains after removal of the sporophyte. The gametophyte is photosynthetic. The mature gametophyte consists of "leaves," a "stem," and rhizoids. How could you determine if these are true stems and leaves?

_____

_____

Polytrichum is a dioecious moss, with the reproductive organs located at the tips of separate male and female plants. With forceps, carefully remove some of the leaves from the apex of a female plant. After removing as many leaves as possible, cut off the stem and mount in a drop of water on a slide. With your probe, gently tease the tip into small fragments. Examine microscopically. Locate the archegonia (Fig. 29-3). Note the canal that leads through the neck and terminates in the venter of the archegonium. Where is the egg located in the archegonium?

_____

_____

In a similar manner, mount a stem tip of a male plant. Locate the antheridia, which are the elongated, saclike structures consisting of an outer sterile jacket and an inner mass of cells destined to become **antherozoids** (sperm).

If available, also examine prepared slides of moss antheridia and archegonia.

3. Fertilization

The nonmotile egg is retained within the venter of the archegonium. When the archegonium is mature, the cells lining the inside of the stalk disintegrate and a canal is opened leading to the female gamete. The male gamete swims through this canal and unites with the egg. What must be present for fertilization to occur?

_____

The zygote undergoes a series of divisions and becomes a mass of undifferentiated cells, still held in the venter. The developing embryo differentiates into three parts—foot, seta, and capsule. The remains of the archegonium is retained as the calyptra and may be found enclosing the capsule. Is the calyptra sporophytic or gametophytic tissue?

_____

Label the various structures in Fig. 29-3 with *N* or *2N* to indicate whether they are haploid or diploid.

C. ADVANCES IN COMPLEXITY SHOWN BY THE BRYOPHYTES

Complete Table 29-1. Indicate the advances shown by the bryophytes over the algae with respect to morphology, habitat, and reproduction. The following suggested terms can be used:

1. Morphology: *unicellular, filamentous, spherical colonies, prostrate thallus, erect thallus, radial symmetry, bilateral symmetry*

2. Habitat: *fresh water, salt water, ditches, stagnant pools, damp woods, terrestrial*

3. Asexual reproduction: *fragmentation, cell division, zoospores, nonmotile spores, gemmae*

4. Sexual reproduction: *unicellular or multicellular reproductive structures, motile or nonmotile gametes, alternation of generations, isogametes or anisogametes, necessity of water for fertilization, dependency or nondependency of sporophyte, antheridia, archegonia.*

REFERENCES

Bell, P. R., and C. Woodcock. 1968. *The Diversity of Green Plants*. Addison-Wesley.

Bold, H. C. 1977. *The Plant Kingdom*. 4th ed. Prentice-Hall.

Delevoryas, T. 1977. *Plant Diversification*. 2nd ed. Holt, Rinehart and Winston.

Gottlieb, J. E. 1968. *Plants: Adaptation Through Evolution*. Reinhold.

Raven, P. H., R. F. Evert, and H. Curtis. 1976. *Biology of Plants*. 2nd ed. Worth.

Smith, G. M. 1955. *Cryptogamic Botany*. Vol. 2, 2nd ed. *Bryophytes and Pteridophytes*. McGraw-Hill.

Kingdom Plantae: Phylum Tracheophyta

The members of this group represent an advancement in the plant kingdom. In these plants, we find for the first time a system of specialized tissues that carry water, dissolved minerals, and other organic products throughout the plant. They are called **vascular tissues** and the plants that have them (ferns, pines, oaks) are called **vascular plants**, or **tracheophytes**. These plants are able to transport great quantities of water and minerals over long distances in relatively short periods of time. As a result, vascular plants grow much larger than the nonvascular mosses, algae, and fungi.

The Tracheophyta consist of several subphyla and numerous classes. Only the following classes will be studied in this exercise:

Class Filicinae (ferns): Gametophyte small, more or less free-living and photosynthetic. Multicellular sex organs (gametangia). Mostly homosporous but may be heterosporous.

Class Gymnospermae (conifers): Seed plants having needlelike leaves. Ovules in cones and not enclosed. Sperm not flagellated.

Class Angiospermae (flowering plants): Seed plants in which seeds are typically enclosed in carpels. Mature seeds contained in fruits, which may be fleshy or hard. The flower is the reproductive structure containing the male (stamen) and female (pistil) parts. Pollination affected by wind and insects. Gametophytes highly reduced. Double fertilization (of egg and endosperm nuclei) is common feature.

In this exercise, you will become familiar with the structure and reproductive patterns of ferns, conifers (which include pines, spruces, and other evergreens), and the lily (a flowering plant).

A. CLASS FILICINAE (FERNS)

1. Sporophyte

Examine the mature sporophyte of *Polypodium*. Locate the horizontal stem, which may lie on, or just beneath,

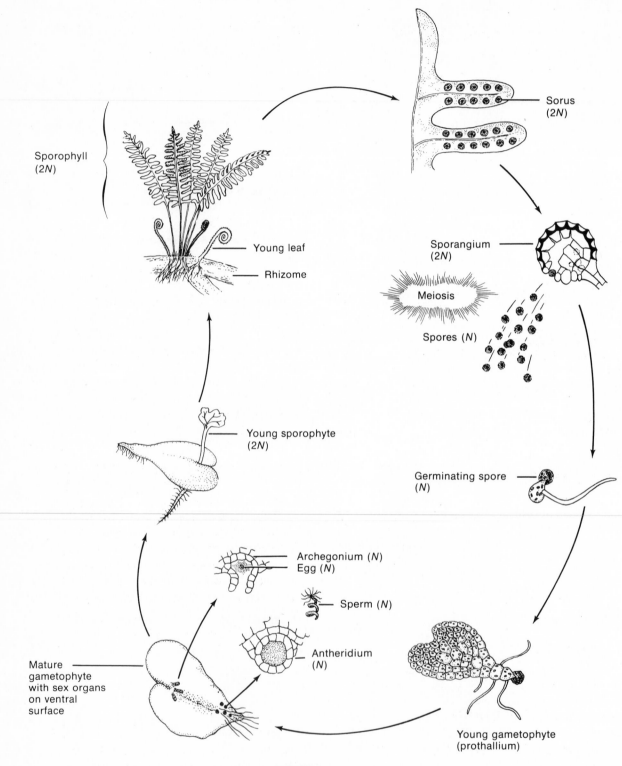

Sorus
(2N)

Sporophyll
(2N)

Young leaf

Rhizome

Sporangium
(2N)

Meiosis

Spores (N)

Germinating spore
(N)

Young sporophyte
(2N)

Archegonium (N)
Egg (N)

Sperm (N)

Antheridium
(N)

Mature
gametophyte
with sex organs
on ventral
surface

Young gametophyte
(prothallium)

FIG. 30-1
Life cycle of a fern.

the surface of the soil. What name is given to this type of stem?

_____

_____

Note the large, deeply lobed leaves, or fronds, of the plant (Fig. 30-1). On the undersurface of some of the leaves, locate small yellowish brown spots or **sori**. Each sorus contains many **sporangia**. What are produced in the sporangia?

_____

What do we call a leaf that produces sporangia?

_____

Obtain part of a fern sporophyll that bears sori. Examine the sorus with a hand lens or dissecting microscope. Scrape the contents of a sorus into a drop of water on a slide. Examine under the low power of the microscope. Each sporangium is composed of a stalk and an enlarged capsule. Examine the capsule under high power. Note a ridge of cells (**annulus**) that extends around the capsule. These cells have thickened inner and radial walls. As the capsule matures, the annular cells lose water and the thin outer walls tend to shrink. This results in a considerable amount of tension on the lateral, thin-walled "cheek cells," which then rupture, releasing the spores.

Remove the cover slip from the slide, and blot the excess water with a piece of filter paper. Examine your preparation (without the cover slip), and observe the sporangia as the slide dries. Describe your observations.

_____

_____

2. Gametophyte

On germination, the fern spore develops into a short filament of cells, which differentiates into a platelike structure called a **prothallium**. The mature prothallium or gametophyte resembles a heart-shaped structure with a notch, containing the growing point, at one end. With a dissecting microscope, examine living fern gametophytes. Locate rhizoids on the ventral surface.

Among the rhizoids of mature gametophytes are found numerous antheridia (Fig. 30-1). Examine the gametophyte with a dissecting microscope. Locate archegonia

on the ventral surface just posterior to the apical notch. Only the neck of the archegonium is visible. The venter is embedded within the gametophytic tissue. The sex organs are found on the ventral surface of the plant. Of what significance is this?

_____

_____

_____

Examine prepared slides of a mature gametophyte, and locate the structures indicated above.

In the development of the new sporophyte, the zygote—following fertilization of the egg—undergoes a series of divisions and develops into an embryo. The young embryo, still held in the venter of the archegonium, differentiates into four lobes. One lobe develops into the "foot." A second lobe grows down into the soil and becomes a primary root. A third lobe develops into the primary leaf, and the last lobe becomes the stem. Until the primary root and leaf become functional the young sporophyte is dependent on the gametophyte; but as soon as the root begins to absorb water and the leaf photosynthesizes, the sporophyte becomes independent. Soon after this, secondary leaves and adventitious roots are formed and the primary root, leaf, and gametophyte die.

B. CLASS GYMNOSPERMAE (CONIFERS)

Conifers are characterized by producing a seed in the life cycle. In the conifers, the seeds are exposed (naked) on scalelike structures. Like the ferns, seed plants have a well-defined alternation of generations. In contrast to the ferns, the gametophyte is microscopic and completely dependent on the large free-living sporophyte, which has stems, leaves, and roots. Although there are several living orders of conifers, your study will be confined to only one of these orders, the conifers, which have familiar representatives in the pines, spruces, cedars, firs, and others.

1. Pine Sporophyte

Study specimens of pine branches, and note that two kinds of leaves are produced by pines. Locate needlelike, photosynthetic leaves borne on short spur shoots and inconspicuous scale leaves found at the bases of the spur

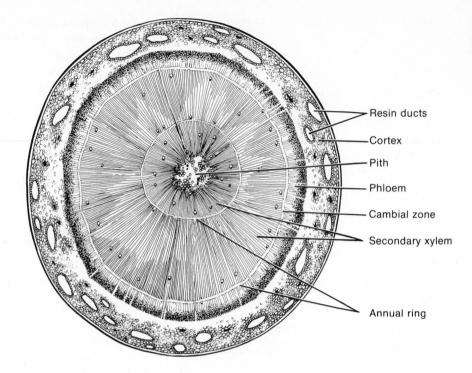

FIG. 30-2
Diagram of an older pine stem.

Resin ducts
Cortex
Pith
Phloem
Cambial zone
Secondary xylem
Annual ring

shoots. How many needle leaves are borne on each spur shoot?

Examine branches of other species of pine. Describe any variation in the number of leaves in a cluster.

Would you consider this difference a means of separating one group of pine from another?

Why are pines called "evergreens"?

Examine cross sections of young and old pine stems (Fig. 30-2). Identify the epidermis, cortex, and vascular tissue, and note the numerous resin canals. What economically important products come from pines?

In the older stems, note the annual rings. How were these formed?

Now examine cross sections of a pine needle (Fig. 30-3). Note the heavily cutinized epidermal cells. Locate a layer of sclerenchyma just beneath the epidermis. Find depressions, or pits, in the epidermis. Where are the stomata located in the pine leaf?

How does the tree benefit by having the stomata located as they are?

Locate the central vascular cylinder surrounded by an endodermis. How many vascular bundles are present?

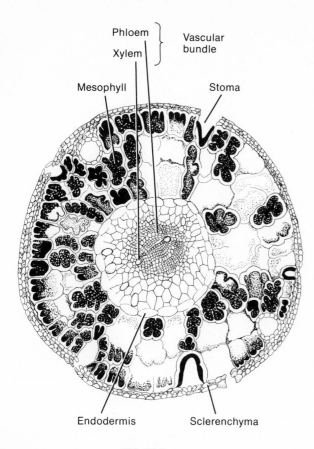

Phloem
Xylem
} Vascular bundle

Mesophyll

Stoma

Endodermis   Sclerenchyma

FIG. 30-3
Pine needle leaf.

Examine cross sections of leaves of other species of pines. Describe any variation in structure among the various needles.

_____

_____

Examine the slides of the various leaves with a dissecting microscope. What correlation exists between the number of leaves in a cluster and the shape of an individual needle leaf?

_____

_____

2. Pine Gametophyte

The pine tree produces two kinds of cones on the same tree. Each cone (**stobilus**) is an auxiliary shoot composed of a central axis that bears spirally arranged sporophylls. Examine branches bearing **staminate** or **pollen cones**,

usually in clusters at the ends. Dissect one of the staminate cones and locate the central axis to which are attached scalelike structures called **microsporophylls** (Fig. 30-4). Remove a microsporophyll, and examine with a dissecting microscope. Note the two saclike **microsporangia**. Break the microsporangia open, and examine the contents under the high power of your microscope. Depending on the stage of development, you will observe either young **microspores** (consisting of a single cell) or microgametophytes (consisting of two prominent cells and two degenerate cells). What is another name for the microgametophyte of pine?

_____

Note the lateral, winglike appendages. How might these "wings" be advantageous?

_____

Examine prepared slides of pine pollen.

A second kind of cone found on the tree is the **seed cone**, which is borne on short, lateral branches near the apex of young branches. They are partially hidden by the terminal bud. Examine branches bearing seed cones, and compare them to the staminate cones on the basis of size, shape, and location. Locate older seed cones that have opened and discharged their seeds. Dissect a seed cone and locate the overlapping, bractlike appendages (Fig. 30-4) attached to the central axis. On the upper surface of each bract, or **megasporophyll**, locate two small, white structures, the ovules. Note that the ovules are not attached directly to the bract but are borne on paper-thin scales, which in turn are attached to each bract. Why are gymnosperms classed as having "naked" seeds?

_____

_____

Examine longitudinal sections of a young pine ovule with a dissecting microscope (Fig. 30-4). Locate an outer layer of tissue that almost encloses the inner tissues except for a small opening at one end. The outer layer is the **integument**; the opening is the **micropyle**. Within the integument, locate the **megasporangium**, in which the **megagametophyte** is found. At the micropylar end of the megagametophyte, locate archegonia. From what cell did the megagametophyte arise?

_____

Note the pollen chamber just inside the microphyle.

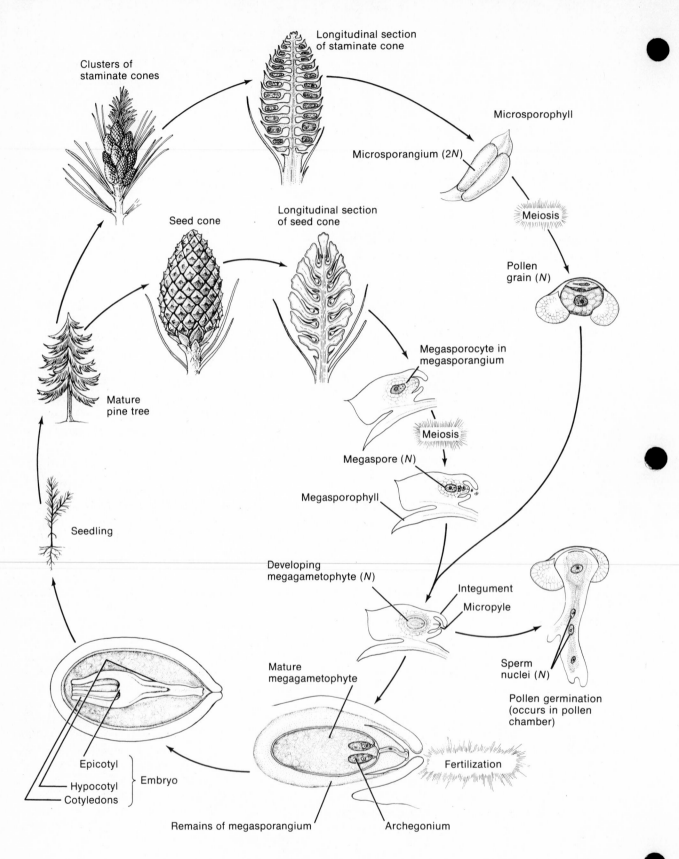

Clusters of staminate cones

Longitudinal section of staminate cone

Microsporophyll

Microsporangium (2N)

Meiosis

Pollen grain (N)

Seed cone

Longitudinal section of seed cone

Megasporocyte in megasporangium

Meiosis

Megaspore (N)

Megasporophyll

Mature pine tree

Developing megagametophyte (N)

Integument

Micropyle

Seedling

Sperm nuclei (N)

Pollen germination (occurs in pollen chamber)

Mature megagametophyte

Fertilization

Epicotyl

Hypocotyl

Cotyledons

Embryo

Remains of megasporangium

Archegonium

FIG. 30-4
Life cycle of a pine.

3. Pollination and Fertilization

The pollen grains are released from the staminate cones toward the end of May. At about the same time, the young seed cones open and the pollen, by sifting down through the cone scales, comes to lie in the pollen chamber. The pollen grain germinates, produces a slender pollen tube containing the male gametes, and digests its way to the archegonia. Because the growth of the pollen tube and the development of the megagametophyte is quite slow, fertilization may not occur for as long as 13 months following pollination.

Remove the seed coats from soaked pine seeds, and cut through the gametophytic tissue to locate the embryo. Locate the epicotyl and hypocotyl. At the tip of the hypocotyl, locate a coiled suspensor, which, by its growth, pushed the developing embryo deeply into the gametophytic tissue that contained large quantities of stored food. If available, examine stages in the germination of a pine seed. Note the peculiar manner in which the embryo comes out of the seed.

C. CLASS ANGIOSPERMAE (FLOWERING PLANTS)

Sexual reproduction requires the union of gametes. The result of this union (fertilization) is a single cell, the zygote, which, by a series of morphogenetic changes, develops into a new individual. In the flowering plants, the gametes are produced in modified branches that we call *flowers*. Examine a flower of a lily and locate the structures described below and as shown in Fig. 30-5, of a typical flower.

1. **Sepals** are modified leaves and are the outermost structures of the flower; they are typically green, although they may be other colors and in some cases may be absent. Collectively, the sepals constitute the **calyx**.

2. **Petals** are internal to the sepals, and may be white or highly colored. Collectively, the petals make up the **corolla**.

3. **Stamens** are structures internal to the petals. Each stamen consists of a stalk (the filament) and a terminal capsule (the anther), which when mature contains the pollen grains. The pollen grains produce the male gametes.

4. **Pistils**—one or more—are found at the center of the flower. Pistils are made up of one or more carpels—leaflike structures bearing ovules. It is postulated that in evolution the carpels have rolled inward, enclosing the ovules. The pistil consists of three parts: an enlarged basal region (the ovary), a slender stalk (the style), and a somewhat flattened tip (the stigma). The ovary contains

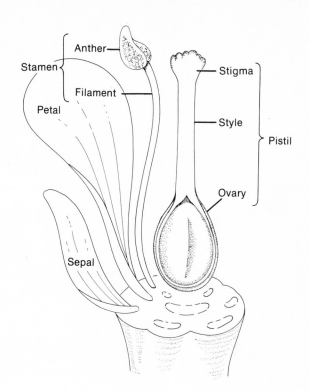

FIG. 30-5
Diagram of a flower.

seedlike structures called ovules, which, when mature, contain the female gametes. In the process of pollination, the pollen grains are transported to the stigma, where they germinate and send a long tube down to the ovules. How does pollination in the flowering plants differ from that in conifers?

_____

_____

_____

_____

The pollen tube penetrates the ovule and releases two male gametes, one of which unites with the egg to form the zygote.

The lily plant is called a *sporophyte*, a stage in the life cycle of the plant during which spores are produced within specialized structures called *sporangia*. These are formed on or within modified leaves called **sporophylls**. What flower parts described above can be considered sporophylls?

_____

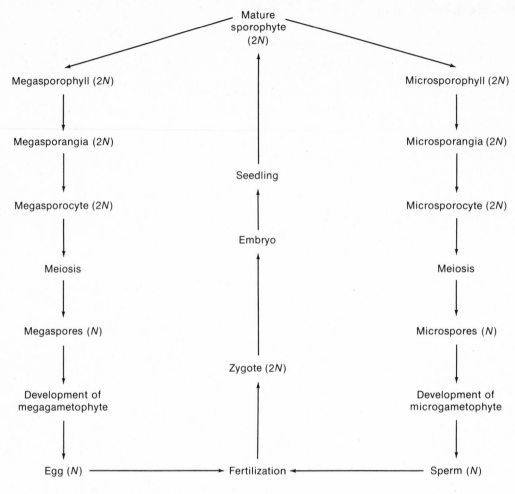

FIG. 30-6
Generalized scheme of the reproductive cycle of higher plants.

Certain cells—**spore mother cells** or **sporocytes**—undergo meiotic division within the sporangium to form these spores. The spore undergoes morphogenetic changes and develops into microscopic plants (gametophytes) that produce the gametes. In the flowering plants, the gametophytic plant is parasitic on the sporophyte. Because the male gamete is smaller than the female gamete, it is called a **microgamete** to distinguish it from the larger female **megagamete**. Similarly, the male gametophyte is called the *microgametophyte* as opposed to the female *megagametophyte*. This same terminology applies to all male and female structures. This scheme is summarized in Fig. 30-6.

In studying the stamens (microsporophylls), recall that the stamen consists of an anther and filament. The anther contains the microsporangium in which are found the microsporocytes. Examine slides of a young lily anther (Fig. 30-7). Locate the microsporcytes. What is the chromosomal condition of these cells (i.e., N or 2N)?

_____

_____

What indication is there that some of the microsporocytes have divided?

_____

_____

What kind of division has occurred?

_____

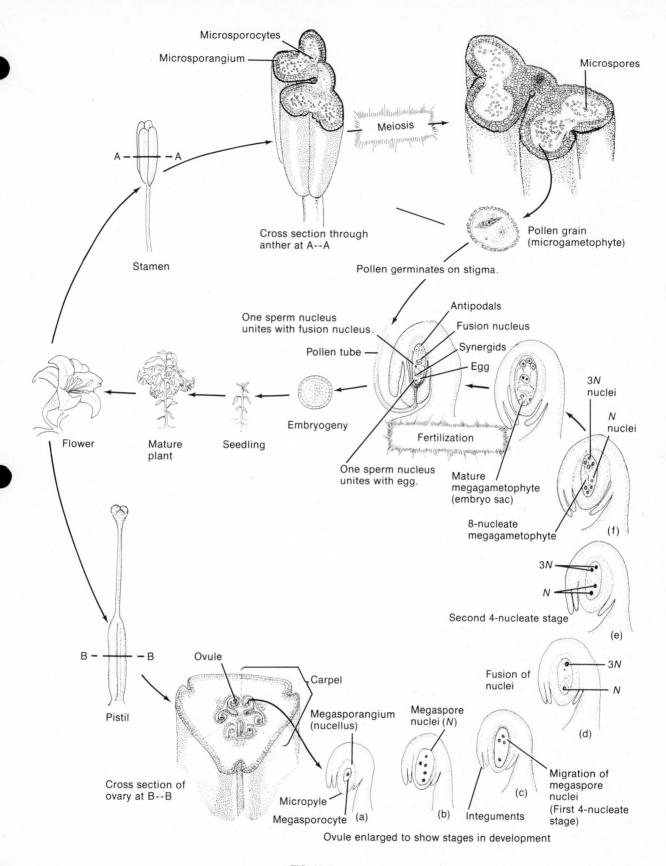

Microsporocytes

Microsporangium

Microspores

Meiosis

Stamen

A — — A

Cross section through
anther at A--A

Pollen germinates on stigma.

Pollen grain
(microgametophyte)

One sperm nucleus
unites with fusion nucleus.

Antipodals

Fusion nucleus

Synergids

Pollen tube

Egg

One sperm nucleus
unites with egg.

Fertilization

Flower

Mature
plant

Seedling

Embryogeny

Mature
megagametophyte
(embryo sac)

8-nucleate
megagametophyte

3N
nuclei

N
nuclei

(f)

3N

N

Second 4-nucleate
stage

(e)

Fusion of
nuclei

3N

N

(d)

B — — B

Pistil

Ovule

Carpel

Megasporangium
(nucellus)

Megaspore
nuclei (N)

Migration of
megaspore
nuclei
(First 4-nucleate
stage)

Cross section of
ovary at B--B

Micropyle

Megasporocyte

(a)

(b)

Integuments

(c)

Ovule enlarged to show stages in development

FIG. 30-7
Life cycle of a lily.

The cells formed as a result of the division of the microsporocytes are called *microspores*. These will develop into mature microgametophytes or pollen grains. Remove an anther from your flower, crush it in a drop of water on a slide, and examine microscopically. For a more detailed examination of the pollen grain, obtain slides showing a section through an older lily anther. Locate the numerous pollen grains. The pollen grains are shed from the anther and are transferred by various means to the stigma of the same or a different flower. In this process of pollination, a pollen tube is formed that is chemotropically oriented to grow down through the style to the ovules. During the growth of the pollen tube, gametes are formed as a result of the division of one of the nuclei in the pollen tube. Examine cultures of germinating pollen and observe the pollen tubes. If possible, locate the two male gametes. In Fig. 30-7, trace the stages in the development of the microgametophyte.

In the ovule, a centrally located mass of tissue enlarges to form the megasporangium or **nucellus** (Fig. 30-7). Concomitant with the development of the megasporangium, adjacent cells grow up and around the nucellus to form the integuments, which later develop into the outer coverings of the seed. The integuments do not fuse but leave an opening (the **micropyle**) at the apex of the nucellus, through which the pollen tube enters the ovule. As the nucellus grows, the nucleus of the centrally located megasporocyte undergoes meiosis to form four megaspore nuclei.

One of the megaspore nuclei migrates to the micropyle end; the other three migrate to the opposite (chalazel) end. This 3 + 1 arrangement represents the first 4-nucleate stage in the development of the embryo sac.

The three haploid nuclei then fuse to form a $3N$ nucleus. This stage is followed by a mitotic division of the $3N$ and N nuclei to form two triploid nuclei and two haploid nuclei. This is the second 4-nucleate stage. A final division occurs resulting in an 8-nucleate embryo sac consisting of four triploid and four haploid nuclei. At this point, three of the triploid nuclei migrate to the chalazel end of the embryo sac where cell walls are formed around them. These cells, called *antipodals,* are probably nutritive in nature.

Three haploid nuclei migrate to the micropylar end of the embryo sac. The middle one becomes the egg. The role of the two lateral ones (called *synergids*) is not fully understood although recent work has shown that the pollen tube enters the synergid first and then the egg. Thus, the synergids might function in guiding the pollen tube. The two remaining nuclei migrate to the center of the embryo sac and form a fusion nucleus. What is the chromosome content of this nucleus?

Examine slides that show the developmental stages indicated above. As you study these slides, refer to Fig. 30-7.

Fertilization is complete when the pollen tube, having reached the micropyle of the ovule, digests its way through the nucellus, reaches the embryo sac, and releases both male gametes. One gamete unites with the egg to form the zygote, which subsequently develops into an embryo. The second gamete unites with the fusion nucleus to form the endosperm nucleus. What is the chromosome condition of the endosperm nucleus?

Subsequent division of the endosperm results in a mass of nutritive tissue that is used as a food source for the developing embryo. This double fertilization is a phenomenon peculiar to flowering plants and has no counterpart in the lower plants or in the animal kingdom.

D. TYPICAL EMBRYO SAC DEVELOPMENT

The events in the development of the lily embryo sac (as given in Part C) are really only one of several different types of development that take place in the formation of the megagametophyte in angiosperms (Fig. 30-8). Many are much more complex than that which occurs in the lily. Of the various examples shown in Fig. 30-8, which plant shows a pattern of embryo sac development comparable to the lily?

(*Note:* The number of "dots" in each nucleus indicates the chromosome complement. For example, two "dots" is diploid, three "dots" is triploid, and so forth.)

Although you should be aware of the complexities that occur, we can simplify this developmental event by describing a composite picture of embryo sac development. This is shown in Fig. 30-9.

E. ADVANCES IN COMPLEXITY SHOWN BY VASCULAR PLANTS

Complete Table 30-1. Indicate the increases in complexity shown by the tracheophytes over the bryophytes with respect to morphology and reproduction. The following are suggested terms to use.

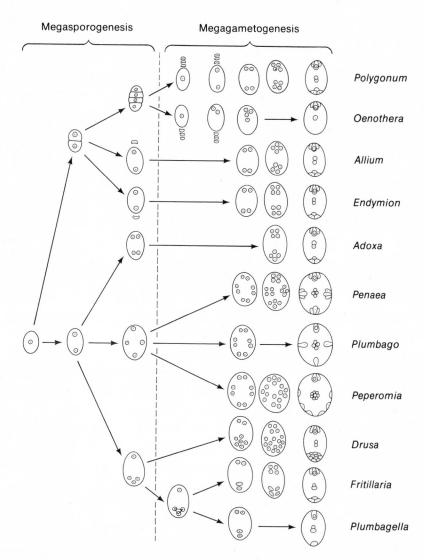

FIG. 30-8
Comparison of megagametophyte development in angiosperms. (Adapted from
Comparative Morphology of Vascular Plants, by Adriance S. Foster and Ernest M.
Gifford, 2nd ed. W. H. Freeman and Company. Copyright © 1974. Redrawn from
Johri in *Recent Advances in the Embryology of Angiosperms*, edited by
P. Maheshwari. University of Delhi, 1963.)

Morphology: *true leaves present or absent, true stems and roots present or absent, vascular tissue present or absent, erect or prostrate plant body*

Asexual reproduction: *spores, fragmentation, gemmae, death and decay of older parts*, and so on

Sexual reproduction: *unicellular or multicellular reproductive organs, motile or nonmotile gametes, alternation of generations, isogametes, anisogametes, water necessary of unnecessary for fertilization, antheridia, archegonia, dependency or interdependence of sporophyte, pollination*

358

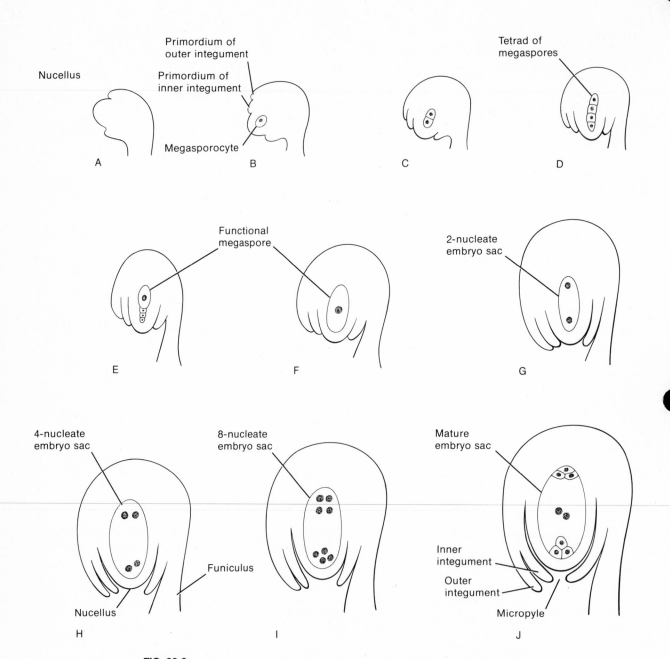

FIG. 30-9
Megagametophyte development in a typical angiosperm. (Adapted from *Comparative Morphology of Vascular Plants,* by Adriance S. Foster and Ernest M. Gifford, 2nd ed. W. H. Freeman and Company. Copyright © 1974. Redrawn from *A Textbook of General Botany,* 4th ed., by R. M. Holman and W. W. Robbins. Wiley, 1951.)

TABLE 30-1
Advances in complexity shown by the vascular plants.

Character	Liverworts and mosses	Vascular plants
Morphology of sporophyte		
Morphology of gametophyte		
Asexual reproduction		
Sexual reproduction		

REFERENCES

Banks, H. P. 1970. *Evolution and Plants of the Past*. Wadsworth.

Bierhorst, D. W. 1971. *Morphology of Vascular Plants*. Macmillan.

Bold, H. C. 1978. *Morphology of Plants and Fungi*. 4th ed. Harper & Row.

Bold, H. C. 1977. *The Plant Kingdom*. 4th ed. Prentice-Hall.

Curtis, H. 1979. *Biology*. 3rd ed. Worth.

Delevoryas, T. 1977. *Plant Diversification*. 2nd ed. Holt, Rinehart and Winston.

Gottlieb, J. E. 1968. *Plants: Adaptation Through Evolution*. Reinhold.

Raven, P. H., R. F. Evert, and H. Curtis. 1976. *Biology of Plants*. 2nd ed. Worth.

Kingdom Animalia: Phyla Porifera and Cnidaria

According to Whittaker's classification scheme, the kingdom Animalia includes multicellular organisms having eucaryotic cells that lack cell walls, plastids, and photosynthetic pigments. Most members of this kingdom take in nutrients by ingestion, with digestion taking place in an internal cavity. Some take in nutrients by absorption and lack an internal digestive cavity.

The higher forms in the animal kingdom have evolved highly sophisticated levels of organization and tissue differentiation, including sensory neuromotor systems and modes of motility based on contractile fibers.

Reproduction for most of the organisms in this kingdom is sexual, and except for some of the lowest phyla haploid cells occur only in the gametes.

In this exercise, you will study representatives of the phyla Porifera (sponges) and Cnidaria (coelenterates), the first of the multicellular or "tissue" animals.

A. PHYLUM PORIFERA (SPONGES)

The phylum Porifera (Latin *porus,* "pore"; *ferre,* "to bear") consists of the sponges, which are characterized by bodies with radial symmetry and an internal skeleton of either minute spicules or fibers made up of **spongin**.

The body surface of sponges has many pores, which are connected to canals and chambers lined by flagellated cells.

Based largely on the structural organization of the internal skeleton, this phylum is divided into three major classes:

Class Calcarea (calcareous sponges): skeletons are composed of limy ($CaCO_3$) spicules

Class Hexactinellida (glass sponges): skeletons are composed of siliceous material (chiefly $H_2Si_3O_7$)

Class Demospongiae: skeletons are composed of organic fibers (spongin) or siliceous spicules or both, and canal systems are complex

1. Class Calcarea

Scypha (formerly called *Sycon* or *Grantia*) is a small, slender sponge that rarely exceeds more than an inch in height and is found in clusters adhering to various objects in shallow marine waters.

Using a dissecting microscope, examine preserved specimens of *Scypha* and note their slender, vase-shaped

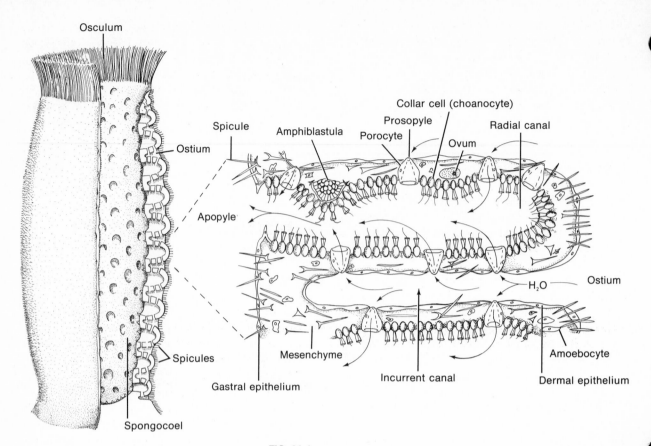

FIG. 31-1
Canal system of *Scypha*.

appearance. Observe the basal end by which this organism attaches itself to various objects and the large single excurrent opening, the **osculum**, at the free end. Minute pores (**ostia**) along the body wall allow water to enter the single tubular central canal, or **spongocoel**. Locate bristlelike structures along the body surfaces. These are the spicules, which give rigidity to the body. The spicules are chiefly of four kinds: (1) long, straight spicules surrounding the osculum that protrude beyond the body surface, producing a bristly appearance; (2) short, straight spicules surrounding the ostia; (3) T-shaped spicules lining the spongocoel; and (4) three-branched spicules embedded in the body wall. Examine slides showing isolated spicules.

Study a prepared stained cross section of *Scypha* under both low and high magnification (Fig. 31-1). Note that the body wall is thick and folded to form many short radial canals. Water enters the sponge through the ostia, which lead into the **incurrent canals**. These canals extend almost to the wall of the spongocoel, or the digestive cavity. The spongocoel connects to the outside through an opening called an **osculum**. The incurrent canals are connected to the **excurrent (radial) canals** by a series of small pores called **prosopyles**. The excurrent

canals, in turn, open into the spongocoel through pores called **apopyles**. The exterior surface of this sponge is covered by a thin **dermal epithelium**; the spongocoel is lined with **gastral epithelium**; and the radial canals are lined with small, flagellated collar cells, or **choanocytes**. These cells bear a resemblance to some of the flagellated protozoans—a fact that indicates a probable evolution of the sponges from protozoans. Between the dermal and gastral epithelium is a gelatinous **mesenchyme**, which contains free cells, or **amoebocytes**.

Water, taken into the body through the ostia, is passed over the collar cells, which remove tiny bits of food, and is then extruded through the osculum. The food consists of plankton (microscopic plants and animals) and bits of organic matter that are digested in the food vacuoles of the choanocytes and amoebocytes. Indigestible material is extruded into the canal system for extrusion through the osculum by way of the spongocoel.

Sponges can reproduce by both asexual and sexual means. Parts of a sponge lost by injury can be replaced asexually by regeneration. Many kinds of sponges reproduce by simple budding; the buds either separating from the original sponge as growth proceeds or remaining attached to form clusters. Because *Scypha* is **monoecious** (**hermaphroditic**), sexual reproduction is accomplished by male (sperm) and female (ova) gametes produced by the choanocytes. Fertilization is internal. When the embryo reaches the oval-shaped **amphiblastula** stage, it escapes through the osculum. It swims about for a short time and then attaches to a solid object to begin growth as a young sponge.

2. Class Hexactinellida

Hexactinellids are beautiful vase- or funnel-shaped sponges whose skeletons are composed of six-rayed spicules made of siliceous materials; they are therefore referred to as "glass sponges." They are deep-water forms of sponges, and usually only the skeleton is recovered.

Examine specimens of the sponge *Euplectella* (Venus's flower blasket). What you are observing is merely the skeleton of the living sponge, because all of the protoplasm has dried and decayed away. Note that the skeleton is composed of a delicate network of siliceous spicules fused at their tips.

3. Class Demospongiae

This class includes the familiar bath sponges and freshwater sponges. Examine the flexible fibrous skeleton of a bath sponge *(Spongia);* it is the sponge we commonly use because of its water-absorbing capacity. The skeleton can hold water because of capillary forces in the fine spaces of the irregular spongin network. Synthetic sponges have largely replaced the natural variety in most areas of the world.

B. PHYLUM CNIDARIA (COELENTERATES)

The phylum Cnidaria consists of a diverse group of radially symmetrical organisms that are characterized by a digestive (**gastrovascular**) body cavity, some muscle fibers, and many minute stinging capsules called **nematocysts**. The members of this phylum may have one of two forms—polypean or medusan. A **polyp** is a tubular organism closed at one end and having a mouth surrounded by tentacles at the other end. A **medusa** is an umbrella-shaped, jellylike, free-swimming organism with a mouth at the end of a central projection called a **manubrium**. The phylum is divided into three classes:

Class Hydrozoa: in which the polyp stage is predominant and gives rise to small free-swimming medusae in many species

Class Scyphozoa: includes the larger jellyfish, in which the medusa stage, consisting largely of gelatinous **mesoglea** or "jelly," is predominant and the polyp stage is minute or lacking (Scyphozoans can be roughly distinguished from the medusae of the hydrozoans by their size, which ranges from 25 mm to 2 m in diameter)

Class Anthozoa: in which there is only a polyp stage

1. Class Hydrozoa

a. Hydra

A common freshwater hydrozoan, *Hydra* is an excellent organism to use for the study of the polyp form of coelenterates. It is also of fundamental interest because it illustrates a definite, though primitive, level of organization into tissues. Commonly studied species are the brown *(Hydra oligactis)* and green hydras *(Hydra viridissimus);* the latter are green because of the presence of minute algae living symbiotically within their bodies.

Using a hand lens or a dissecting microscope, examine living hydras in a Syracuse dish or deep-well slide containing pond water. These slender organisms vary from 10 to 25 mm in length. At the upper end of the animal, observe several elongate, actively moving tentacles, which are used to capture food. At the center of this circle of tentacles is the mouth. Tap the edge of your slide or dish, and observe the extreme contractility of this organism. Note that the animal expands after contracting. Compare the rate of elongation with that of contraction.

So that you can observe the hydras ingesting food, your instructor will add to your slide or dish several brine shrimp or *Daphnia* that have been thoroughly rinsed with tap water. Why are the brine shrimp washed before being fed to the hydra?

Using a dissecting microscope, observe your specimen and describe the feeding process, beginning with the first contact of the hydra's tentacles with its food.

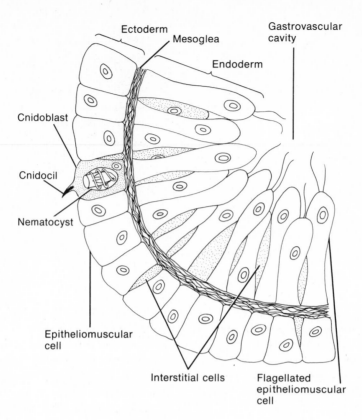

FIG. 31-2
Section of body wall of *Hydra*.

It is not unusual for a single hydra to capture and ingest 10 or more *Daphnia* in the course of a 2-hour feeding period.

While observing the feeding process, you may have noticed that as the tentacles of the hydra came in contact with its prey, the shrimp or *Daphnia* jerked for several minutes before becoming still. The food organism reacted in this way because it had been stung by numerous stinging cells released by the tentacles of the hydra. Close examination of the tentacles of your specimen will reveal the presence of wartlike structures called **nematocysts**. Until it is discharged, each nematocyst is enclosed in a **cnidoblast** cell, with the coiled thread inside it. Observe the trigger (**cnidocil**) located on the edge of the undischarged nematocyst. When it is discharged, the coiled thread is turned inside out as it is released from the cnidoblast. Note the barbs and long thread in the discharged nematocyst. The release of these nematocysts can be observed by placing a hydra in a drop of water on a clean slide and then adding a drop of dilute acetic acid at the edge of the water. Observe the tentacles as the acid diffuses toward them. Note the discharge of the nematocysts. The structures of the various types of nematocysts can be observed by adding a drop of dilute methylene blue or other suitable stain at the edge of the water.

Hydras reproduce asexually by simple budding and sexually by the production of sperm and ova. Budding consists of a simple outgrowth from the body wall (its gastrovascular cavity continuous with that of the parent) separating upon maturity from the parent. Examine specimens of budding hydras.

The gametes are produced in organs called **spermaries** and **ovaries**, which are protuberances along the body wall. Both sex organs may be present in a single organism. Examine prepared slides showing the location and structure of these organs.

To study the histology of *Hydra,* examine stained cross sections. Note that the body wall surrounding the **gastrovascular cavity** consists of two distinct layers of cells—an outer layer of **ectoderm** and an inner layer of **endoderm** (Fig. 31-2). These two layers are held together by a thin, noncellular layer—the **mesoglea**. In the ectoderm are two principal cell types—the larger **epitheliomuscular cells** containing contractile fibrils at their base and the smaller **interstitial cells** located between them.

● What might you expect the function of the epitheliomuscular cells to be?

_____

_____

The ectoderm of the tentacles also contains nematocysts.

Many of the large endodermal cells contain food vacuoles in which intracellular digestion takes place. These food vacuoles are formed as a result of the engulfing of food particles by pseudopodia that are extended into the gastrovascular cavity. Many of the digestive cells also contain flagellae, whose beating activity directs food toward the pseudopodia. Extracellular digestion in hydra is by means of the secretion of enzymes directly into the gastrovascular cavity, followed by absorption of the digested food material.

b. Obelia

Unlike *Hydra,* most members of the hydrozoans are colonial marine organisms. *Obelia* is such a typical coelenterate and is found attached to seaweeds (particularly the kelps), rocks, shells, or pilings in the shallow waters off seacoasts. Reproduction in this animal is **metagenetic** (alternation of sexual and asexual generations), a common characteristic of plants. The **polyp** stage is the asexual generation, and the **medusa** stage is the sexual one.

Place a small piece of *Obelia* in a Syracuse dish and examine under a dissecting microscope. The plantlike colony consists of numerous branches, which terminate in two kinds of polyps. The feeding, or **nutritive, polyps (hydranths)** possess tentacles and resemble *Hydra.* The **reproductive polyps (gonangia)** are club-shaped and lack tentacles (Fig. 31-3). The branches of the colony are covered by a transparent, noncellular sheath—the **perisarc**. This covering expands around the hydranths and gonangia to form vase-shaped protective structures called **hydrothecae** and **gonothecae**, respectively. The inner cellular core of the colony is called the **coenosarc**.

c. Gonionemus

Because the medusae of *Obelia* are too small to study in detail, the large medusa stage of *Gonionemus,* a common jellyfish, will be used to illustrate the typical structure of a coelenterate medusa.

Using a hand lens or dissecting microscope, examine a specimen in a Syracuse dish (Fig. 31-4). Note that the medusa is umbrella-shaped. Turn the organism over, and note that the margin of the "umbrella" extending inward is a muscular ring of tissue called the **velum**. What might a function of the velum be?

_____

_____

The medusa usually swims with its convex surface upward so that the tentacles are facing the surface of the water. Observe the number of tentacles around the bell. Extending into the cavity of the medusa is the **manubrium**, which contains a mouth at its tip surrounded by four **oral lobes**. Extending from the manubrium along the inner surfaces are four **radial canals** that join with the circular canal at the margin and connect with the cavities of the tentacles. What is the function of these canals?

_____

_____

Observe the numerous **nematocyst batteries** and the **suctorial pads** on the tentacles.

At the base of each tentacle are round, pigmented structures that are believed to be **photoreceptors**. Between tentacles is a **statocyst**, a small capsule containing a tiny, solid body, which serves as a balancing organ. The reproductive organs (**gonads**) are attached to the radial canals. *Gonionemus,* like most coelenterates, is **dioecious**; that is, it has the male and female organs in separate organisms. The eggs and sperm are released into the sea, where fertilization takes place. The zygote develops into a **planula larva**, which swims about and then settles and attaches to a submerged object, where it transforms into a microscopic polyp. The polyp may reproduce asexually by budding or it may form tiny medusae as described for *Obelia.*

d. Other Hydrozoans

Examine demonstration specimens of other hydrozoans to see the great diversity of structure among the individuals forming a colony. In this respect, pay particular attention to *Physalia,* the Portuguese man-of-war, which shows a highly specialized form of **polymorphism** (many forms). In addition to a modified medusa that forms the gas-filled float, there are several kinds of tentacles that serve to paralyze and capture food for the colony.

2. Class Scyphozoa

In scyphozoans (Greek *skyphos,* "cup"; *zoon,* "animal"), the medusa stage is quite large, ranging from 25 mm to 2 meters in diameter. The polyp stage is minute or lacking.

Aurelia, one of the commonest of the scyphozoan jellyfish, exists throughout the world. Aurelias are often

366

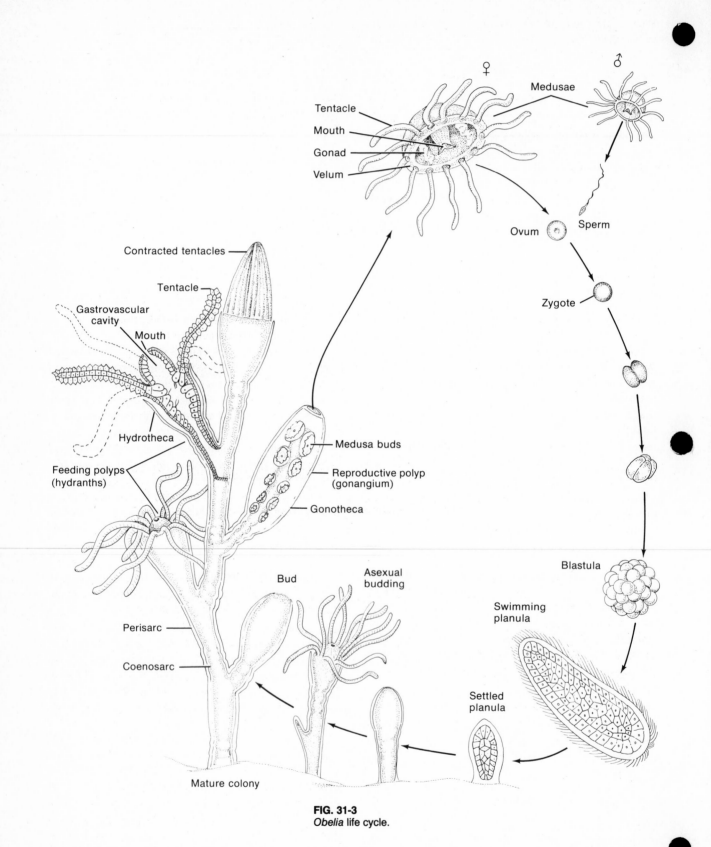

FIG. 31-3
Obelia life cycle.

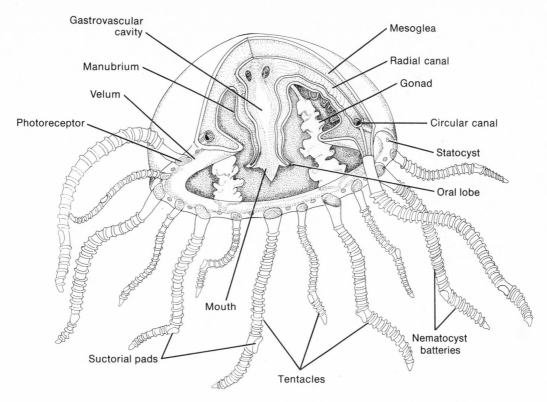

Gastrovascular cavity

Manubrium

Velum

Photoreceptor

Mesoglea

Radial canal

Gonad

Circular canal

Statocyst

Oral lobe

Mouth

Suctorial pads

Tentacles

Nematocyst batteries

FIG. 31-4
The internal anatomy of *Gonionemus*.

seen in large shoals, drifting along together or swimming slowly by rhythmic contractions of the shallow, almost saucer-shaped bell. Great numbers are sometimes cast on shore during storms.

Examine a specimen of *Aurelia*. Identify as many of the following structural characteristics of this jellyfish as you can.

The body is shallowly convex above and concave below and is fringed by a row of closely spaced marginal tentacles (Fig. 31-5). These tentacles are interrupted at eight equally spaced intervals by indentations, each of which contains a sense organ. The sense organs consist of a pigmented eyespot, sensitive to light; a hollow statocyst, containing minute calcareous particles whose movements set up stimuli that direct the swimming movements; and two sense pits, lined with cells that are thought to be sensitive to food or to other chemicals in the water. Many circular muscle fibers are present in the margin. What is the function of these muscle fibers?

_____

_____

The mouth is located in the center of the oral (concave) surface at the end of a vary short manubrium. The manubrium lies between four tapering oral arms, each of which has a ciliated groove. Stinging capsules in the lobes paralyze and entangle small animals, which are then swept up the grooves, through the mouth, and into a digestive cavity that extends into four pouches, in which there are tentaclelike projections. These projections are covered with nematocysts that paralyze prey that arrives in the pouches still alive and struggling. Many radial canals extend through the mesoglea from the pouches to a ring canal in the bell margin. Flagella lining the entire gastrovascular cavity maintain a steady current of water, which brings a constant supply of food and oxygen to the animal's internal parts and removes waste from them.

The four horseshoe-shaped, colored bodies by which *Aurelia* is recognized are the testes or ovaries; they are located on the floor of the large central part of the gastrovascular cavity. In a male medusa, the sperm cells are discharged into the gastrovascular cavity and then to the outside through the mouth. The eggs of the female are discharged into the cavity, where they are fertilized by sperm cells entering the mouth along with incoming food.

The zygotes emerge and lodge on the oral lobes, where each develops into a ciliated planula larva. This larva soon escapes, swims about for a while, and then settles and attaches to the sea bottom. Losing the cilia, it becomes a minute trumpet-shaped polyp (**scyphistoma**) with a basal disc, mouth, and tentacles. This polyp feeds and stores food and may survive in this stage for many

FIG. 31-5
Life cycle of *Aurelia*.

months, meanwhile budding off other small polyps like itself.

Usually in the fall and winter, the polyp develops a series of horizontal constrictions (**strobilation**) that resembles a pile of minute "saucers" (**ephyra**) with fluted borders. One by one the "saucers" pinch off from the parent and swim away as little medusas that will develop into adult jellyfish.

Examine demonstration specimens and slides showing the stages in the life cycle of *Aurelia*.

3. Class Anthozoa

Anthozoa (Greek *anthos*, "flower"; *zoon* "animal") are marine polyps of flowerlike form that have no medusa stage. They are distinguished from hydrozoan polyps by having a gastrovascular cavity that is divided by a series of vertical partitions and surface ectoderm that turns in

at the mouth to line the gullet. Externally, there is no difficulty in distinguishing the large sea anemones or the stony corals of this class from most of the small, fragile hydrozoan polyps. Besides the familiar sea anemones and stony corals, this class includes the soft, horny, and black corals; the colonial sea pens and sea pansies; and others. They are abundant in warm, shallow waters, but also inhabit polar seas. Other species inhabit areas ranging from the tide lines to depths of 5,000 meters.

a. Sea Anemones

Of the polyp type of coelenterates, sea anemones are among the most highly specialized. They have a well-developed nerve net, mesenchyme cells between ectoderm and endoderm, and several sets of specialized muscles.

Examine the common sea anemone *Metridium*, and note the stout cylindrical body, expanded at its upper end

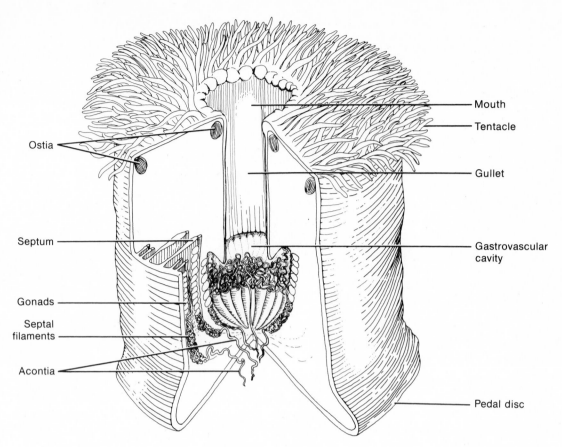

FIG. 31-6
Internal anatomy of *Metridium*.

into an oral disc around a slitlike mouth surrounded by several rows of tentacles. When undisturbed and covered by water, the body and tentacles are widely extended. If irritated or exposed by a receding tide, the oral disc may be completely turned inward and the body tightly contracted. Cilia on the tentacles and oral disc beat to keep these surfaces free of debris. The basal end forms a smooth, muscular, slimy **pedal disc** on which the anemone can slide about very slowly and by which it holds to rocks so tenaciously that it is likely to be torn if someone tries to pry it loose. They commonly attach themselves to the shells of crabs or other shelled animals in the ocean. In this way the anemones are widely dispersed. Many anemones are exquisitely colored. Examine a preserved or a living specimen, and identify the external and internal features described in the following discussion.

From the mouth, a muscular gullet hangs down into the gastrovascular cavity (Fig. 31-6). The gullet is not cylindrical but is flattened and lined with cilia that beat downward, thus drawing a current of water into the gastrovascular cavity and steadily supplying the internal parts with oxygen. At the same time, other cilia lining the gullet beat upward, creating an outgoing current of water that takes with it carbon dioxide and other wastes. When small animals touch the tentacles, the cilia of the gullet reverse their beat, and the food is swept down the gullet into the digestive cavity. The gullet is connected with the body wall by a series of vertical partitions (**septa**). What is the function of these septa?

_____

_____

In the septa, beneath the oral disc, are openings, or **ostia**, through which water can pass between the internal compartments. The free, inner margin of each septum is a thick convoluted **septal filament** that becomes a threadlike **acontium** toward the bottom. Both parts bear nematocysts for paralyzing prey and gland cells for the secretion of enzymes needed in digestion.

Anemones sometimes reproduce asexually by pulling apart into two longitudinal halves; each half then regenerates into a new adult. Sexual reproduction is accomplished by the small, rounded gonads located at the edges of the septa. The sexes are separate. Eggs and sperm leave the gonads through the mouth, and fertilization takes place in the water. The fertilized egg develops into a ciliated planula larva, which finally settles down in a rocky crevice and grows into an adult anemone.

b. Corals

Although small and fragile polyps, corals can combine to form huge colonies consisting of millions of individuals. Each member of a colony secretes a protective skeleton of limestone containing a pocket into which the polyp partly withdraws when attacked. New individuals build their skeletons on the skeletons of dead ones, and thus, over many years, huge undersea ledges known as coral reefs are built up by the action of these minute animals. Three main types of coral reefs are recognized. A **fringing reef** grows in shallow water, bordering the coast or separated from it by only a narrow stretch of water that can be waded when the tide is out. A **barrier reef** also is parallel to the coast but is separated from it by a channel (lagoon) deep enough to accommodate large ships. The best-known of these is the Great Barrier Reef along the northwest coast of Australia, which is about 2,000 kilometers long and from a few to 150 kilometers off shore. An **atoll** is a ring-shaped island surrounding a central lagoon. Atolls are hundreds or thousands of kilometers from the nearest land and slope off into the depths of the ocean.

Examine samples of coral on demonstration in the laboratory, and note the variety of different forms. Locate and examine the small pockets that contained the polyps.

REFERENCES

Buchsbaum, R. 1948. *Animals Without Backbones*. 2nd ed. University of Chicago Press.

Fry, W. G., ed. 1970. *The Biology of the Porifera*. Academic Press.

Meglitsch, P. A. 1972. *Invertebrate Zoology*. 2nd ed. Oxford University Press.

Storer, T. I., R. L. Usinger, R. C. Stebbins, and J. W. Nybakken. 1979. *General Zoology*. 6th ed. McGraw-Hill.

Kingdom Animalia: Phylum Platyhelminthes

The members of this phylum are characterized by a dorsoventrally flattened body and are therefore commonly called *flatworms*. The space between the ectoderm-derived body wall and the endoderm-derived internal organs is filled with loose parenchymal tissue of mesenchymal origin. Because these organisms possess a third tissue layer, the mesoderm, they are considered to be **triploblastic**. They have advanced considerably beyond the coelenterates in that they possess well-developed nervous, excretory, muscular, digestive, and reproductive systems. The phylum includes the following three major classes:

Class Turbellaria: free-living flatworms, most of which inhabit fresh or salt water or moist places on land

Class Trematoda: flukes, which are internal or external parasites

Class Cestoda: tapeworms, the adults of which are intestinal parasites of vertebrates

A. CLASS TURBELLARIA (FREE-LIVING FLATWORMS)

The free-living flatworms are best exemplified by a group of small freshwater organisms collectively called the *planarians*. The genus *Dugesia* is commonly found in slow streams or ponds of cool, fresh water, either adhering to or crawling over sticks, stones, leaves, and other debris.

Examine a living planarian with a hand lens or dissecting microscope. Observe its general shape and size. From its movements, determine its anterior, posterior, dorsal, and ventral sides. What type of symmetry is evident?

_____

What is its coloration?

_____

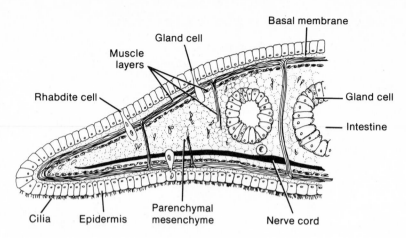

FIG. 32-1
Cross section of *Dugesia*.

What are its reactions to such stimuli as jarring, contact with a toothpick, or being turned on its dorsal surface?

_____

_____

Observe the protrusible **pharynx** on the ventral surface. What is the advantage of such a structure?

_____

_____

Note the large "eyes" on the anterior dorsal surface.

Using a dissecting microscope, examine a prepared slide of a whole mount of a planarian cleared to show the internal anatomy. Observe the branched digestive tract leading from the pharynx. What is the function of the numerous lateral projections from each of the three main branches of the digestive tract?

_____

_____

Excretory tubes and nervous elements are difficult to observe because of the thickness of the animal.

Examine cross sections of a planarian cut through the pharynx and through regions anterior and posterior to the pharynx. Observe the parts of the digestive tract in each of these regions (Fig. 32-1). There is no body cavity: the space between the surface epidermis and the endodermal

linings of the digestive tract is filled with a mass of cells of mesenchymal origin (**parenchyma**). Observe cilia on some of the ectodermal surface cells. Where are they most prominent?

_____

_____

The epidermis contains small bodies, called **rhabdites**, and many unicellular glands that open on the surface. It is thought that the rhabdites are dislodged into the water where they swell and form a protective gelatinous sheath around the animal. What is the arrangement of the muscle layers?

_____

_____

How does such an arrangement of muscles give the planarian flexibility?

_____

_____

Locate the two nerve cords just inside the ventral epidermis, one on either side.

Planarians have been used extensively in studies of **regeneration**. Their regenerative powers are readily demonstrated. Add several drops of the anesthetic tricaine methanesulfonate or magnesium sulfate to a Syracuse dish, and allow 15 minutes for the planarian to become completely anesthetized. Carefully cut the planarian with a sharp razor blade wiped clean of any oil. Diagram your cut in Fig. 32-2. (Your instructor will indicate different cuts to be made.) Add fresh pond water and place your

FIG. 32-2
Regeneration in *Dugesia*.

dish, covered to prevent evaporation, in a cool, dark spot in the laboratory. Observe the planarian throughout the next 2 weeks, and make sketches of the regeneration.

B. CLASS TREMATODA (FLUKES)

Flukes are characterized as having a thick cuticle with no cilia. The mouth is usually surrounded by a sucker. Rarely, one or more suckers may also be present on the ventral surface. All members of this class are parasitic; most of their hosts being vertebrates.

1. Opisthorchis (Clonorchis) sinensis (Chinese Liver Fluke)

Although not normally found in the Western Hemisphere, *Opisthorchis sinensis,* which is prevalent in certain parts of Asia, is commonly used to illustrate the typical mor-

phology and life cycle of flukes. The Chinese liver fluke lives in human beings and has a life cycle that requires two intermediate hosts. It is a common parasite in China, Japan, and Korea, where it has infested an estimated 19 million human beings.

The adult fluke, about 15 mm long, lives in the bile ducts of the human liver where it remains firmly attached by means of a pair of suckers. It is hermaphroditic and capable of self-fertilization, though cross-fertilization is much more common. What advantage is gained from possessing the capability to self-fertilize?

_____

_____

_____

The fertilized eggs that are released into the bile ducts are eventually voided in the feces of the host. If the feces get into water, the eggs might then be eaten by snails

374

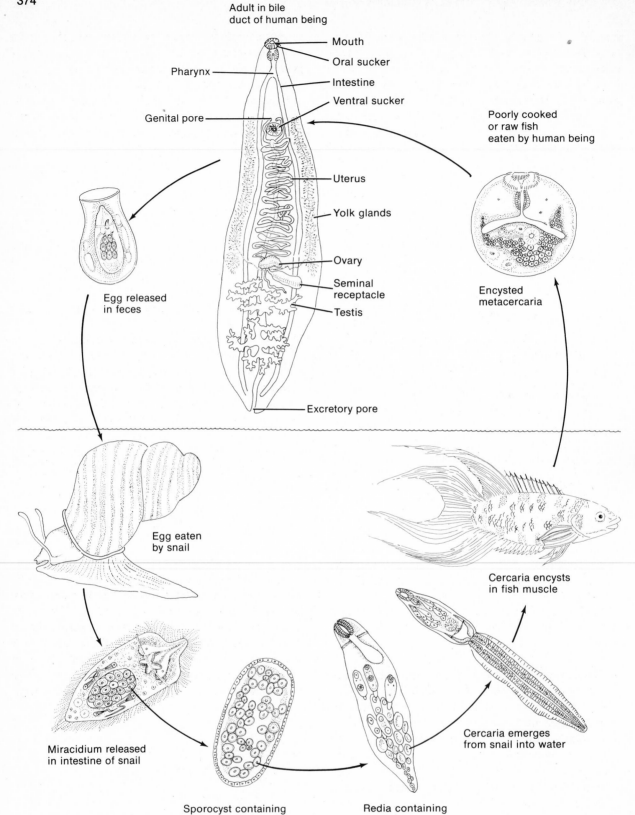

Adult in bile
duct of human being

Mouth

Oral sucker

Pharynx

Intestine

Ventral sucker

Genital pore

Poorly cooked
or raw fish
eaten by human being

Uterus

Yolk glands

Ovary

Seminal
receptacle

Testis

Encysted
metacercaria

Egg released
in feces

Excretory pore

Egg eaten
by snail

Cercaria encysts
in fish muscle

Miracidium released
in intestine of snail

Cercaria emerges
from snail into water

Sporocyst containing
rediae

Redia containing
cercariae

FIG. 32-3
Life cycle of *Opisthorchis sinensis*.

(Fig. 32-3). Within the digestive system of the snail, the egg opens and a larval form, called a **miracidium**, emerges and makes its way through the tissues of the snail, where it becomes asexually transformed into other larval forms. It has been estimated that a single miracidium can ultimately give rise to 250,000 infective larvae called **cercariae**. Why is it essential that one miracidium give rise to such a large number of cercariae in the life cycle of the fluke?

_____

_____

_____

The cercariae escape from the snail and swim about until they come in contact with a second, intermediate host, a Chinese golden carp *(Macropodus opercularis)*. They burrow through the skin of the fish, lose their tails, and encyst to form **metacercariae**. When raw or partly cooked fish is eaten by human beings, the cyst walls are digested in the stomach and metacercariae are released. They then migrate to the bile ducts and mature into adult flukes to complete the life cycle. In light of what you know about the life cycle of the fluke, what would be the most effective methods of controlling the infestation of human beings by this organism?

_____

_____

_____

_____

_____

Examine a prepared slide of the Chinese liver fluke, and note the flattened, leaflike shape of the worm. Observe an anterior **oral sucker**, in the center of which is the mouth, and a **ventral sucker** about one-third of the way back. Observe the bilobed intestine, and note that it has no opening other than the mouth. A pair of irregularly branched testes occupies the posterior third of the body. Tiny **sperm ducts** convey sperm cells to the **genital pore** located just anterior to the ventral sucker. The long, coiled uterus lies behind the ventral sucker. The **ovary**, a single body lying near the middle of the animal is connected to a lighter-staining **seminal receptacle** used for the storage of sperm. After copulation, the sperm cells

of each animal are stored in the seminal receptacle of the other. Also connected to the ovary by means of two delicate tubules are the **yolk glands**, which consist of many small, rounded bodies characteristically found in the lateral midparts of the body. These glands supply the eggs with yolk as they develop. At the posterior end of the fluke is the **excretory pore**, through which nitrogenous wastes are excreted.

2. Fasciola hepatica (Sheep Liver Fluke)

Although generally similar to *Opisthorchis*, *Fasciola hepatica* is considerably larger, ranging from 15 to 50 mm, and it has a more complex reproductive system. It commonly infests the livers of sheep and cattle, but it may also infest horses, rabbits, camels, pigs, goats, and even human beings.

Examine a demonstration slide of this fluke, and note its flat, leaflike body, which is rounded anteriorly and bluntly pointed posteriorly (Fig. 32-4). Locate the **anterior sucker** surrounding the mouth and the **ventral sucker** a short distance back from it. The digestive system consists of the mouth, a short muscular pharynx, and a branched intestine that extends along both sides of the fluke. Each of the branches has many smaller lateral branches, called **caeca**. What is the function of these caeca?

_____

_____

The female reproductive system, found mainly in the anterior half of the body, consists of a branched ovary connected to a median **ootype** by an oviduct. The ootype is surrounded by a **Mehlis gland**. Along each side of the body are many yolk glands that are joined to two yolk ducts with a common entry into the ootype. The male reproductive system has two highly coiled testes, each of which is connected by a vas deferens to a seminal receptacle.

3. Fasciolopsis buski (Giant Intestinal Fluke)

This organism, measuring approximately 75 mm in length, is probably the largest of the flukes found in human beings. It is common in Southeast Asia, where it is estimated to have infested 10 million people. Except for an unbranched intestine, the arrangement of organs

376

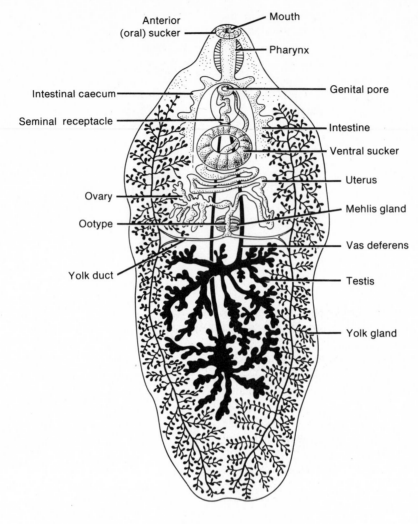

Anterior (oral) sucker

Mouth

Pharynx

Intestinal caecum

Genital pore

Seminal receptacle

Intestine

Ventral sucker

Uterus

Ovary

Mehlis gland

Ootype

Vas deferens

Testis

Yolk duct

Yolk gland

FIG. 32-4
Fasciola hepatica.

in *Fasciolopsis buski* generally resembles that of the Chinese liver fluke. Examine demonstration slides of this fluke.

From your study of the life cycles and morphologies of flukes, explain how they are adapted to their parasitic life.

_____

_____

_____

_____

_____

4. Schistosoma (Blood Fluke)

The schistosomes are trematodes that inhabit the intestinal veins of human and other vertebrates and are therefore commonly called **blood flukes**. Examine demonstration slides of the adults of one of the species of *Schistosoma*, and observe that they are long slender flukes in which the sexes are separate (Fig. 32-5).

The life cycle of *Schistosoma* is very similar to that of *Opisthorchis* and *Fasciola;* the snail is the intermediate host for the various larval stages. However, rather than being ingested with food, the cercariae invade their human hosts primarily by burrowing through the skin, particularly that of the feet, or by being taken in with drinking water. Cercariae of certain schistosomes that do not normally infest human beings can burrow into the skin and produce a "swimmer's itch."

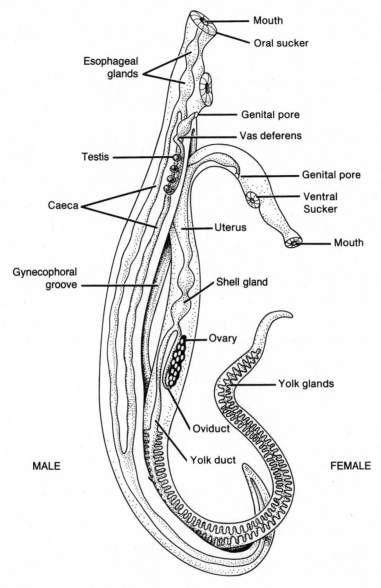

FIG. 32-5
Adult male and female *Schistosoma*.

C. CLASS CESTODA (TAPEWORMS)

Tapeworms are usually long, flat, ribbonlike organisms. The extent to which the tapeworm has adapted to a parasitic existence is manifest in its degenerate digestive and nervous systems and its highly developed reproductive system. The flatness of these worms enhances cellular diffusion so that there is no need for respiratory and circulatory systems.

1. Dipylidium caninum (Dog Tapeworm)

In this exercise, the common cat or dog tapeworm, *Dipylidium caninum,* will be studied as a typical tapeworm.

Fleas are the hosts for the larval stage of this species, and children are sometimes infected by it if they accidentally swallow fleas while playing with dogs or cats.

378

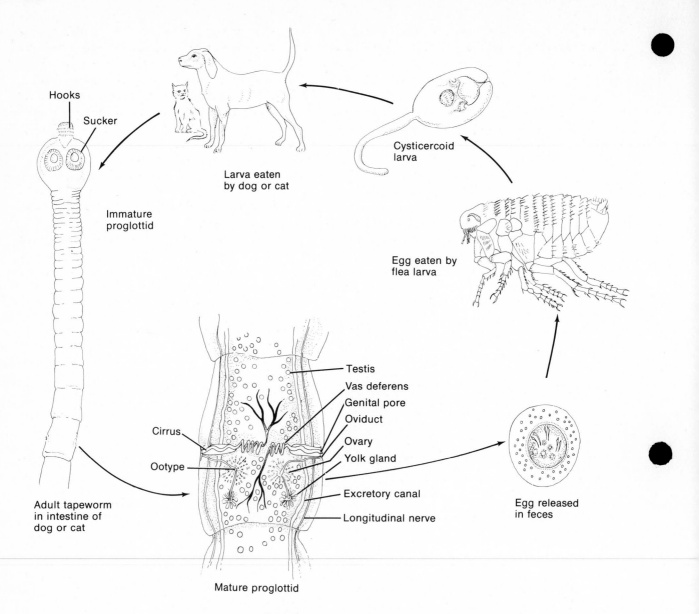

FIG. 32-6
Life cycle of *Dipylidium caninum*.

Examine a prepared slide showing characteristic segments of an adult tapeworm (Fig. 32-6). Note the head, or **scolex**, with its four suckers and several rows of hooks used for attachment to the intestine of its host. Behind the scolex is a short neck, followed by a row of segments, called **proglottids**. The mature proglottids possess a high degree of internal organization. They contain both male and female reproductive organs in duplicate. The smaller ducts leading from the lateral **genital pores** are the oviducts, which lead into the diffuse ovaries. The testes are distributed throughout the proglottid and the **vas deferens**, by which the sperm leave the proglottid, is the larger duct leading to the genital pore. Lateral and transverse **excretory canals** are present in the mature proglottids, as are thin, longitudinal nerve cords.

The proglottids near the posterior end of the tapeworm become filled with many ovarian capsules, each of which contains a number of eggs. The reproductive organs observed in the mature proglottids have atrophied in these **gravid** segments, and the uterus has enlarged, filling them entirely. The gravid segments break loose from the tapeworm and are released in the feces of the host. The embryos released from these segments are eaten by the larvae of the dog or cat flea and develop into **cysticercoids**, which are infective. When swallowed by a dog or cat, such an infected flea will be digested by the host and the cysticercoid released. It attaches to the intestinal wall and develops into an adult tapeworm.

2. Taenia saginata (Beef Tapeworm)

The most common intestinal tapeworm to infest human beings is the beef tapeworm, which ordinarily grows to a length of 5 to 7 meters. In addition to cattle, the buffalo, giraffe, and llama have been recorded as natural hosts for the cysticercus stage. Meat inspection has reduced the occurrence of this parasite to about 1% of the cattle in the United States. In countries in which beef is prepared by broiling large pieces over open fires, the incidence of infection is quite high. Why?

_____

_____

_____

Examine preserved specimens of this tapeworm, as well as slides showing scolices and mature and gravid proglottids.

3. Taenia solium (Pork Tapeworm)

The pork tapeworm that infests human beings closely resembles the beef tapeworm and has a similar life cycle, except that the larval stages, called **bladderworms** (cysticerci), develop in pigs. A mature pork tapeworm can be from 2 to 8 meters long. People are infested by eating raw or partly cooked pork. Meat inspection has made it uncommon in the United States.

4. Dibothriocephalus latus (Fish Tapeworm)

The broad, fish tapeworm, which can grow to a length of 18 meters, is the largest tapeworm to live in human beings. This tapeworm requires two intermediate hosts to complete its life cycle. The eggs, when released into water, develop into larvae that are eaten by small crustaceans, called *copepods*. These in turn are eaten by fish, in which the larval stage (**plerocercoid**) develops. People acquire the parasite when they eat raw or partly cooked fish. This tapeworm has recently become well established in the western Great Lakes region of North America, where it commonly infests pike and pickerel.

Examine prepared slides of the fish tapeworm, and note that the scolex has sucking grooves, rather than the suckers and hooks found in the other tapeworms you have studied. Also note that the proglottids are broader than they are long and that the reproductive organs are located in the center of a proglottid. Do you consider tapeworms to be more, or less, adapted to parasitism than flukes? Give the reasons for your answer.

_____

_____

_____

_____

REFERENCES

Bushsbaum, R. 1948. *Animals Without Backbones*. 2nd ed. University of Chicago Press.

Chandler, A. C., and C. P. Read. 1961. *Introduction to Parasitology*. 10th ed. Wiley.

Cheng, T. C. 1973. *The Biology of Animal Parasites*. Academic Press.

Meglitsch, P. A. 1972. *Intvertebrate Zoology*. 2nd ed. Oxford University Press.

Noble, E. R., and G. A. Noble. 1976. *Parasitology*. 4th ed. Lea and Febiger.

Russell-Hunter, W. D. 1969. *A Biology of the Lower Invertebrates*. Macmillan.

Schmidt, G. D., and L. S. Roberts. 1977. *Foundations of Parasitology*. Mosby.

Storer, T. I., R. L. Usinger, R. C. Stebbins, and J. W. Nybakken. 1979. *General Zoology*. 6th ed. McGraw-Hill.

Kingdom Animalia: Phylum Aschelminthes and Parasites of the Frog

The phylum Aschelminthes (Greek *asco,* "sac"; *helmin,* "worm") consists of a heterogeneous group of organisms that includes rotifers, gastrotrichs, kinoryncha, nematomorphs (horsehair worms), and one of the most successful groups in the animal kingdom, the nematodes, or roundworms. All of the organisms are characterized by having a complete digestive tract with a separate musculature, a nonliving body covering, called a **cuticle,** and a body cavity lacking a mesodermal lining, called a **pseudocoel.** The reproductive organs are found in the fluid-filled pseudocoel.

This phylum includes five major classes:

Class Rotifera: microscopic animals found primarily in freshwater habitats and characterized by an anterior locomotor and feeding organ and a specialized internal grinding organ

Class Gastrotricha: microscopic aquatic animals in which the cuticle is covered by scales or spines

Class Kinorhyncha: microscopic marine organisms in which the cuticle is superficially segmented, with lateral spines along the body

Class Nematoda: roundworms, including both free-living and parasitic worms having elongate cylindrical bodies tapered at both ends

Class Nematomorpha: horsehair worms that are long and slender, having a cylindrical body rounded at both ends

In this exercise, you will study representatives of the rotifers and nematodes and parasites of the frog.

A. CLASS ROTIFERA

Rotifers are microscopic organisms that are common and abundant in freshwater lakes, ponds, quiet streams, and wayside ditches; they are even found in street gutters and eave troughs of buildings. They constitute an important component of the plankton that is a source of food for many fish species.

Prepare a wet mount on a clean slide of a culture of rotifers that contains one or more of the genera shown in Fig. 33-1. Observe the elongate cylindrical body, which

382

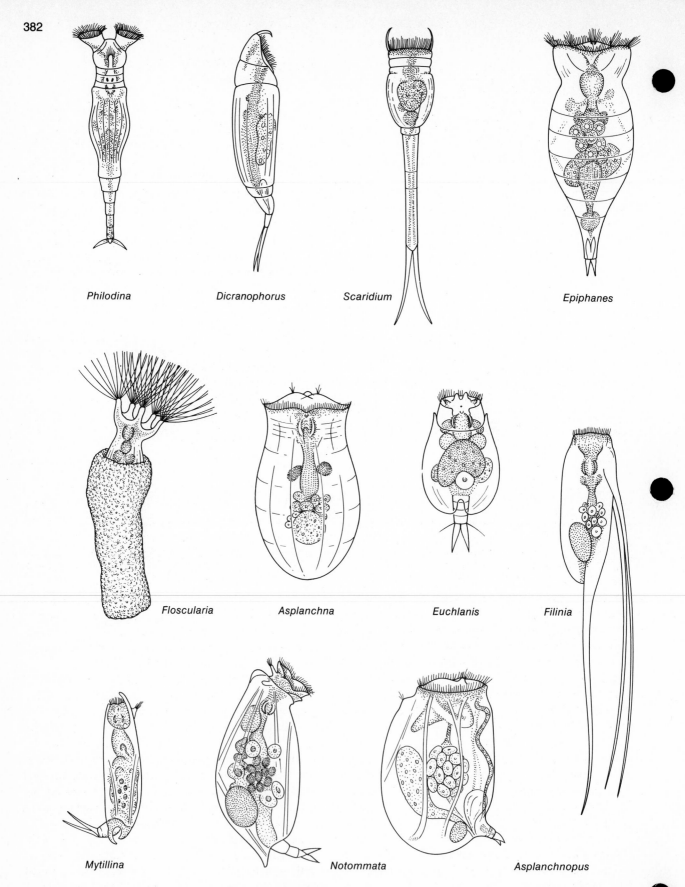

Philodina *Dicranophorus* *Scaridium* *Epiphanes*

Floscularia *Asplanchna* *Euchlanis* *Filinia*

Mytillina *Notommata* *Asplanchnopus*

FIG. 33-1
Representative rotifers.

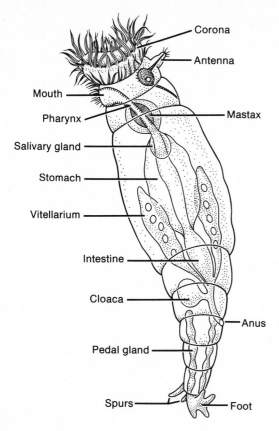

FIG. 33-2
Anatomy of a representative rotifer.

is divided into three general regions: the head, trunk, and foot. Although the cuticle is divided into several segments, the internal organs are not; therefore, this segmentation is not true, as it is in the annelids. You may observe, in a rotifer that is moving about, a telescoping of these segments as the animal expands and contracts. Observe the long, tapering **foot** and its two **spurs** at the posterior end of the body. The anterior end of the body is expanded into a crown of cilia, called a **corona**, which is used primarily for locomotion and for gathering food (Fig. 33-2). The coronal cilia create a current of water that draws food particles toward the mouth. Because the beating motion of these cilia gives the impression of two wheels turning, the organisms are sometimes called "wheel animalcules." The mouth leads into a muscular pharynx that has a grinding apparatus, called a **mastax**. This structure can be readily observed in living rotifers because of its constant movement. Posterior to the pharynx is the narrow **esophagus**, surrounded by the large **salivary glands** and saclike **stomach**. The digestive tract is lined with cilia that move food into the **intestine** and waste products to the **cloaca**, where they are then eliminated through the **anus**, located near the base of the foot.

B. CLASS NEMATODA (ROUNDWORMS)

Among multicellular animals, roundworms are probably second only to insects in number. Most of the 500,000 species of nematodes are free-living. Some are found in fresh water, some in salt water, and some in mud, field, or garden soils. Other nematodes are parasites of roots, stems, leaves, and even the seeds of many horticultural and agricultural plants, damaging crops inestimably. Many thousands of species of roundworms are parasites of invertebrate and vertebrate animals. Among the vertebrates, it is doubtful that any species is not parasitized by one or more of the roundworms. Although more than 50 species are known to infest human beings, only about a dozen are parasitic in human beings. Most of the species that are either free-living or parasitic in plants or invertebrates are barely visible to the eye, transparent, and have simple life cycles. The species that are parasitic in vertebrates, on the other hand, can be several feet in length and have more complicated life cycles.

1. Ascaris lumbricoides (Pig Roundworm)

Ascaris is a roundworm commonly parasitic in the intestine of hogs. The sexes are separate, the male worm being shorter and more slender than the female and readily distinguished by a sharply curved posterior end. In addition, the male has a pair of hairlike structures (**spicules**) extending from the anal opening, which are used during copulation. Both male and female worms are several centimeters long. Examine preserved specimens of males and females. Using a hand lens or dissecting microscope, observe the terminal **mouth** surrounded by three lobelike **lips**. Locate the **excretory pore** just behind the mouth. Note the external chitinous cuticle.

Using a scalpel, carefully slit a female worm along the whole length of the body. Expose the internal organs by pinning the body wall back in a dissecting pan (Fig. 33-3). Cover the worm with water. Locate the long, flat digestive tract extending the length of the worm. The Y-shaped female reproductive system occupies most of the body cavity. Identify the single **vagina**, which divides into a pair of large, straight, and uncoiled **uterine tubes**. The uteri narrow down into the **oviducts**, which in turn continue into the long, thin, extremely coiled **ovaries**.

The male reproductive tract consists of a single, long, very coiled tube, which is divided into a long slender **testis, sperm duct,** an enlarged **seminal vesicle,** and a small **ejaculatory duct** opening into the terminal end of the digestive tract.

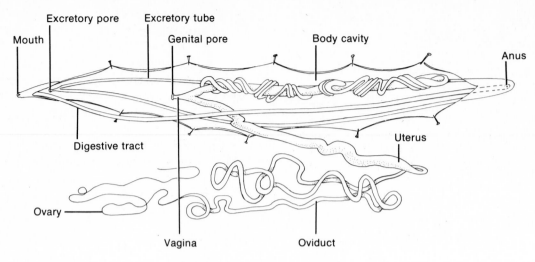

FIG. 33-3
Internal anatomy of female *Ascaris*.

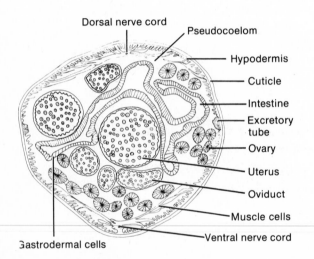

FIG. 33-4
Cross section of female *Ascaris*.

Examine a prepared slide of a cross section of the female (Fig. 33-4). The body wall consists of an outer, noncellular **cutile** and an inner **hypodermis**. What is the function of the cuticle?

_____

_____

The hypodermis has four extensions into the body cavity. Two of these extensions contain the **dorsal** and **ventral nerve cords**, and the other two contain the **excretory tubes**. The greater part of the body wall is composed of muscle tissue. The digestive tract is centrally located. Observe the thin-walled intestine, and note that the intestinal wall consists of a single layer of large gastrodermal

cells. The body cavity of *Ascaris* is a **pseudocoelom**. Locate the two large cross sections of the uteri, and note the shelled ova. Identify as many meiotic stages as are evident in your slide.

_____

_____

Sections through the oviducts and ovaries can be distinguished by their smaller sizes and by the absence of shells around the egg cells.

2. Trichinella spiralis

Infection by this parasitic roundworm, which causes **trichinosis** in human beings, results from eating raw or partly cooked pork containing the encysted larvae of this parasite. In the human intestine, the larvae are released from their cysts and develop into adult worms. The mature female worm gives birth to larval worms, which then migrate through the body and **encyst** in the muscles of the diaphragm, ribs, and tongue. The greatest damage is done during this migration phase. Why?

_____

_____

This incidence of human infection in the United States is astonishingly high—approximately 17% of the population is infected.

Examine prepared slides of adult worms and encysted larvae.

3. Necator americanus (Hookworm)

No group of nematodes causes more injury to human beings or greater economic loss through attacks on domestic animals than the hookworms. These tiny parasites have highly developed mouth cavities that contain plates by which the worm holds onto the intestine while it sucks blood and tissue. Larvae develop from eggs on moist soil in the warm climates. Infestation of human beings is by penetration of the skin by the larvae and is very often a result of going barefoot in areas where the parasite is prevalent.

Examine prepared slides of hookworms. Locate the **buccal capsule** at the anterior end of this worm, and note the cutting plates inside the capsule. At the posterior end, locate the **bursa**, an umbrellalike expansion of the cuticle, which is used in copulation.

4. Enterobius vermicularis (Pinworm)

This roundworm is one of the most common parasites of children, and its incidence in Canada and the United States is estimated to be between 30% and 60%. The parasite enters the body as an ovum through either the mouth or the anus: ova are easily carried under fingernails, get into the bedclothes of an infected person, or may be on toilet seats. Infections in children lead to severe itchiness in the anal region, insomnia, restlessness, loss of appetite, and irritability.

Examine slides of adult pinworms. These small, spindle-shaped worms are characterized by a lateral expansion of the cuticle at their anterior ends. The posterior end of the male is strongly curved.

5. Free-Living Nematodes

Free-living nematodes can be found in almost any loose soil containing organic matter. Using a dissecting microscope or the low power of a compound microscope, examine a small pile of loose soil that your instructor placed in a petri dish containing agar several days earlier. Scrape several of the worms onto a slide, add a drop of water, and examine under the low and high magnifications of your microscope. With the exception of the nervous system, these nematodes are transparent, and the various organ systems can be observed. If the movements of the worms are too rapid, add a drop of dilute hydrochloric acid to your slide. Describe and account for the type of movement exhibited by these worms.

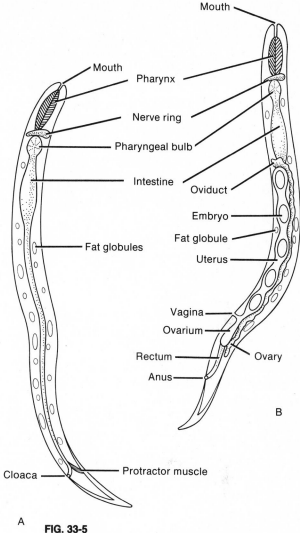

FIG. 33-5
Anguillula aceti: (A) male and (B) female adults.

Compare their structure with those of organisms already studied.

A very common free-living nematode is the vinegar eel *(Anguillula aceti,* formerly *Turbatrix aceti),* which is frequently found on the bottom of a vinegar barrel where it feeds on the bacteria and yeasts that have settled there. Mount a drop of vinegar-eel culture on a slide and examine microscopically. Because the vinegar eel is quite transparent, its internal organs can be easily seen and, being viviparous (i.e., giving birth to living young), all stages of development can be studied. For better observation, add a drop of 0.2% neutral red stain to the drop of vinegar and add a cover slip. If the animals are moving too vigorously for observation, slow them down by withdrawing solution with a small piece of filter paper or paper toweling placed at the edge of the cover slip.

Use Fig. 33-5 to identify the sexes and study the internal anatomy of this free-living nematode.

386

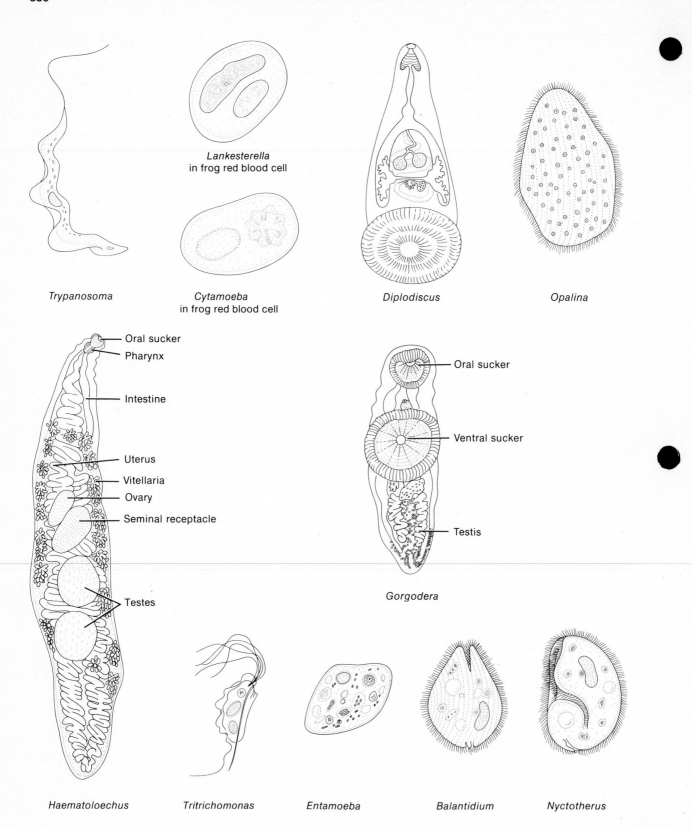

Lankesterella
in frog red blood cell

Trypanosoma

Cytamoeba
in frog red blood cell

Diplodiscus

Opalina

Oral sucker
Pharynx

Intestine

Uterus
Vitellaria
Ovary
Seminal receptacle

Testes

Oral sucker

Ventral sucker

Testis

Gorgodera

Haematoloechus

Tritrichomonas

Entamoeba

Balantidium

Nyctotherus

FIG. 33-6
Common parasites of the frog.

C. PARASITES OF THE FROG

Frogs are the hosts of a number of animal parasites and are therefore excellent organisms for the study of parasite-host relationships. Pith a frog supplied by your instructor, and then cut through the ventral body wall to expose the internal organs. For the pithing procedure, see Appendix D. Refer to Fig. 33-6 in identifying some of the more common frog parasites.

1. Parasites of the Blood

Take blood from one of the larger blood vessels or the kidney, place a drop on a clean slide, and draw it out in a thin film, using the edge of another slide. Add a cover slip, and examine for blood parasites. The most easily recognized forms are the extracellular flagellate trypanosomes, which are about twice the size of a red blood cell. Less readily observed are the intercellular parasites of the red blood cells. Examine the red blood cells under high power, and locate clear oval or spindle-shaped parasites in the cytoplasm. Two genera are known to parasitize the frog, *Lankesterella* and *Cytamoeba*.

2. Parasites of the Lung

Carefully remove the lungs by cutting them at their point of attachment to the larynx. Place them in a Syracuse dish containing room-temperature frog Ringer's solution, and examine for dark bodies. Cut open the lungs, and observe the movements of these parasites. Among the species of trematodes commonly found in the lung is a relatively large one called *Haematoloechus*. Mount the parasites on a slide, add a drop of water, and examine for details of internal anatomy.

3. Parasites of the Digestive Tract

With a scissors, slit open the digestive tract from the rectum to the esophagus. Examine each region for the presence of roundworms and flatworms. Several species of parasites are commonly found in the frog digestive tract. Carefully examine the contents of the intestine for small trematodes. *Diplodiscus*, a relatively large trema-

tode, lives in the rectum and is recognized by its large ventral sucker.

Take a small part of the contents of the rectum, smear it thinly on a slide, add a cover slip, and identify the parasites that are present. Protozoans common to the rectum of the frog are *Opalina*, which is a large, wedge-shaped, multinucleate ciliate, and *Nyctotherus*, a bean-shaped ciliate with a well-developed cytostome and cytopharynx. Other protozoan parasites that may be found in the digestive tract are *Tritrichomonas* and *Entamoeba*.

4. Parasites of the Bladder

Cut open the urinary bladder, and examine for the presence of parasites. At least six species of trematodes have been reported to exist in the frog bladder. One of the more common trematodes is *Gorgodera*.

5. Other Parasites

Carefully examine all other regions of the frog body for parasites (e.g., lining of body cavity, mesenteries, mouth, and surfaces of internal organs). Identify and list the kinds of parasites found (e.g., roundworms, flukes, tapeworms, or protozoa).

REFERENCES

Chandler, A. C., and C. P. Read. 1961. *Introduction to Parasitology.* 10th ed. Wiley.

Chitwood, G. G., and M. B. Chitwood. 1974. *Introduction to Nematology.* University Park Press.

Meglitsch, P. A. 1972. *Invertebrate Zoology.* 2nd ed. Oxford University Press.

Rainis, K. G. 1976. Enteric Protozoa in Frogs. *Carolina Tips* 39(13):49–50.

Russell-Hunter, W. D. 1969. *A Biology of the Lower Invertebrates.* Macmillan.

Schmidt, G. D., and L. S. Roberts. 1977. *Foundations of Parasitology.* Mosby.

Storer, T. I., R. L. Usinger, R. C. Stebbins, and J. W. Nybakken. 1979. *General Zoology.* 6th ed. McGraw-Hill.

Kingdom Animalia: Phylum Mollusca

Molluscs (Latin *molluscus,* "soft"), as the origin of the name suggests, are soft-bodied animals such as snails, oysters, slugs, clams, octopuses, and squids. Most molluscs are **bilaterally symmetrical** and have well-developed respiratory, excretory, circulatory, and digestive systems. Some may have a calcareous shell surrounding the body mass.

Molluscs are similar to annelids in their development. The larvae of both are **trochophores.** Molluscs differ from annelids, however, in the absence of **segmentation.** Further, the coelom, so prominent in the annelids, is greatly reduced in the molluscs and is generally restricted to an area surrounding the heart.

Most molluscs are slow moving, but the bodies of several species have been highly modified for rapid locomotion. Although primarily marine organisms, some molluscs are found in fresh water and on land.

The organisms in the phylum Mollusca are characterized by having three main body regions: a **head-foot,** which is the sensory and locomotive part of the body; a **visceral mass** containing the excretory, digestive, and circulatory organs; and the **mantle,** which secretes the **shell.** The **gills,** which function in respiration, are located between the shell and the mantle.

Representatives of the following classes of molluscs will be studied in this exercise.

Class Pelecypoda: characterized by having the visceral mass contained in a shell that has right and left valves that are hinged together and a hatchet-shaped foot that extends out between the valves during locomotion (mussels, clams, and oysters)

Class Amphineura: characterized by having an elliptical body covered by a shell of eight plates (chitons), although some species do not have these plates

Class Scaphopoda: characterized by having the visceral mass enclosed in an elongated, tapered, and toothlike shell; the foot cone-shaped; and the gills absent (tooth or tusk shells)

Class Gastropoda: characterized by having the viscera contained in a spirally coiled shell (although the shell in some is greatly reduced or absent); a distinct head with one or two pairs of tentacles; and a large, flat foot (snails and slugs)

Class Cephalopoda: characterized by having either an internal or an external shell; a large and prominent head with conspicuous, complex eyes; and a mouth surrounded by eight to 10 or more tentacles (squid and octopus)

A

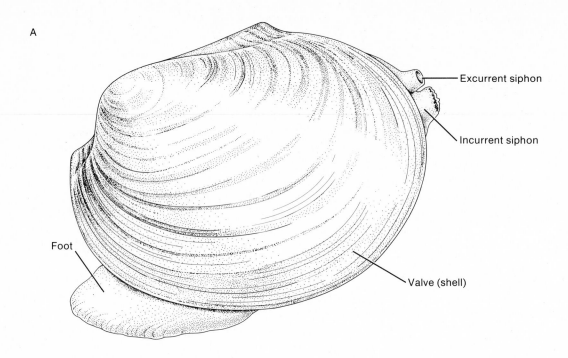

Excurrent siphon

Incurrent siphon

Foot

Valve (shell)

B

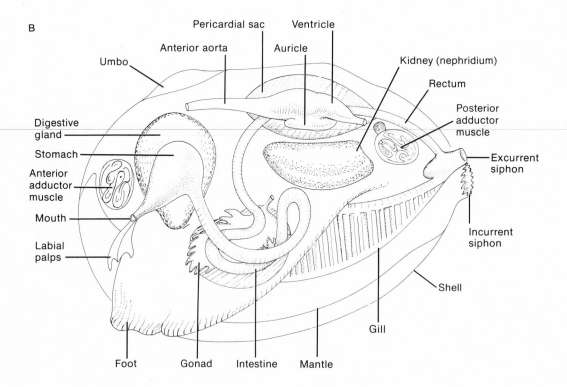

Pericardial sac

Ventricle

Anterior aorta

Auricle

Umbo

Kidney (nephridium)

Rectum

Posterior
adductor
muscle

Digestive
gland

Stomach

Anterior
adductor
muscle

Mouth

Excurrent
siphon

Labial
palps

Incurrent
siphon

Shell

Foot

Gonad

Intestine

Mantle

Gill

FIG. 34-1
Morphology of the freshwater clam *Anodonta*: (A) external and (B) internal anatomy.

Shell

Periostracum ⎫
Prismatic layer ⎬ Shell

Nacreous layer ⎭

Nacre-secreting cells ⎫
Connective tissue ⎬ Mantle
Ciliated epithelium ⎭

Foreign body (sand or a parasite) between shell and mantle

Pearl formed by secretion of nacre around foreign body

FIG. 34-2
Diagram of structure of shell and mantle.

A. CLASS PELECYPODA (MUSSELS, CLAMS, OYSTERS)

Members of this class, characterized by having a shell consisting of two **valves**, include common freshwater clams and mussels and marine varieties of clams and oysters. Freshwater clams, which will be studied in this section, are abundantly distributed and live on the bottoms of lakes, rivers, ponds, and streams where they feed on **plankton**—microscopic plant and animal life.

1. General Structure

Study the shell of the freshwater clam, *Anodonta,* and note that it consists of two valves hinged together along the dorsal side (Fig. 34-1A). On the anterior part of each valve is a protruding region, the **umbo.** The concentric lines that extend outward from the umbo are lines of growth. The valves are held together by two large **adductor muscles** located at opposite ends of the shell (Fig. 34-1B). Cut these muscles by inserting a knife or scalpel between the two valves of the shell and cutting toward the "hinge" where the valves are joined together. Open the valves, and observe that they are lined by a glistening

mantle. The outer epithelial layer of the mantle secretes the shell, which is made up of three layers (Fig. 34-2). The thin outer layer, the **periostracum,** functions to protect the underlying parts of the shell from acids in the water. It also gives the shell its color. The middle **prismatic layer** is composed of calcium carbonate. The inner **nacreous layer,** called *mother-of-pearl,* is made up of numerous layers of calcium carbonate and has an iridescent sheen.

At the posterior margin of the shell, the mantle is thicker, coming together to form two openings called the **siphons.** Water enters the clam through the ventral **incurrent siphon**, circulates through the mantle cavity and over the gills, and then leaves through the dorsal **excurrent siphon.**

Remove one of the valves and its mantle, thus exposing the mantle cavity and the internal organs. Observe the large muscular **foot** extending down from the visceral mass. Locate the **gills**, which hang down into the mantle cavity. How many gills are there? What is their function?

_____

_____

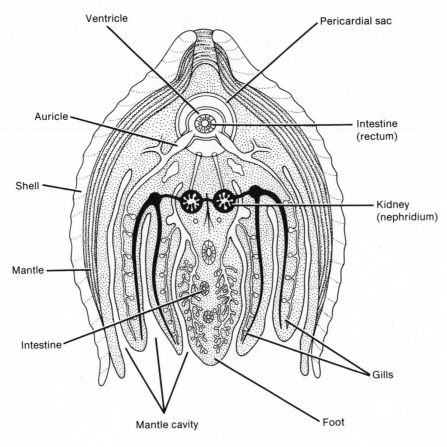

FIG. 34-3
Cross section of a clam.

Locate two pair of flaplike **palps** on the anterior edge of the visceral mass, near the anterior muscle. These palps surround the mouth. Dorsal to the gills is the **pericardial sac**, which encloses the heart. Carefully cut open this sac, and locate the heart. Note that the heart consists of three chambers: two lateral **auricles** and one **ventricle** (Fig. 34-3). Carefully cut away the gills, and locate the kidney (**nephridium**), a dark-colored organ lying near the gills and just below the pericardial cavity. What is the function of this organ?

_____

_____

Most of the digestive system is located within the visceral mass (Fig. 34-1B). *Carefully* cut the visceral mass lengthwise into left and right halves. The **mouth**, located between the palps, leads by way of a short **esophagus** into an expanded **stomach**, which is flanked on either side by two large **digestive glands**. Remove these glands carefully, and note that the stomach leads into an **intestine** that winds through the visceral mass and then passes through the pericardial sac as the **rectum**. The rectum empties into the **excurrent siphon** through the **anus**. Locate as many parts of the digestive tract as possible in your dissection.

2. Reproduction

Most mussels and clams are male or female; a few species are hermaphroditic. The reproductive cycle in these organisms is quite interesting in that the juvenile stage is parasitic on fish (Fig. 34-4). The eggs are released into the cavity of the gills where fertilization takes place. Each zygote then develops into a larva, called a **glochidium**. The larvae stay within the gill through the winter and are released into the water the following spring. If they come into contact with a fish, a contact stimulus causes them

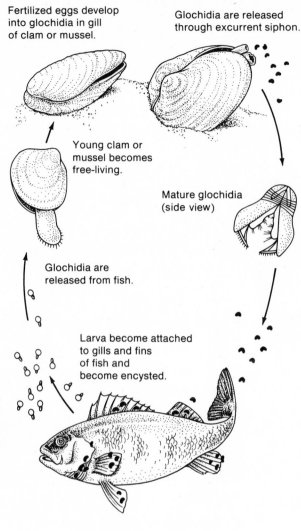

Fertilized eggs develop into glochidia in gill of clam or mussel.

Glochidia are released through excurrent siphon.

Young clam or mussel becomes free-living.

Mature glochidia (side view)

Glochidia are released from fish.

Larva become attached to gills and fins of fish and become encysted.

FIG. 34-4
Life cycle of a clam or mussel.

to close their valves and thus become attached to the gills or the fins of the fish host. What is the advantage of their being attached to the gills or fins instead of the body wall?

_____

_____

_____

_____

_____

The tissue of the fish reacts by growing around the larva.

After several weeks, the parasitic larval form is released and begins a free-living existence. Examine slides or preserved specimens of glochidia. Note the toothlike appendages on the valves, which function to attach the larva to the fish.

B. CLASS AMPHINEURA (CHITONS)

These molluscs, sometimes called *coat-of-mail shells,* are primitive marine organisms. They have a characteristic shell composed of eight plates (Fig. 34-5A). A large, broad, flat muscular foot occupies the greater part of the ventral surface. They are usually found on rocky seashores or in water less than 25 fathoms deep. They attach tightly to rocks by means of the suction produced by the foot. When pulled off, they tend to roll up, much like an armadillo, with their soft parts covered by the hard shell. Examine the chitons on demonstration.

C. CLASS SCAPHOPODA (TOOTH, OR TUSK, SHELLS)

The visceral mass of these marine molluscs is enclosed in a long, tubular, toothlike shell (Fig. 34-5B). The foot is typically cone-shaped and is used for burrowing in the sand. Examine the tooth shell on demonstration.

D. CLASS GASTROPODA (SNAILS AND SLUGS)

This is by far the largest class of molluscs (Fig. 34-5C). For all forms, the visceral mass is enclosed in a coiled shell during the early stages of development. In most species of gastropods, adults retain the coiled shell, but, in slugs, not only has the shell been lost but some species have become land dwellers.

Snails have an unusual mode of locomotion: a **slime gland**, located in the forward part of the foot, secretes a thin film of mucus over which the snail then moves by means of wavelike contractions of the muscles of the foot.

Slugs, because they lack a protective shell, are restricted to moist areas to prevent desiccation. Consequently, they are not very active in the daytime, feeding at night instead.

Sea slugs (**nudibranchs**) live among the seaweeds. Some species so resemble the plants that they are difficult to see. Others have **warning coloration** and are protected by stinging cells.

Examine demonstrations of various gastropods.

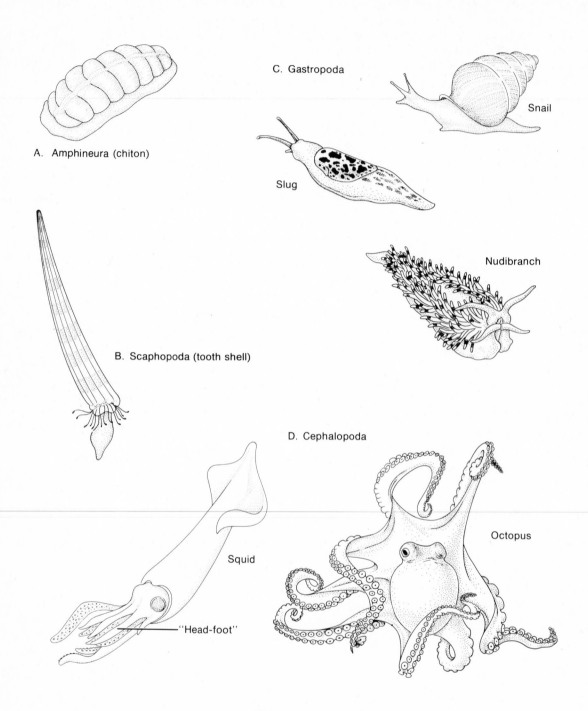

A. Amphineura (chiton)

B. Scaphopoda (tooth shell)

C. Gastropoda

Snail

Slug

Nudibranch

D. Cephalopoda

Squid

"Head-foot"

Octopus

FIG. 34-5
Representative classes of molluscs.

E. CLASS CEPHALOPODA
(SQUIDS AND OCTOPUSES)

The cephalopods are considered to be the most advanced and highly developed class of molluscs (Fig. 34-5D). All cephalopods are marine organisms characterized by having a foot modified to form tentacles and a head with prominent, highly developed eyes. The eye is remarkably similar to the vertebrate eye in that it has an eyelid, iris, pupil, lens, cornea, and retina. In some species in the class Cephalopoda, the shell is external; in others, it is internal. In contrast with other molluscs, the cephalopods are active, free-swimming animals.

Examine a squid. What morphological characteristics can you see on this organism that are adaptations to a predatory existence?

_____

_____

_____

_____

_____

Because the squid relies on its ability to swim rapidly for protection, it has no need of a cumbersome external shell. Consequently, the shell is a vestigial structure, consisting of a horny plate buried in the visceral mass. Interestingly, the shell, called a **cuttle bone**, is sold in pet stores. It is attached to a bird's cage to be used by the bird to "sharpen" its beak.

Next examine an octopus. How are the squid and octopus similar?

_____

_____

_____

How are they different?

_____

_____

_____

REFERENCES

Buchsbaum, R. 1948. *Animals Without Backbones*. 2nd ed. University of Chicago Press.

Hyman, L. H. 1968. *The Invertebrates*. Vol. 6: *Mollusca I*. McGraw-Hill.

Meglitsch, P. A. 1972. *Invertebrate Zoology*. 2nd ed. Oxford University Press.

Morton, J. E. 1967. *Molluscs: An Introduction to Their Form and Function*. 4th ed. Hutchinson.

Purchon, R. D. 1977. *The Biology of the Mollusca*. 2nd ed. Pergamon.

Rounds, H. D. 1968. *Invertebrates*. Reinhold.

Russell-Hunter, W. D. 1969. *A Biology of Lower Invertebrates*. Macmillan.

Wilbur, K. M., and C. M. Younge, eds. 1966. *The Physiology of Molluscs*. Academic Press.

Kingdom Animalia: Phylum Annelida

Organisms in the phylum Annelida (Latin *anellus,* "ring") are referred to as segmented worms to distinguish them from nonsegmented flatworms and roundworms. The body is composed of a series of similar parts called **somites, metameres**, or **segments**.

Annelids exhibit **cephalization**; that is, the nervous system is concentrated at the anterior end of the organism in structures called **cerebral ganglia**. A ventral nerve cord arises from these ganglia and passes posteriorly. The excretory and circulatory systems are well developed. The digestive tract is straight and tubular and, in contrast with that of the roundworms, is supplied with its own musculature allowing it to function independently of the muscular activity associated with the body wall. Annelids, like roundworms, have a fluid-filled body cavity separating the digestive tract from the body wall. However, in annelids this cavity is a **true coelum** in that it is formed through splitting of the mesoderm in the course of development.

The habitats of members of this phylum are widespread: they are found in marine or fresh waters, or on the land. The phylum includes both parasitic and free-living species. The following classes will be studied in this exercise:

Class Polychaeta: having conspicuous segmentation and lateral projections called **parapodia**, a prominent head that has tentacles, and separate sexes in most species; most are marine organisms (*Neanthes:* clam worm)

Class Oligochaeta: having conspicuous segmentation but lacking a well-defined head; members are hermaphroditic and are usually found in fresh water or moist soils (earthworms)

Class Hirudinea: having dorsoventrally flattened bodies with a large posterior sucker and inconspicuous segmentation; members are hermaphroditic and are found in fresh and marine waters (leeches)

A

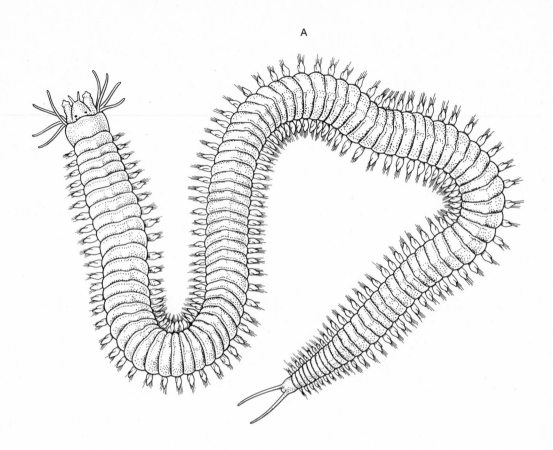

B. Dorsal view of head
   with pharynx retracted

C. Dorsal view of head
   with pharynx everted

Mouth (below)

Tentacle — Jaw

Palp

Prostomium

Eyes

Peristomium

Tentacle

Somite

Parapodium

Seta

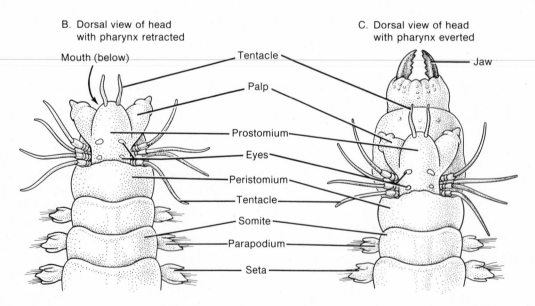

FIG. 35-1
External anatomy of *Neanthes virens*.

A. CLASS POLYCHAETA

The polychaetes consist primarily of free-living marine organisms that are abundant in depths ranging from the low-tide line to about 50 meters. Many are found in the intertidal zone and a few have been found in depths of more than 4,500 meters.

Because of their abundance (thousands have been found in a square meter), these animals are important in the marine food chain. They are eaten by hydroids, flatworms, starfish, fish, and even other marine annelids.

Polychaetes have a particularly interesting external form to study. Even with the numerous and varied modifications that have enabled them to adapt to a wide variety of habitats, these organisms have retained a fundamental organization that is common to all polychaetes. This basic body structure can be observed in *Neanthes virens,* the marine clam worm that lives in burrows in the sand at tide level (Fig. 35-1A). It remains in its burrow throughout the day, coming out at night to feed.

Examine a specimen of *Neanthes*. Note that the long, slender body is somewhat compressed, being rounded dorsally and flattened ventrally. It is composed of about two hundred segments, called **somites**. The head is generally well developed and contains the mouth, which is retracted except when the organism is feeding, at which time the pharynx is everted and the jaws used in capturing small animals are exposed (Fig. 35-1B, C). Over the mouth region is the highly modified segment called the **prostomium**, which has a pair of **tentacles**, two pairs of **simple eyes**, and laterally placed conical **palps**. The **peristomium** bears another four tentacles. What function might these tentacles serve?

_____

_____

_____

Posterior to the head region are a variable number of similar segments, each of which bears a pair of fleshy outgrowths called **parapodia**. Each parapodium contains several terminal, bristlelike structures called **setae**. Suggest a function for the setae.

_____

_____

B. CLASS OLIGOCHAETA

The common earthworm, *Lumbricus terrestris,* will be studied to illustrate the main characteristics of the oligochaetes. The bodies of most earthworms are divided externally and internally into well-defined segments that are separated from each other by membranous partitions. Except for the tail and head regions, all segments are essentially alike. The earthworm hunts food at night and thus has been called a "night crawler." It extends its body from the surface opening of a small tunnel, which it makes by "eating" its way through the soil. The rear end of the worm's body remains near the opening while the head end forages for decaying leaves and animal debris.

It has been estimated that an acre of good soil contains more than 50,000 earthworms. By their continual foraging and tunneling, these worms turn over from 18 to 20 tons of soil per acre and bring more than 25 mm of rich soil to the surface every 4 or 5 years. Thus, indirectly, the earthworm enriches farmland, assisting farmers in the production of greater quantities of food for a rapidly expanding population.

1. External Anatomy

Obtain a specimen of *Lumbricus* and, using Fig. 35-2 as a guide, study its external anatomy. A hand lens or dissecting microscope will be helpful in identifying the smaller features.

At the anterior end (**prostomium**) is a small fleshy projection over the mouth. It is not considered to be a segment of the worm. At the posterior end is the **anus**, the opening at the end of the digestive tract through which solid wastes are expelled.

About one-third of the way back from the mouth region is a thick cylindrical collar—the **clitellum**. This structure, which functions in reproduction, will be considered later.

Place the worm so that the ventral side is uppermost. The ventral surface of a living worm is a lighter color than the dorsal (upper) surface. With your finger, lightly stroke the ventral surface in an anterior direction. The bristles you feel are the setae and are used by the worm in movement. How many pairs of setae are there in each segment of the worm?

_____

Which segments do not have setae?

_____

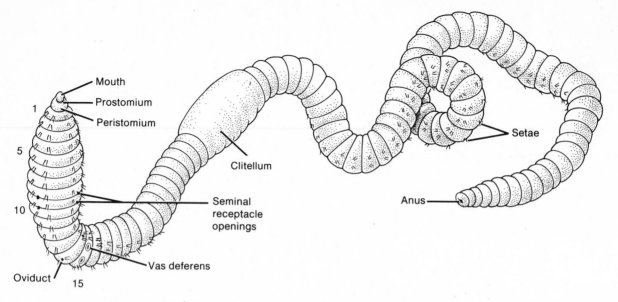

FIG. 35-2
External anatomy of the common earthworm, *Lumbricus terrestris.*

Each segment (except the first three and the last one) contains pores, called **nephridiopores**. These small openings connect with the **metanephridia**, which are the primitive kidneys of the earthworm. Liquid wastes, which collect in the body cavity, are excreted through these nephridial openings. A pair of rather large openings of the **vas deferens** (male) are located on each side of Segment 15. Sperm are released from the worm through these openings. Eggs are released through openings of the **oviducts** (female) located in Segment 14.

2. Internal Anatomy

Place the earthworm on the dissecting tray, *dorsal side up,* and pin into position. To expose the internal organs, dissect the worm as outlined in Fig. 35-3. With the help of Figs. 35-4 and 35-5, locate the structures described next.

a. Digestive System

The **mouth** is located at the anterior end. The opening is just below the overlapping prostomium.

The mouth leads to a slightly expanded and muscular **pharynx**. Food taken in by the animal is passed on by muscular contractions in the pharynx through the **esophagus**, which is covered by three pairs of whitish **seminal vesicles**, to the **crop** where it is temporarily stored.

The crop opens into a thick-walled, highly muscular **gizzard** where, with the aid of small soil particles taken in during feeding, food is ground up. It is then passed into the **intestine**, where it is digested and absorbed.

Solid waste products of digestion are passed to the exterior through the **anus**.

b. Circulatory System

An interesting feature of the circulatory system is that it is a "closed" system in which the blood circulates within a series of blood vessels. The blood is red because it contains hemoglobin, the same pigment that gives the red color to human blood. The hemoglobin, however, is not contained in cells but is dissolved in the plasma.

The major vessels of the circulatory system are a **dorsal longitudinal vessel** lying on top of the digestive tract and a **ventral blood vessel** lying below it. These two vessels are connected to each other by five pairs of vessels passing around the esophagus. They are larger than the other blood vessels and constitute the **hearts.** Although the hearts contain valves and contractile tissue and serve as pumps to circulate blood through the animal, they are thought to play a minor role in circulation. The dorsal and ventral blood vessels are the major circulatory pumps. Associated with the hearts and surrounding the esophagus are two pairs of **esophogeal** (calciferous) **glands**, which are considered to be excretory organs that function in controlling the amount of calcium in the blood.

A. Place worm in tray, dorsal side up. Pin through anterior and posterior segment.

B. Lift skin with forceps. With scissors cut through skin (off center) to the anus. Do not damage internal organs.

C. With scalpel or razor, cut through septa on both sides of intestine. Pin body wall to tray as shown.

D. Cut through clitellum toward anterior end. Sever septa and pin as shown in E.

E. Internal structure of earthworm.

FIG. 35-3
Procedure for dissecting earthworm.

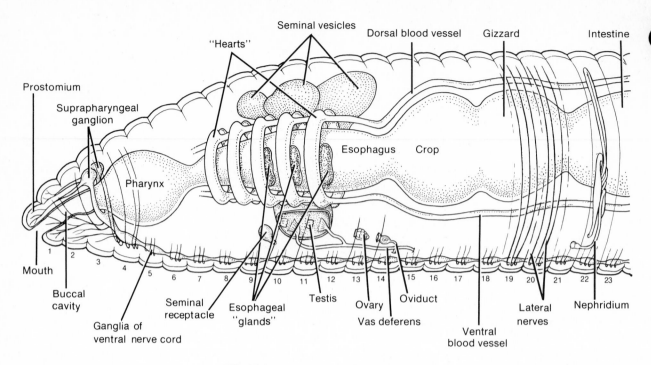

FIG. 35-4
Internal structure of *Lumbricus:* lateral view.

Most of the other blood vessels are difficult to observe unless the material has been sectioned for microscopic study.

c. Reproductive System

To obtain a clear view of the reproductive organs, cut through the intestine near the clitellum. Carefully lift the intestine and tease it free as far forward as the posterior end of the pharynx. Then cut it out.

As previously stated, earthworms are **hermaphroditic**, having complete sets of male and female reproductive organs. The male system consists of a pair of trilobed **seminal vesicles** located between Segments 9 and 13 (Fig. 35-5). Within these vesicles, sperm are produced in the **testes**. Tear off one of the lobes, smear it in a small drop of water on a slide, and add a cover slip. By using high magnification, you should be able to observe sperm. The vesicles connect with the **vas deferens** (sperm duct), which exits to the outside in Segment 15.

To observe the female reproductive organs, it may be necessary to remove the seminal vesicles. The female system consists of (1) a pair of **ovaries** in Segment 13; (2) a pair of **oviducts**, opening into Segment 13 by way of a ciliated **egg funnel** and an opening to the outside

through the ventral surface of Segment 14; (3) an **egg sac** (a small pouch branching from the egg funnel); and (4) two pairs of **seminal receptacles** in Segments 9 and 10.

Although earthworms are hermaphroditic, they do not undergo self-fertilization. Rather, sperm are transferred between worms during **copulation**: two worms come together along their ventral sides and become temporarily joined together by the secretion of a "slime tube"; sperm are discharged from the seminal vesicles of each worm, pass along seminal grooves on the ventral body surfaces, and enter the **seminal receptacles** of the other worm.

When eggs leave the ovaries, the glandular clitellum secretes a tube of mucus that slides over the anterior segments and picks up eggs from the oviducts in Segment 14 and sperm from Segments 9 and 10. The tube of mucus finally slips over the anterior end of the worm to form the egg cocoon, from which the young eventually hatch.

d. Nervous System

The nervous system in the worm is difficult to study. Its major component is the **ventral nerve cord**, which runs the length of the worm on the inner ventral surface. At its anterior end, the cord divides and passes around the front part of the pharynx where it enlarges to form two

403

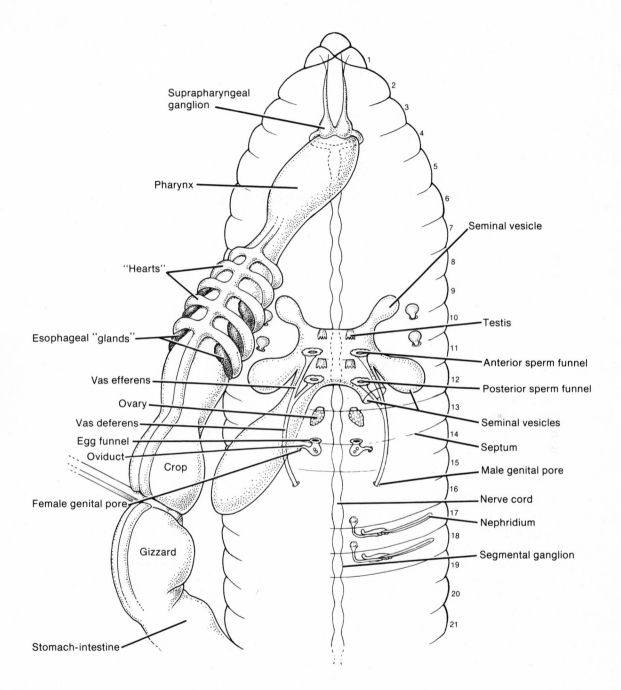

FIG. 35-5
Internal structure of *Lumbricus:* dorsal view.

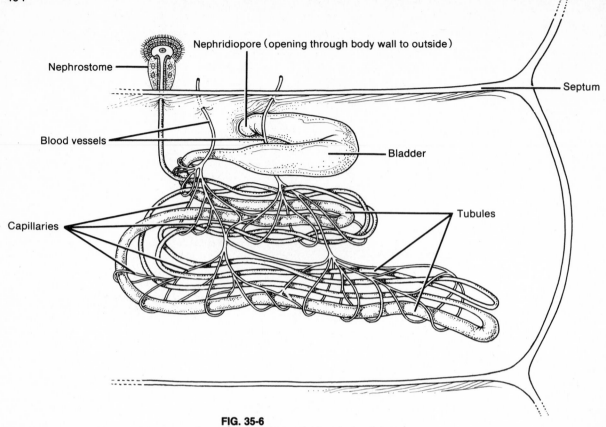

FIG. 35-6
Structure of a nephridium in *Lumbricus*.

FIG. 35-7
Cross section through segment of earthworm.

swellings, the **suprapharyngeal ganglia**. These might be considered primitive "brains."

Along the length of the cord, lateral nerves extend from segmental ganglia to the muscles of the body wall.

e. Excretory System

In *Lumbricus,* every body segment, except the first three or four and the last, contains an excretory organ called a **nephridium** (Fig. 35-6). Each nephridium opens into the coelomic cavity just anterior to the segment in which it is located through a ciliated funnel (**nephrostome**). The nephrostome continues as a finely coiled tubule, surrounded by capillaries, that leads to a **bladder**. The bladder discharges to the outside through a **nephridiopore**, located near the ventral surface of the body wall.

The cilia of the nephrostome create currents that draw wastes from the coelom into the tubule. Various materials are exchanged and reabsorbed by the blood in the capillaries surrounding the convoluted tubules, and thus a salt and water balance in the body is maintained.

3. Microscopic Anatomy

Examine a cross section of *Lumbricus* for details of its internal anatomy (Fig. 35-7).

The body surface is covered by a noncellular **cuticle**, which is secreted by the **epidermis** directly beneath. The epidermal layer consists of a layer of columnar epithelial cells and mucus-secreting cells, sensory cells, and photoreceptor cells that function in orienting the animal to its environment.

Under the epidermis is a layer of **circular muscles**. What effect would contraction of this muscle layer have on locomotion of the worm?

_____

_____

_____

Under the circular-muscle layer is a thick band of **longitudinal muscles** that are arranged in a featherlike pattern. What effect would contraction of this muscle layer have on the body?

_____

_____

_____

The innermost layer of the body wall is covered with thin, flattened cells that form the **peritoneum**. The space between the body wall and the digestive cavity is the **coelom**. Locate the **dorsal** and **ventral blood vessels** and the **ventral nerve cord** in the coelomic cavity. You may be able to observe nephridia, located in the coelomic cavity on either side of the intestine, in your cross section, as well as setae.

The wall of the intestine is composed of three layers. The innermost layer is the **mucosa**, a layer of narrow, ciliated, columnar cells. The intermediate layer is the **submucosa**, which contains circular and longitudinal muscle fibers and numerous small blood vessels. The outermost layer is made up of slender columnar epithelial cells containing numerous granules and **chloragogue cells**, which aid in the elimination of wastes from the blood. What is the function of these muscle layers and blood vessels in the intestine?

_____

_____

_____

C. CLASS HIRUDINEA

Leeches are highly specialized annelids, most of which live in freshwater habitats although a few are marine organisms and some have become adapted to a terrestrial existence in tropical countries.

Contrary to common belief, leeches are not true parasites. Rather, they can be considered predaceous animals, feeding on the blood of various invertebrates and vertebrates. It is true that some species of leeches live permanently on a single animal and might be termed **ectoparasites**. However, many others do not.

Examine various leeches on display in the laboratory. Note that they are dorsoventrally flattened and tapered at both ends (Fig. 35-8). Most species are between 20 and 60 mm long. The largest is said to be as long as 0.5 meter when it is crawling. Note the **anterior** and **posterior suckers**, which are used for attachment. The anterior sucker contains the mouth, which has jaws covered with chitinous teeth for biting. Blood that is sucked up is stored in an enormous crop, allowing the animal to ingest three times its weight in blood. This permits the leech to go as long as nine months between feedings.

In most leeches, respiration takes place directly through the moist body surface, although some leeches have gills for this purpose. Waste products are removed from the coelomic fluid and blood by nephridia.

A

B

Anterior sucker

Posterior sucker

FIG. 35-8
Leeches: (A) *Placobdella,* commonly found on turtles;
and (B) *Hirudo medicinalis,* a leech once used for bloodletting.

Leeches are hermaphroditic, but reproduction is by cross-fertilization. Copulation and the formation of a cocoon is similar to that of earthworms.

REFERENCES

Bell, A. W. 1947. The Earthworm Circulatory System. *Turtox News* 25:89–94.

Buchsbaum, R. 1948. *Animals Without Backbones.* 2nd ed. University of Chicago Press.

Dales, R. P. 1963. *Annelids.* Hutchinson.

Edwards, C. A., and J. R. Lofty. 1972. *Biology of Earthworms.* Chapman and Hall.

Hickman, C. P. 1973. *Biology of the Invertebrates.* 2nd ed. Mosby.

Mann, K. H. 1962. *Leeches (Hirudinea): Their Structure, Physiology, Ecology and Embryology.* Pergamon.

Pennak, R. W. 1953. *Freshwater Invertebrates of the United States.* Ronald.

Kingdom Animalia: Phyla Onycophora and Arthropoda

The phylum Onycophora (Greek *onychus,* "claw"; *phorus,* "bearing") includes a group of terrestrial organisms that have a distinct head, a somewhat cylindrical, unsegmented body, and a number of short, unjointed legs. They are primarily found in very moist land habitats, beneath stones, leaves, or logs in forests. In this exercise, you will study *Peripatus,* a representative genus of this phylum.

The phylum Arthropoda (Greek *arthros,* "joint"; *podos,* "foot") is the largest of all animal phyla. Of the million or so known species of animals, more than three-quarters are arthropods. The arthropods are considered to have attained the greatest "biological success": they comprise the largest number not only of species, but also of organisms; they occupy the greatest variety of habitats, consume the largest amounts and kinds of food, and are capable of defending themselves against their enemies.

The arthropods are characterized by their rigid, chitinous body covering, called an **exoskeleton**. The body is segmented externally and internally to varying degrees, depending on the species, and the appendages are jointed and highly modified for a large variety of functions.

The classification of the Arthropoda is quite complex because of its large number of species and the tremendous diversity in form among its members. It is divided into 3 subphyla, which are subdivided into classes. Some of the major classes are included in the following:

Subphylum Trilobita: primitive marine arthropods that are now extinct were characterized by having a distinct head, a segmented body and appendages

Subphylum Chelicerata: relatively simple, chiefly terrestrial arthropods lacking antennae and mandibles but having six pairs of jointed appendages

Class Xiphosura: aquatic arthropods having compound lateral eyes, a cephalothorax (fused head and thorax), and an abdomen with five or six pairs of appendages

Class Pycnogonida (sea spiders): small marine organisms having a short, thin body and a mouth on a long proboscis

Class Arachnida: terrestrial arthropods having simple eyes, no gills, and six pairs of jointed appendages

408

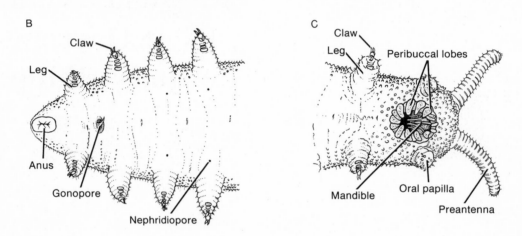

FIG. 36-1
Peripatus: (A) lateral view of whole organism,
(B) posterior ventral surface, and (C) anterior ventral surface.

Subphylum Mandibulata: the largest group of arthropods, which are characterized by having three or more pairs of legs, one or two pairs of appendages modified to serve as antennae, and one pair adapted to function as mandibles (jaws)

Class Crustacea: the most common aquatic arthropods, which are characterized by respiring mainly by gills and having two pairs of antennae, one pair of jaws, and two pairs of maxillae

Class Insecta: mainly terrestrial arthropods having a distinct head, thorax, and abdomen and one pair of antennae, three pairs of legs, and two pairs of wings

Class Chilopoda: terrestrial arthropods having long, flattened bodies with many somites (segments), each somite having a pair of legs

Class Diplopoda: terrestrial arthropods characterized by having a long, usually cylindrical body with many somites, each somite having two pairs of legs

A. PHYLUM ONYCOPHORA

The members of this phylum possess characteristic features that are common to both the annelids and arthropods and thus come closer than any others to being the "missing link" between any two phyla.

Examine a preserved specimen or plastic mount of *Peripatus,* which resembles the annelids in the structure of the eyes, the nephridia, the ciliated reproductive ducts, and the simple gut. It resembles the arthropods in having a **hemocoel** (body cavity that functions as part of a blood-vascular system) and a dorsal heart, and in the general structure of the reproductive organs. Note the absence of external segmentation, although there is a pair of legs for each internal segment of the body (Fig. 36-1). The legs terminate in claws, which superficially resemble those of arthropods but differ in not being jointed. The head has three segments, each of which bears three pairs of appendages: two short **antennae**, two blunt **oral papillae**, and

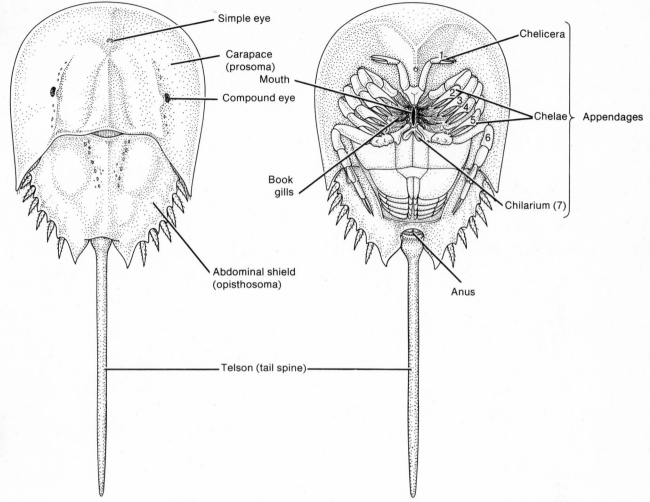

FIG. 36-2
Limulus: (A) dorsal view and (B) ventral view.

two small horny **jaws**. *Peripatus* possesses an internal system of excretory **nephridia** with external openings (**nephridiopores**) at the base of each appendage. The **anus** opens at the blunt posterior end and is preceded by a single genital opening, the **gonopore**.

B. PHYLUM ARTHROPODA

1. Subphylum Chelicerata

a. Class Xiphosura

This class includes many fossil forms and living species of horseshoe crabs. Examine a preserved specimen of *Limulus polyphemus*, a horseshoe crab that is common in the shallow marine waters off the Atlantic coast from Nova Scotia to Yucatan. The dark brown outer covering, or **carapace**, is shaped like a horseshoe, thus giving it

its common name of horseshoe crab (Fig. 36-2). Posterior to the carapace is an **abdominal shield** with short, lateral movable spines, to which is attached a tail spine (**telson**). The telson is used to right the body when it is overturned and to push it forward when burrowing into the ocean floor.

Turn your specimen over, and observe the seven pairs of jointed appendages. The first pair consists of two **chelicerae**, which function to some extent in locomotion but are used mainly in capturing and macerating food organisms. The next four pairs are leglike and end in small pincers, or **chelae**. The appendages in the next pair, also leglike, end in leaflike tips used to sweep away mud that clings to the body when burrowing. The seventh pair consists of very small, modified appendages, called **chilaria**, attached to the pregenital somite. Respiratory organs consisting of deep pleats that resemble the leaves of a book ("**book gills**") are on the hind surface of appendages 2 through 6. Gaseous exchange between the

FIG. 36-3
Representative mite (A), tick (B), scorpion (C), and spiders (D). The spiders shown are
(1) black widow, (2) common garden, (3) crab, (4) jumping, and (5) wolf.

blood and the water that is constantly moving past these organs takes place across them as the book gills wave back and forth.

b. Class Arachnida

The arachnids are a diverse group of arthropods that include spiders, scorpions, ticks, and mites. They are characterized by having body segments fused into two main regions: a cephalothorax bearing four pairs of walking legs and an abdomen. Arachnids further differ from the other arthropods by the absence of compound eyes, antennae, and true jaws.

Examine preserved specimens or plastic mounts of spiders, scorpions, ticks, and mites (Fig. 36-3).

2. Subphylum Mandibulata

a. Class Crustacea

This class of arthropods includes fairy shrimps, water fleas, barnacles, crayfish, and crabs. Most crustaceans are marine, but many others inhabit inland waters, and a few, such as sow bugs, live in moist places on land. Many crustaceans are microscopic whereas others, such as giant crabs, may be as long as 5 meters.

Crustaceans have three important arthropod features. The body is segmented and covered by a chitinous exoskeleton, and the appendages are jointed. However, the segmentation of the crustaceans is more specialized than that of the annelids. In the latter, the segments are nearly identical, whereas in the crustaceans and most arthropods there is considerable regional specialization, including a well-developed head.

The common crayfish (*Cambarus* or *Procambarus* sp.) is a cannibalistic scavenger that lives on the muddy bottoms of freshwater lakes, streams, and ponds. It emerges at night to feed on dead and decaying matter, insect larvae, worms, and other crayfishes. It can be as much as 15 cm long, and its appendages are differentiated to serve specific purposes.

If available, observe a living specimen of a freshwater crayfish in a shallow pan of water or in an aquarium. Study its manner of walking and swimming. In which direction does a crayfish normally crawl?

_____

Hold a crayfish firmly against the bottom of the container, and then introduce a drop of India ink at the posterior end of the abdomen. From your observations,

describe the direction of water flow and the mechanism used by the crayfish to set up such water currents.

_____

_____

_____

Feed a crayfish a live insect (cockroach or cricket), and note the coordinated activity of the mouth parts.

1. **External Anatomy.** Examine a preserved specimen of the crayfish. The body is divided into an anterior **cephalothorax** (fused head and thorax) and a posterior **abdomen** (Fig. 36-4). The chitinous exoskeleton effectively protects the crayfish from predators. In order to grow, however, the crayfish periodically **molts** (i.e., sheds its exoskeleton). During the period in which a new skeleton is being formed, the crayfish is defenseless; it hides to escape its enemies.

The **carapace** is a saddlelike covering over the cephalothorax. A transverse groove separates the fused head from the thoracic region. Laterally, the carapace covers the gills. The **rostrum** is an anterior, pointed extension of the head. The eyes are located on either side of the rostrum.

The **abdomen** consists of several segments and is terminated by the telson, an extension of the last abdominal segment. To escape its enemies, the crayfish spreads the telson and the wide **uropods** like a fan, rapidly drawing the telson forward under its body. This motion causes the crayfish to dart backward into the muddy bottom, which becomes cloudy because of the flipping movements. Each abdominal segment contains a dorsal plate, a ventral plate, and two lateral plates. Examine the appendages on the lower side of the abdomen. These appendages are the **swimmerets**. What is the function of these appendages?

_____

_____

_____

Note that all other appendages are modifications of this three-part plan. Although male and female crayfish have an equal number of swimmerets, in male crayfish those adjoining the thorax have been modified: The exopodites

412

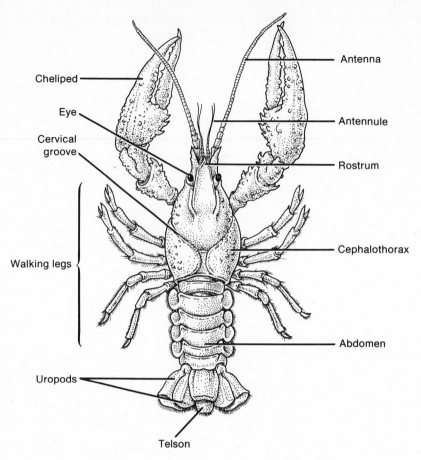

FIG. 36-4
Dorsal view of a crayfish *(Cambarus* or *Procambarus).*

and endopodites are elongate and can be brought together to form a troughlike channel, used for the transfer of sperm from the male to the seminal receptacles of the female. In female crayfish, the eggs, which look like clusters of grapes, are attached to the abdominal swimmerets and are aerated by gentle, waving movements of the swimmerets.

Examine the five pairs of walking legs and count the number of segments in each leg (Fig. 36-5). Note that there are no pincers on the fifth (posterior) pair of legs. Locate the male genital pores, which open into the base of the legs of this pair. The openings of the oviducts in the female are located at the base of each third walking leg. Carefully cut the membrane at the base of each leg, and remove the right walking legs, starting with the most posterior one and working forward. Arrange these appendages in order on a piece of paper. How many of these legs have feathery gills attached to them?

_____

What is the advantage of the featherlike structures in these gills?

_____

_____

_____

The legs of the first pair, the **chelipeds**, are much larger than the rest. Cut the exoskeleton from the dorsal surface of the claw, and study the action of the muscles in opening and closing the pincer.

The appendages of the crayfish and other crustaceans are **homologous** organs; that is, they are all fundamentally similar in structure and arise from a similar embryonic rudiment. The basic structural plan is evident in the simple abdominal appendages, consisting of a single protopodite and the exopodite and endopodite. The structural adaptations of the appendages in different regions are correlated with their functions (Fig. 36-4). When corre-

LOCATION	APPENDAGES OF CEPHALOTHORAX (HEAD AND THORAX)	FUNCTION
Front of mouth	Antennules	Senses other organisms and helps to balance crayfish
Front of mouth	Antenna	Senses other organisms
Mouth	Mandible or jaw	Crushes food
Behind mandibles	First maxilla	Moves food to mouth
Behind mandibles	Second maxilla	Bails water in gill chamber
At anterior and ventral part of thorax region	First maxilliped	Holds food, touches, and tastes
At anterior and ventral part of thorax region	Second maxilliped	Holds food, touches, and tastes
At anterior and ventral part of thorax region	Third maxilliped	Holds food, touches, and tastes
Posterior to maxillipeds at ventral part of thorax	Cheliped	Grasps food
Posterior to maxillipeds at ventral part of thorax	Gill Walking leg	For locomotion

APPENDAGES OF THE ABDOMEN

LOCATION		FUNCTION
Ventral side of abdomen	Swimmeret	First swimmeret in male transfers sperm to female, which uses 2nd, 3rd, 4th, and 5th swimmerets to hold eggs and young
Posterior end	Telson	For swimming

FIG. 36-5
Structure and function of crayfish appendages.

414

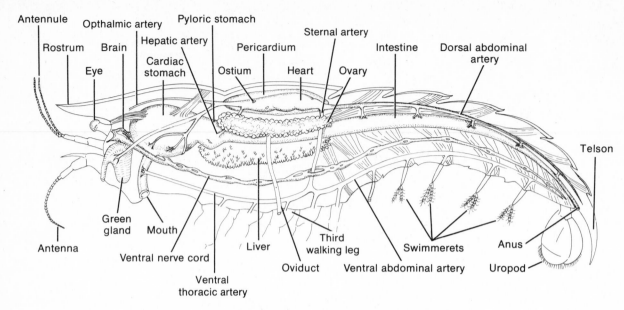

FIG. 36-6
Internal anatomy of the crayfish.

sponding structures in different segments of the same animal are homologous, it is called **serial homology**. On the other hand, **analogous** organs are similar in function but not necessarily in structure. Cite examples of analogous organs.

_____

_____

_____

2. **Internal Anatomy.** Using a sharp scalpel and scissors, carefully dissect away the dorsal half of the exoskeleton to expose the internal organs (Fig. 36-6). In the middorsal region, locate the diamond-shaped heart perforated by three pairs of openings called **ostia**. Identify the following blood vessels: **ophthalmic artery** extending anteriorly from the heart to the eyes; **hepatic arteries**, a pair of short arteries going to the digestive gland; **antennary arteries** going to the antennae; **dorsal abdominal artery**, a single artery leading posteriorly from the heart to the dorsal part of the abdomen; **sternal artery**, a single vessel leading from the heart to the ventral part of the crayfish where it splits and becomes the **ventral thoracic artery** anteriorly and the **ventral abdominal artery** posteriorly. Because there are no veins in the crayfish, the blood flows from the arteries into open spaces or **sinuses** instead of capillaries as it does in the earthworm. The blood, after being oxygenated in the sinuses of the gills, returns through efferent channels to the heart. This type of circulatory system is known as an **open system** to distinguish it from the **closed system**

found in the annelids and many higher forms, including human beings.

Remove the heart, and locate the gonads. In the female crayfish, the ovaries are a pair of tubular structures bilaterally arranged in front of the heart and continuing behind it as a single mass. In the male, the testes are highly coiled white tubes.

Locate the mouth. This leads to a short, tubular esophagus, which in turn leads to a large, saclike stomach. The stomach is made up of two parts: the larger anterior **cardiac stomach**, in which food is stored, and the small, posterior **pyloric stomach**. Most of the digestion takes place in the pyloric stomach as a result of the grinding action of the gastric mill and the enzymes that are secreted into the region by the digestive glands. The remaining part of the digestive system is the intestine, a small, straight tube leading to the anus. Anterior to the stomach and just behind each antenna are the excretory structures, commonly called the **green glands**. Find their external openings at the bases of the antennae.

The nervous system is similar to that of annelids, except for the fusion of several originally separated nervous elements. Remove the main organs from the thoracic and abdominal regions of your crayfish and locate the **ganglion**, or brain, in front of the esophagus. Expose the brain by careful dissection and find the nerves passing to the eyes, antennae, and antennules. The brain is connected to the **ventral nerve cord** by a pair of nerves that pass around the esophagus. Follow the ventral nerve cord as it passes through the thorax and abdomen, and count the number of ganglia. Each ganglion gives off pairs of nerves to the appendages and internal organs of the segment in which it lies.

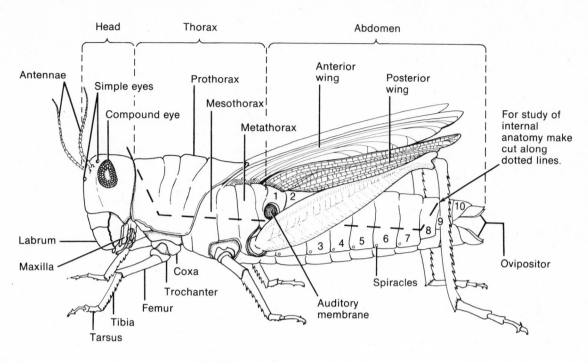

FIG. 36-7
External anatomy of a female grasshopper.

b. Class Insecta

It has been estimated that there may be as many as 5 million insect species, of which fewer than a million have been identified and classified (there are, for example, more than 300,000 species of beetles alone). Insects range in size from those no larger than a dust particle, and a species of hairy, winged beetle that can crawl through the eye of a needle, to the Atlas moth of India, which has a 30-cm wingspan. It has been estimated that the insect population of the world is at least 1×10^{18} and, taking the average weight of insects as 2.5 mg (i.e., less than 0.001 ounce), the weight of the earth's insect population exceeds that of its human inhabitants by a factor of 12.

Clearly, insects are the most successful and abundant of all land animals. They are the principal invertebrates that can live in dry environments and the only ones able to fly. Some insects can survive in temperatures as low as $-30°F$ ($-35°C$); others in temperatures as high as 120°F (49°C). These abilities are due to the chitinous body coating (**exoskeleton**) that protects the internal organs against injury and loss of moisture and to the system of tracheal tubes that enables insects to breathe air. The ability to fly permits them to readily find food. Under favorable conditions, insects can multiply rapidly.

The insect's small size frees it from the need to compete with larger animals for a place in the environment.

Although insects are exceedingly diverse organisms, the basic external and internal organization can be effectively illustrated by a study of the large black lubber grasshopper, *Romalea microptera*. The following description, although primarily pertaining to the short-winged lubber grasshopper, will serve for any common species.

1. **External anatomy.** The body of the grasshopper is divided into a head consisting of six fused segments (**somites**); a thorax of three somites, to which are attached the legs and wings; and a long, segmented abdomen that terminates with the reproductive organs (Fig. 36-7). The outer **exoskeleton** consists largely of chitin, which is secreted by the epidermis. In order to grow, the grasshopper periodically sheds this exoskeleton (**molts**); adults do not molt. Pigment in and under the cuticle gives the grasshopper coloration resembling that of its surroundings, affording protection from predators.

The **head** (Fig. 36-8) has one pair of slender, jointed **antennae**, two **compound eyes**, and three simple eyes or **ocelli**. The mouth parts are of the chewing type and include a broad upper lip or **labrum**; a tonguelike **hypo-**

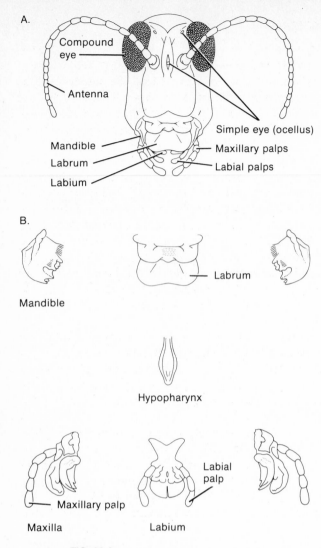

A.

Compound eye

Antenna

Mandible

Labrum

Labium

Simple eye (ocellus)

Maxillary palps

Labial palps

B.

Mandible

Labrum

Hypopharynx

Maxillary palp

Maxilla

Labial palp

Labium

FIG. 36-8
Grasshopper head (A) and mouth parts (B).

pharynx; two heavy blackish lateral jaws or **mandibles**, each with teeth along the inner lateral margin for chewing food; a pair of **maxillae** of several parts, including palps (sensory appendages) at the side; and a broad lower lip or **labium**, with two short palps.

The **thorax** consists of three parts: a large anterior **prothorax**, the **mesothorax**, and the posterior **metathorax**. Each part bears a pair of jointed legs. Identify the leg segments indicated in Fig. 36-7. The meso- and metathorax each bear a pair of wings. The anterior wings of the grasshopper are thick and shield the larger pair of flight wings. Both pairs of wings are derived from the cuticle and have thick parts (veins) that strengthen them. Stretch out the wings, and examine the anterior protective wings and the flight wings.

The slender **abdomen** consists of 11 somites, the posterior ones being modified for reproduction. The male has a blunt terminal segment, whereas the female has four sharp conical prongs, the **ovipositors**, which are used in egg laying (Fig. 36-7). Along the lower sides of the thorax and abdomen are 10 pairs of **spiracles**, the small openings of elastic air tubes, or **tracheae**, that branch to all parts of the body and constitute the respiratory (**tracheal**) system of the grasshopper. This system of air tubes brings atmospheric oxygen directly to the cells of the body. The spiracles open and close to regulate the flow of air. The three most anterior pairs of spiracles are inhalatory, piping air directly to all body tissues. The other spiracles are exhalatory.

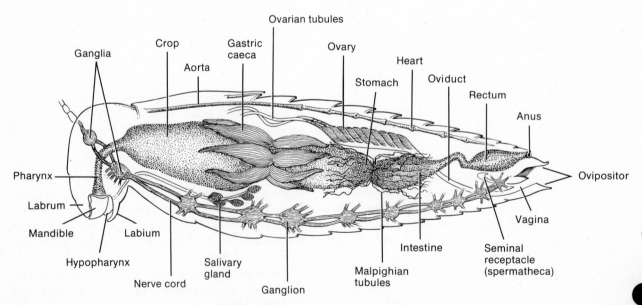

Ovarian tubules

Crop

Gastric caeca

Ovary

Ganglia

Aorta

Heart

Stomach

Oviduct

Rectum

Anus

Pharynx

Labrum

Mandible

Labium

Oviposito r

Hypopharynx

Nerve cord

Salivary gland

Ganglion

Malpighian tubules

Intestine

Vagina

Seminal receptacle (spermatheca)

FIG. 36-9
Internal anatomy of a female grasshopper.

2. **Internal Anatomy.** It is difficult to preserve the internal organs of the grasshopper because the preservative often fails to penetrate the exoskeleton. Careful dissection is necessary to study the internal anatomy.

After removing the wings, start at the posterior end, and make two lateral cuts toward the head with a pair of scissors or fine scalpel as indicated in Fig. 36-7. Remove the dorsal wall. Locate the muscles on the inside of the body wall, and note their arrangement. What is their function?

_____

_____

A space between the body wall and digestive tract, the **hemocoel**, is filled with colorless blood.

Study the digestive tract and identify its parts (Fig. 36-9). Beginning at the anterior end, find the **mouth**, which is located between the mandibles and leads to a short **esophagus** followed by the **crop**. Next is the **stomach**, to which are attached six double finger-shaped digestive glands (**gastric caeca**); these glands produce enzymes that are secreted into the stomach to aid digestion. The digestive tract continues as the **intestine**, which consists of a tapered anterior part, a slender middle part, and an enlarged **rectum** that opens to the outside at the **anus**. During feeding, food held by the forelegs, labium, and labrum is lubricated by secretions from the salivary glands and chewed by the mandibles and maxillae. Chewed food is stored in the crop. Because most of the digestive tract, except for the stomach and crop, is lined with chiton, which is impervious, digestion and absorption take place mainly in the stomach. Excess water is absorbed from any undigested food in the rectum.

The excretory system is made up of numerous tiny tubules—the excretory, or **Malpighian, tubules**—which empty their products into the anterior end of the intestine. These tubules remove urea and salts from the blood.

The sexes are separate, and their reproductive organs are in the terminal abdominal segments. In the male, each of the two **testes** is composed of a series of slender tubules, or follicles, and is located above the intestine; each testis is joined to a longitudinal **vas deferens** (Fig. 36-10). The vas deferens are joined to a single ejaculatory duct, to which **accessory glands** are attached. In the female, each **ovary** is composed of several tapering egg tubes (**ovarioles**), which produce the ova. Each ovary is joined to an **oviduct** leading to the **vagina**, to which a pair of accessory glands and a single **spermatheca** are attached. The latter organ is used to store sperm received at copulation.

The insect circulatory system can be studied by examining the wing veins of a living adult grasshopper or cricket. This can be done by preparing a plasticene or wax cell large enough to hold the insect on a microscope slide. Pin the animal down with two strips of paper, one across the thorax and the other across the body beneath

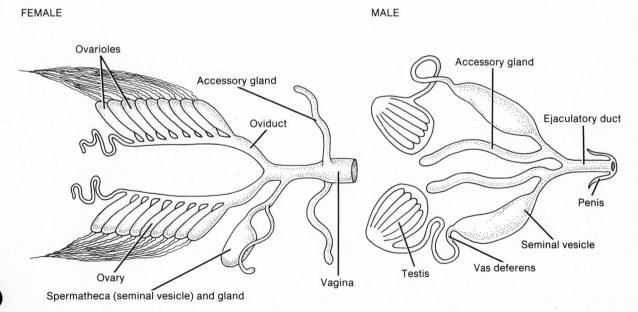

FEMALE

MALE

FIG. 36-10
Reproductive systems of the grasshopper.

418

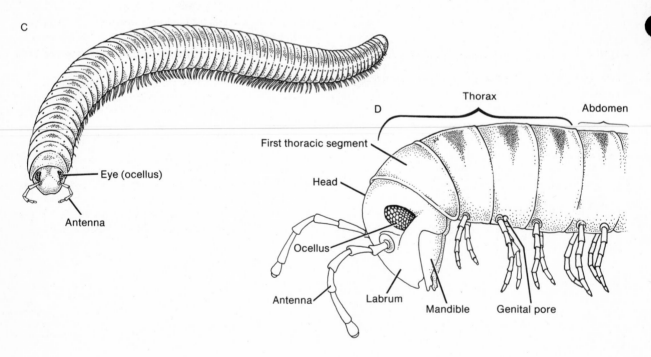

FIG. 36-11
(A) A centipede *(Scolopendra)*. (B) Lateral view of head of *Scutigera*.
(C) A millipede *(Spirobolus)*. and (D) Lateral view of head of *Spirobolus*.

the wings. Slip a piece of tinfoil or glazed white paper beneath the anterior wing, and examine under a dissecting microscope. Note the moving blood cells and the direction of flow of the hemolymph in various parts of the wing. In order to observe the beating heart, pin the insect's wings out to the side and focus light through the body with the concave mirror. What is the direction of blood flow in the dorsal tubular heart?

c. Class Chilopoda (Centipedes)

Centipedes live mainly in warm climates. They usually hide by day in a place that affords protection—in the soil or under stones, bark, or rotten logs. At night, they are very active, fast-running animals that prey on insects, earthworms, spiders, and other small animals, which are paralyzed by the centipede's poisonous claws. The smaller centipedes of the northern United States are harmless to human beings, but the larger ones of the South and the tropics inflict a painful bite.

Examine preserved or plastic-mounted specimens of centipedes. Observe that centipedes are elongate, flattened, wormlike animals with 15 or more pairs of legs (Fig. 36-11A). Each body segment bears a single pair of legs with the last 2 pairs being directed backwards and often different in form from the other pairs. The head bears a pair each of **mandibles** and long, jointed **antennae** and 2 pairs of **maxillae** (Fig. 36-11B). The first somite bears a pair of jointed **maxillipeds** that function as poisonous claws. The genital openings are located at the posterior end of the body, usually on the next to the last segment.

d. Class Diplopoda (Millipedes)

Millipedes, like centipedes, are found in humid, dark places—under leaves, in moss, under stones or boards, in rotting wood, or in the soil. Many species have "stink glands," which give off a foul-smelling fluid that can be so strong as to kill insects that are placed in a jar with the millipede. Millipedes, unlike some of the centipedes, do not bite human beings. Most millipedes are scavengers and feed on decaying plant material, but they also eat animal material.

Examine preserved or plastic-mounted specimens of millipedes. Observe that they are elongate, wormlike animals with 30 or more pairs of jointed legs (Fig. 36-11C). Most body segments have two pairs of legs. The head bears two clumps of many simple eyes and a pair each of mandibles and antennae (Fig. 36-11D). The thorax is short, of four single somites, all but the first having a pair of legs.

REFERENCES

Borror, D. J., and D. M. DeLong. 1976. *An Introduction to the Study of Insects*. 4th ed. Holt, Rinehart and Winston.

Buchsbaum, R. 1948. *Animals Without Backbones*. 2nd ed. University of Chicago Press.

Chapman, R. F. 1969. *The Insects: Structure and Function*. American Elsevier.

Cloudsley-Thompson, J. L. 1958. *Spiders, Scorpions, Centipedes and Mites*. Pergamon.

Horn, D. J. 1976. *The Biology of Insects*. Holt/Saunders.

Jacques, H. E. 1947. *How to Know the Insects*. 2nd ed. Brown.

Klots, A. B., and E. B. Klots. 1959. *Living Insects of the World*. Doubleday.

Meglitsch, P. A. 1972. *Invertebrate Zoology*. 2nd ed. Oxford University Press.

Romoser, W. S. 1973. *The Science of Entomology*. Macmillan.

Russell-Hunter, W. D. 1969. *A Biology of Lower Invertebrates*. Macmillan.

Storer, T. I., R. L. Usinger, R. C. Stebbins, and J. W. Nybakken. 1979. *General Zoology*. 6th ed. McGraw-Hill.

Kingdom Animalia:
Phylum Echinodermata

The phylum Echinodermata (Greek *echinos*, "hedge-hog"; *derma*, "skin") consists of familiar seashore animals commonly known as starfish, sea urchins, sand dollars, sea cucumbers, and sea lilies. The phylum is so named because of the presence of spiny plates (**calcareous ossicles**), which form a dermal skeleton. Echinoderms are typically radially symmetrical (although the larva is bilaterally symmetrical), and they have true coeloms arising as outpocketings from embryonic mesoderm of the gut. It is on the basis of this last characteristic, and because the bipinnaria larva more closely resembles the chordate larva, that the echinoderms are said to be more closely related to the chordates.

A unique feature of the echinoderms is a derivative of the coelom known as the *water vascular system*. Although a circulatory system is present, it is greatly reduced. Thus the coelomic fluid acts as the principal medium for the transport of food, respiratory gases, and so forth. There are no excretory organs, and thus echinoderms have little capacity for ionic exchange, which explains why this group of organisms has never invaded fresh waters.

The phylum is divided into at least 10 distinct classes but only the following 5 include living species:

Class Asteroidea (starfish): having a star-shaped body, with from 5 to 25 arms, that is covered by a flexible, spiny skeleton

Class Crinoidea (feather stars and sea lilies): having a flowerlike body with many slender, branched arms

Class Ophiuroidea (brittle stars): having a body with a central disc and 5 distinct, slender, jointed arms

Class Echinoidea (sea urchins and sand dollars): having a cylindrical or disc-shaped body in a shell of fused plates that bear movable spines

Class Holothuroidea (sea cucumbers): having a soft, wormlike body with no arms or spines

A. CLASS ASTEROIDEA (STARFISH)

The simplest and perhaps the most familiar of all echinoderms is the starfish. The common starfish, *Asterias*, found along the Atlantic coast of North America, is a typical example of this class. Starfish crawl on the shallow bottom or in tide pools among the rocks and sand of the seashore and coral reefs. They have been serious predators of oysters. At one time oyster fishermen caught starfish, cut them up, and threw them back into the ocean. Then it was discovered that each of the pieces could regenerate and grow into another starfish. Today, "sea mops" made of cloth are dragged over the oyster beds to entrap the starfish. They are then exposed to the sun to dry.

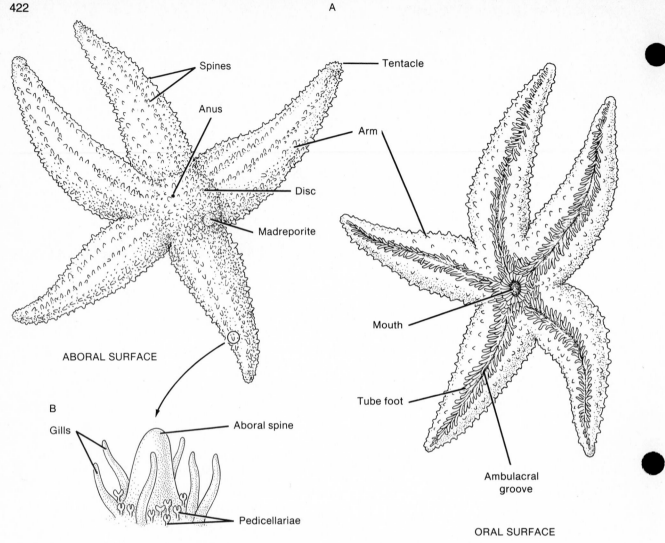

FIG. 37-1
(A) External features of the oral and aboral surfaces of *Asterias,*
and (B) spines and pedicellariae.

1. External Anatomy

Examine a preserved specimen, and note that the body is composed of a central **disc** from which radiate 5 **arms** or **rays** (Fig. 37-1A). Some specimens may have fewer arms, but this is usually because they have been broken off in handling. Some starfish have more than 5 arms; in rare cases, specimens with as many as 25 have been found. The oral, or ventral, surface of each arm contains grooves extending outward from the centrally located mouth. The spiny surface is the aboral, or dorsal, surface. Locate the **madreporite**, a small, porous, buttonlike structure, at one side of the aboral surface. The spines of the aboral surface are part of small calcareous plates (ossicles) that lie buried beneath the integument. These plates form the endoskeleton. Around the spines are many minute pincerlike **pedicellariae** (Fig. 37-1B). Each pedicillaria has 2 jaws that are moved by muscles and that open and shut when touched; they keep the body surface

clean of debris and may also help to capture food.

The groove in the oral surface of each arm is called the **ambulacral groove**. Along the sides of the ambulacral groove are a series of flexible **spines** that can lie across the groove for protection. Located in these grooves are rows of small, fingerlike projections called **tube feet**, which are organs of locomotion. If you separate the tube feet, you may be able to see the thick, white **radial nerve cord** that runs down the center of each arm. At the tip of each arm, locate the small, light-sensitive eye spot. These light-sensitive tips are thrust upward during locomotion.

2. Internal Anatomy

Cut off the tip of one of the arms, and then make longitudinal cuts on one side of the arm to the central disc. Carefully remove the aboral surface to expose the internal organs (Fig. 37-2A). Note that most of the coelom in

A

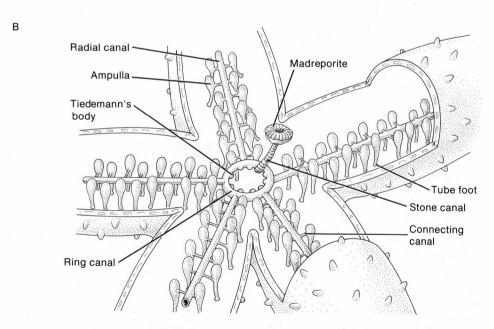

FIG. 37-2
(A) Internal organs of the starfish, and (B) the water vascular system.

424

FIG. 37-3
(A) Feather star *(Antedon)*, and (B) sea lily *(Metacrinus)*.

each arm is taken up by two highly branched digestive glands, the **hepatic caeca**. Examine the glands with a hand lens or dissecting microscope, and note the numerous lobes that secrete digestive enzymes. The 2 main ducts of these glands join at the base of the arm to form the **pyloric duct**, which enters the centrally located, sac-like stomach. A ventral **mouth** and a short **esophagus** lead directly into the stomach, which consists of a lower cardiac stomach, which is lobed, and an upper **pyloric stomach**. During feeding, the cardiac stomach is everted through the mouth. The food is partly digested and passed into the pyloric stomach, which empties into the anus located in the center of the aboral disc. Two small **rectal caeca** can usually be found near the anus. These caeca

are thought to function as temporary storage areas for waste products.

Cut the pyloric duct where it enters the stomach, and remove the hepatic caeca. If the starfish was caught during the breeding season, the arms will be filled with the **gonads** (reproductive organs). At other times the gonads are normally very small.

The male and female gonads look alike. To determine the sex of the starfish, the gonads must be examined microscopically. To do this, remove a small piece of the reproductive organ, and mince it in a drop of water on a slide. Add a cover slip, and examine under the low and the high power of the microscope. The testes of the male will have flagellated sperm. The ovaries of the female produce spherical eggs that are considerably larger than the sperm. Eggs and sperm are discharged into the water, where fertilization takes place.

The **water vascular system** of the starfish consists of a series of seawater-filled ducts that function in locomotion and feeding (Fig. 37-2B). To study this system, carefully remove the reproductive organs and the remaining parts of the digestive system—the stomach and anus. Be careful not to damage the sieve plate. Water enters this system through a sievelike **madreporite**, which is connected to a circular **ring canal** by the **stone canal**. The water is then distributed to the **radial canals** that are in each of the rays. The margin of the ring canal bears **Tiedemann's bodies,** which apparently produce the free amoebocytes found in the water vascular system. Lining the ridge through which each radial canal passes is a double row of bulblike structures called **ampullae**. These structures are connected to the **tube feet**, which project from the **ambulacral groove** on the undersurface of each ray. Water from the radial canal collects in the ampullae. Contraction of the ampullae causes the tube feet to elongate as water is forced into them. Expansion of the ampullae results in shortening of the tube feet. Thus, through the use of small suction discs at the end of each tube foot and the alternate expansion and contraction of the ampullae, the starfish is able to move.

B. CLASS CRINOIDEA (FEATHER STARS AND SEA LILIES)

Examine preserved or plastic-mounted specimens of feather stars and sea lilies. These flowerlike echinoderms live from just below the tideline to depths of more than 3,600 meters. The body of a feather star *(Antedon)* is a small cup-shaped **calyx** of calcareous plates, to which are attached 5 flexible arms that branch to form 10 or more narrow appendages, each bearing many slender lateral **pinnules**, arranged like barbs on a feather, thus giving rise to its common name (Fig. 37-3A). The sea lily has a long, jointed **stalk** that extends from the lower surface of the calyx and attaches it to the sea bottom by rootlike outgrowths called **cirri** (Fig. 37-3B). Both mouth and anus are on the aboral surface of the calyx. Each arm has an ambulacral groove, lined with cilia and containing tentaclelike tube feet.

C. CLASS OPHIUROIDEA (BRITTLE STARS)

Examine preserved or plastic-mounted specimens of brittle stars. This echinoderm has a small, rounded disc with five distinct arms that are long, slender, jointed, and very fragile (Fig. 37-4). The skeleton of the arms consists of

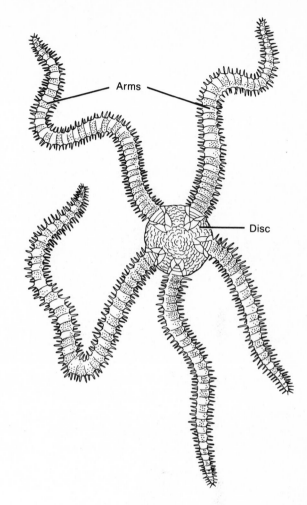

FIG. 37-4
Brittle star.

two parts: an outer, superficial endoskeleton and a deeper, internal, articulated series of vertebral ossicles. This arrangement permits the solidly armored arm to move quite freely and thus enables this animal to crawl rapidly and swim. The arms break or can be cast off easily, such parts being readily regenerated.

D. CLASS ECHINOIDEA (SEA URCHINS AND SAND DOLLARS)

Members of this class have globose, oval, or disc-shaped bodies lacking free arms or rays but covered with slender movable spines.

1. Sea Urchin

Examine a preserved specimen of the sea urchin *Arbacia* or *Strongylocentrotus*. Study the surface of this animal and observe the sharp, movable spines that are anchored

426

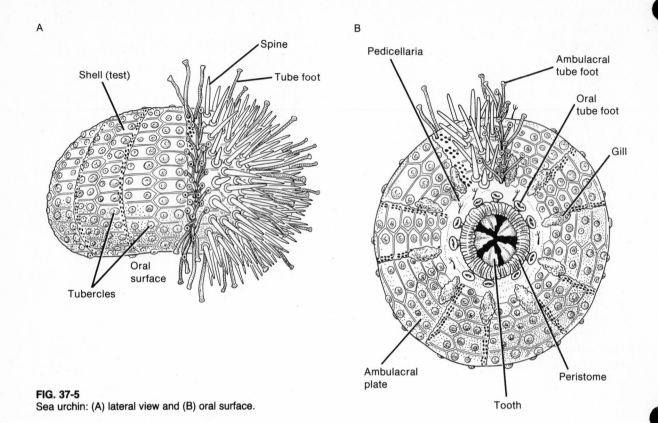

FIG. 37-5
Sea urchin: (A) lateral view and (B) oral surface.

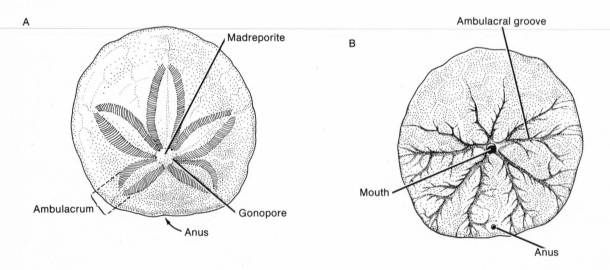

FIG. 37-6
Sand dollar: (A) aboral and (B) oral surfaces.

Tentacles

Tube foot

Ambulacral
region

FIG. 37-7
Sea cucumbers: (A) *Cucumaria* and (B) *Thyone*.

which bears five protrusible teeth; these teeth are the principal chewing organs, making up the jaw apparatus known as **Aristotle's lantern**. A soft, membranous area called the **peristome** surrounds the mouth; it has specialized oral tube feet, which are believed to be chemoreceptive in function. At the edge of the peristome are five pairs of **gills**.

2. Sand Dollar

Examine the concave aboral surface of the sand dollar *Echinarachnius* (Fig. 37-6). Observe the arrangement of the **ambulcra** on the surfaces. In the center of the aboral surface, you will find the madreporite, at the end of which are 5 genital pores (**gonopores**). Turn your specimen over, and locate the mouth in the center of the disc and the anus at the edge.

E. CLASS HOLOTHUROIDEA (SEA CUCUMBERS)

Examine preserved specimens of the sea cucumber *Cucumaria* or *Thyone* (Fig. 37-7). Note that the body surface has no spines. The endoskeleton is reduced to microscopic spicules, thus giving the body wall a tough, leathery quality. The mouth is located at the center of a conspicuous crown of **tentacles**, which are modified tube feet. In *Cucumaria*, you will also observe lengthwise zones of tube feet that are tactile and respiratory in function. In *Thyone*, the tube feet are distributed over the whole body.

The body wall of the sea cucumber is composed of a cuticle over a nonciliated epidermis, a dermis, a layer of circular muscles, and five double bands of longitudinal muscles. The action of these muscles enables the sea cucumber to extend or contract its body and to move by wormlike movements.

to the solid shell, or **test** (Fig. 37-5A). Among the spines are pedicellariae on long, flexible stalks. Some echinoids have several kinds of pedicellariae; a few bear poison-producing glands. Locate the long, slender tube feet, and note that they are restricted to five regions of the shell known as the **ambulacra**.

Turn the sea urchin so that the oral side faces you (Fig. 37-5B). In the center of the oral surface is the mouth,

REFERENCES

Barnes, R. D. 1980. *Invertebrate Zoology*. 4th ed. Saunders.
Buchsbaum, R. 1948. *Animals Without Backbones*. 2nd ed. University of Chicago Press.
Hyman, L. H. 1955. *The Invertebrates*. Vol. 4: *Echinoderms*. McGraw-Hill.
Meglitsch, P. A. 1972. *Invertebrate Zoology*. 2nd ed. Oxford University Press.
Nichols, D. 1969. *Echinoderms*. Hutchinson.
Storer, T. I., R. L. Usinger, R. C. Stebbins, and J. W. Nybakken. 1979. *General Zoology*. 6th ed. McGraw-Hill.

Kingdom Animalia: Phyla Hemichordata and Chordata

Representatives of the phylum Hemichordata (Greek *hemi,* "half"; *chorda,* "string") are a group of soft-bodied animals that are entirely marine. They are often found in U-shaped burrows on sandy or muddy sea bottoms. The hemichordates, because they possess both echinoderm and chordatelike characteristics, presumably represent an evolutionary link between the echinoderms and chordates. In this exercise, the acorn worm *Saccoglossus* will be studied as a representative of this phylum.

The phylum Chordata (Greek *chorda,* "string") is the largest and ecologically most significant phylum. It is divided into 3 subphyla, the Urochordata (tunicates), Cephalochordata (lancelets), and Vertebrata, all of which share 3 important characteristics: a notochord and pharyngeal gill slits (or pouches) and a dorsal hollow nerve cord at some stage in their development.

Representatives of the following phyla and classes of vertebrates will be studied in this exercise:

Phylum Hemichordata (acorn worms): wormlike animals characterized by having bilateral symmetry, a well-developed enterocoelom, and gill slits, as well as a primitive dorsal nervous system and an internal skeleton in the form of a notochord

Phylum Chordata: chordates possessing, at some stage in their life cycles, well-developed gills or gill slits, a dorsal tubular nerve cord, and a notochord

Subphylum Urochordata (tunicates): having a larval stage in which chordate characteristics are present, the neural tube and notochord being lost in the sedentary adult, although it does possess a primitive circulatory system

Subphylum Cephalochordata (lancelets): having a well-developed coelom, a circulatory system without a discrete heart, and a fusiform body that has prominent muscle segments (myotomes)

Subphylum Vertebrata (vertebrates): having a cranium (skull), visceral arches, and a spinal column of segmented vertebrae that are cartilaginous in lower forms and bony in higher forms; notochord extends from cranium to base of tail; enlarged brain; head region with specialized sense organs

Class Agnatha (cyclostomes): having a long, slender, and cylindrical body with median fins, a mouth located ventrally, from 5 to 16 pairs of gill arches and a persistent notochord, but lacking true jaws and scales (hagfish and lampreys)

Class Chondrichthyes: having a cartilaginous skeleton with notochord, tough skin that is covered with scales, median and paired lateral fins, a mouth that is ventrally located and has both upper and lower jaws, and pectoral and pelvic girdles (sharks, skates, and rays)

Class Osteichthyes: having a skeleton that is somewhat bony, a terminal mouth, gills covered by an operculum, median and paired fins, and (usually) skin that is covered with scales, although some are scaleless (perch, carp, and trout)

Class Amphibia: having moist, glandular skin that lacks scales; two pairs of limbs, but no fins; a bony skeleton; a terminal mouth with upper and lower jaws and a tongue that is often protrusible; being aquatic in the larval stage but usually terrestrial as an adult (frogs, toads, salamanders, and newts)

Class Reptilia: having a body that is dry and covered with scales; two pairs of limbs (absent in snakes), with digits adapted to running, crawling, climbing, or swimming; and a bony skeleton (lizards, snakes, turtles, crocodiles, and alligators)

Class Aves: warm-blooded animals having a body covered with feathers, forelimbs modified as wings, a bony but light skeleton, and a beak (includes all birds)

Class Mammalia: having mammary glands that secrete milk for nourishing the young, hair in varying quantities, and young that are born alive (human beings, dogs, cows, and mice)

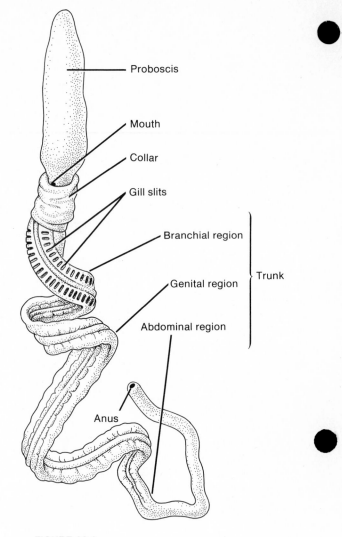

FIGURE 38-1
External anatomy of the acorn worm *Saccoglossus.*

A. PHYLUM HEMICHORDATA

Hemichordates are common marine animals of broad distribution. They are small, soft-bodied organisms that live singly or in colonies on sandy or muddy sea bottoms or in open ocean waters. The most common representatives are the acorn worms *Balanoglossus* and *Saccoglossus.*

Examine a preserved or plastic-mounted specimen of *Saccoglossus.* Note the softness of the body and its wormlike form (Fig. 38-1). The epidermis is ciliated and well supplied with mucus-secreting cells, which are important in burrowing and feeding. The body is divided into three regions: an anterior **proboscis**, a short **collar**, and an elongate **trunk**. The **mouth** opening is ventral and located at the base of the proboscis. The trunk is divisible into 3 regions: an anterior **branchial region** containing gill slits; a **genital region,** which, in other species, may be enlarged into large genital ridges; and, posteriorly, an **abdominal region** containing the intestine and lateral pouches of the hepatic caeca. The **anus** is terminal.

B. PHYLUM CHORDATA

1. Subphylum Urochordata

The urochordates are a group of exclusively marine and sessile organisms that are covered by a firm **test**, or **tunic**, from which they get the common name of *tunicates.*

Examine a preserved or plastic-mounted specimen of the tunicate *Ciona* or *Molgula* (Fig. 38-2A). The adult animal is saclike in appearance and is usually attached by its base to rocks, seaweeds, shells, wharf pilings, or ship hulls. At its free end, there are 2 openings: a mouth, or **branchial siphon**, and an **atrial siphon**. The body wall consists of a firm test, or tunic, below which lies the **mantle**. The mantle secretes the tunic and contains the muscles by means of which the shape of the body can be

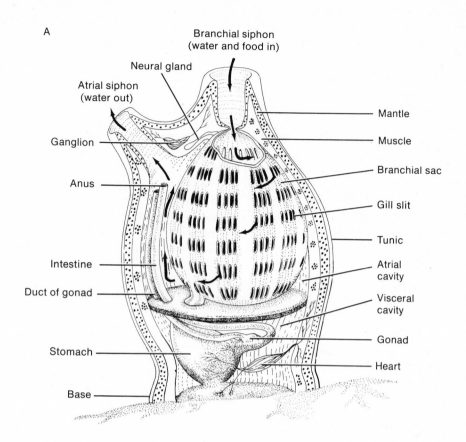

A

Branchial siphon
(water and food in)

Neural gland

Atrial siphon
(water out)

Ganglion

Anus

Intestine

Duct of gonad

Stomach

Base

Mantle

Muscle

Branchial sac

Gill slit

Tunic

Atrial
cavity

Visceral
cavity

Gonad

Heart

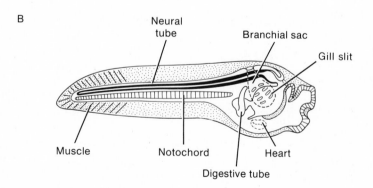

B

Neural
tube

Branchial sac

Gill slit

Muscle

Notochord

Digestive tube

Heart

FIGURE 38-2
(A) External anatomy of an adult tunicate, *Molgula*. (B) Tadpole larva.

altered. The body is divided into an **atrial cavity**, in which there is a large **branchial sac** that has many **gill slits**, and a **visceral cavity**, which contains the viscera (**gonads, stomach**, and **heart**).

Examine a prepared slide of the larval stage of *Molgula*. This transparent, free-swimming larva somewhat resembles an amphibian tadpole and thus is commonly called a **tadpole larva**. A larva has true chordate characteristics that an adult does not possess. Its tail contains a supporting **notochord**, a dorsal tubular **nerve cord**, serial pairs of lateral, segmental muscles, and **gill slits** (Fig. 38-2B). It swims about like a tadpole, settles down on some object, and then transforms into a sedentary adult. During this transformation, most of the chordate features (i.e., the notochord and nerve cord) disappear.

2. Subphylum Cephalochordata

Amphioxus *(Branchiostoma)*, the most commonly studied member of the cephalochordates, is a small, fishlike animal found in shallow marine waters in many parts of the world. Although the animal can swim with lateral, undulating movements of its body, it spends most of the time buried in the sandy bottom with its anterior end projected.

a. External Anatomy

Examine a preserved or plastic-mounted specimen of amphioxus. The animal is pointed at both ends and compressed laterally (Fig. 38-3A). Notice the absence of a distinct head, and the conspicuous chevron-shaped **muscle bands (myotomes)** of the body. A median **dorsal fin** extends almost the entire length of the body and a median **ventral fin** covers the posterior third of the animal. At the anterior end of the body is the funnel-shaped **buccal cavity** surrounded by a circle of oral tentacles (**cirri**). Approximately two-thirds of the way back from the anterior end, on the ventral side, locate the **atriopore**, through which water leaves after having been pumped through the pharynx.

b. Internal Anatomy

Study the internal anatomy of amphioxus by examining preserved or stained specimens under the dissecting microscope (Fig. 38-3A). Identify the **nerve cord**, which extends nearly the entire length of the animal's body. Above the nerve cord are short rods of connective tissue, called **fin rays**, that strengthen the dorsal fin. Locate the **notochord**, a cartilagelike rod that lies ventral to the

nerve cord and extends the length of the body. The notochord is a longitudinal elastic rod of cells and serves as an internal skeleton. Ventral to the notochord is the digestive tract. The mouth, located in the buccal cavity, leads into the relatively large **pharynx**. Observe the gill slits in the wall of the pharynx. The pharynx is lined with cilia that beat inward to produce a steady current of water that enters the mouth, passes over the **gill slits** (leaving behind suspended food particles), and is then eliminated through the atriopore. Posteriorly, the pharynx joins the intestine. Close to the point at which it does is a ventral outgrowth, the **liver,** that secretes digestive enzymes into the intestine.

Examine a cross section of amphioxus taken from the region of the pharynx, and locate the following structures shown in Fig. 38-3B; the dorsal fin with its dorsal fin ray; **metapleural folds**; the skin consisting of a one-celled layer of **epidermis** and a thicker **dermis**; muscle bands (**myotomes**); the **nerve cord** and its **central canal**; the **notochord**; **dorsal aortae**, a pair of small blood vessels ventral to the notochord; the **pharynx,** which contains a middorsal furrow, the **hyperbranchial groove** lined with cells, and a midventral groove, the **endostyle**, having both gland cells and cilia; the "**liver**" (hepatic caecum), a tube on the right side of the pharynx; the **ventral aorta**, a small blood vessel just ventral to the endostyle; the **atrial cavity**; and the **coelom**.

On either side of the pharynx, locate the **gonads**, paired bodies containing the sex cells. Where would you expect fertilization to take place?

_____

_____

The sex of your specimen can be determined by examining the cells of the gonads. The testes are made up of a large number of small, dense cells. The ovaries contain fewer, larger cells with vesicular nuclei. What is the sex of your specimen?

_____

_____

3. Subphylum Vertebrata

a. Class Agnatha

The Agnatha include the hagfishes and lampreys (Fig. 38-4). Organisms in this class are also called *cyclostomes* ("round mouths"). All hagfishes are marine, whereas lampreys inhabit both marine and fresh waters.

433

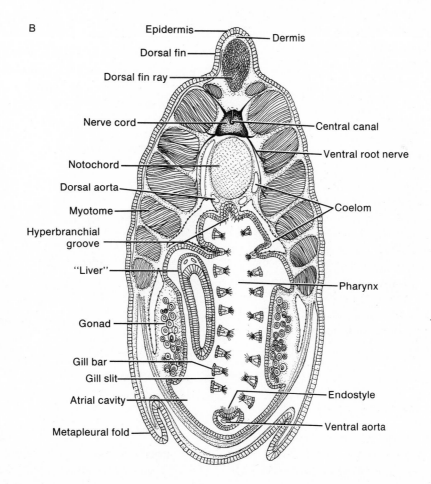

FIGURE 38-3
(A) Lateral view of internal anatomy of amphioxus *(Branchiostoma).* (B) Cross section of amphioxus.

FIG. 38-4
Agnatha: (A) hagfish, (B) sea lampry, (C) oral funnel of lamprey, and (D) lamprey
attached to fish. (Parts B–D after *Atlas and Dissection Guide for Comparative Anatomy*,
2nd ed., by Saul Wischnitzer. W. H. Freeman and Company. Copyright © 1972.)

Examine the sea lamprey on demonstration. Note the shape of its body, which is similar to that of an eel, and the median fins. How many dorsal fins are there?

_____

How many ventral fins?

_____

At the anterior end of the body, locate the seven circular gill slits, which open to the gills. Just anterior to the gill slits are the **eyes**. Between the eyes, on the dorsal surface, is a single **nasal opening** that functions as an olfactory (smell) organ. The ventrally located mouth lies within a suctorial disc called the **oral (buccal) funnel** (Fig. 38-4B). Lampreys attach themselves to their prey through the suction generated by the oral funnel. Then, using the pointed horny teeth inside the oral funnel and the rasplike tongue, the lamprey penetrates the flesh of the animal and feeds on the blood (Fig. 38-4D). Several years ago, the sea lamprey all but eliminated the commercial fish (whitefish, lake trout, lake perch) of the Great Lakes. Successful eradication measures, including chemical control and electric barriers to block migration, have virtually eliminated the lamprey, and the population of fish that are used commercially has steadily increased.

Examine the **ammocoete larva** of the lamprey. To which organism already studied does it bear a striking resemblance?

_____

In terms of evolutionary relationships, what is the significance of this similarity?

_____

_____

_____

b. Class Chondrichthyes

Chondrichthyes (Greek *chondros*, "cartilage"; *ichthys*, "fish") include sharks, skates, and rays. All are predaceous, and most live in the ocean, although a few are found in tropical rivers and lakes, and in fresh and brackish waters.

Sharks are active swimmers and usually swim in the open oceans. A typical diet includes fish, squid, and small crustaceans. Some of the larger sharks capture sea lions and seals. A few species are "man eaters," although some well-known biologists claim the shark has been badly maligned with respect to this last category. Rays and skates have a principal diet of small invertebrates.

In many countries, including the United States, sharks and rays are used for food, although it is usually not identified as such. In Asia, the shark's fins are boiled to yield a gelatinous substance that is widely used as a flavoring for soups.

Examine the dogfish shark *(Squalus acanthias)*, a relatively small species frequenting the eastern shore of the United States (Fig. 38-5A). Locate the following external features:

1. The **head**, which is bluntly pointed, contains a broad mouth having several rows of sharp teeth. The teeth, unlike those of the bony fishes and higher vertebrates, are not attached to the jaw but are embedded in the flesh. Teeth are continuously being formed and move forward to replace those that are lost.

2. The two **nostrils** contain olfactory organs, enabling the shark to smell materials dissolved in the water.

3. The **eyes** are without lids and are adapted for use in dim light.

4. Anterior to each **pectoral fin** are six gill slits. Five of them look like slits, but the sixth, which is located just behind the eye, is modified as the **spiracle**.

The **vent**, or **anus**, is located between the **pelvic fins**. In the male, the pelvic fins possess **claspers**, which are brought close together during mating and inserted into the cloaca of the female. Seminal fluid containing sperm thus flows down the channel formed and enters the female.

6. There are separate medially located **dorsal fins**, each having a characteristic spine just preceding the fin. The **caudal (tail) fin** is bilobed and is used to propel the animal through the water.

7. The **lateral line**, a fine groove along each side of the body, contains a canal having numerous openings to the surface. In the canal are sensory hair cells that connect to the tenth cranial nerve. These sensory cells respond to low-frequency pressure stimuli in the water, serving in a way as a response to touch at a great distance.

8. The body itself is covered evenly by diagonal rows of **placoid** scales. Each scale is covered by enamel and has an inner dentine layer.

The internal anatomy of the shark is shown in Fig. 38-5B. A peculiar feature of the digestive system is the **spiral valve**, a spirally arranged partition covered with a mucous membrane that functions to increase the area for absorption.

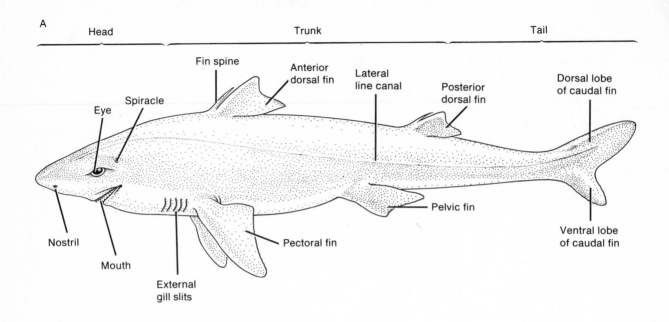

A

Head   Trunk   Tail

Fin spine

Anterior dorsal fin

Lateral line canal

Posterior dorsal fin

Dorsal lobe of caudal fin

Spiracle

Eye

Nostril

Mouth

External gill slits

Pectoral fin

Pelvic fin

Ventral lobe of caudal fin

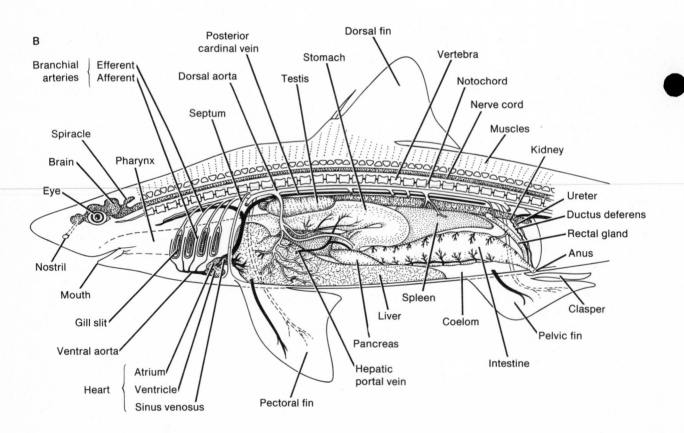

B

Branchial arteries
Efferent
Afferent

Posterior cardinal vein

Dorsal aorta

Septum

Testis

Stomach

Dorsal fin

Vertebra

Notochord

Nerve cord

Muscles

Kidney

Spiracle

Brain

Pharynx

Eye

Nostril

Mouth

Gill slit

Ventral aorta

Heart
Atrium
Ventricle
Sinus venosus

Pectoral fin

Hepatic portal vein

Pancreas

Liver

Spleen

Coelom

Intestine

Ureter

Ductus deferens

Rectal gland

Anus

Clasper

Pelvic fin

FIG. 38-5
Dogfish shark: (A) external anatomy and (B) internal anatomy. (After *Atlas and Dissection Guide for Comparative Anatomy,* 2nd ed., by Saul Wischnitzer. W. H. Freeman and Company. Copyright © 1972.)

c. Class Osteichthyes

The members of this class, referred to as the *bony fish,* range from the common perch to the more unusual lungfish (Fig. 38-6). They share the characteristics of having scales, jaws, a bony skeleton, and gills covered by an operculum. Fish are a highly successful and adaptable group that inhabit virtually all types of water, including fresh, brackish, and salt. Although most fish are streamlined in shape, they have developed a wide variety of forms to assure success in given habitats. As a group, fish are vitally important as a source of food throughout the world. Many species are also game caught for sport.

The common perch *(Perca flavescens)* is typical of the bony fish and is a good example to study.

1. **External Anatomy.** The main body regions of the perch are the head, trunk, and tail (**caudal fin**). The **head** extends from the tip of the snout to the hind edge of the operculum, the **trunk** from this point to the anus, and the **tail** is the remainder (Fig. 38-7). Examine the head, and observe the large mouth, which has distinct upper and lower jaws, the upper jaw being the **maxilla** and the lower jaw the **mandible.** Dorsally on the snout are two double external **nares (nostrils);** they are the openings to the **olfactory sacs,** which are highly sensitive to dissolved chemicals in the water. There is no external ear, but each internal ear contains semicircular canals that are balancing organs that enable the fish to maintain the proper position in the water. The lateral eyes are without lids. Behind each eye is a bony **operculum,** which is a protective covering for the four comblike respiratory gills. Cut away the operculum from the left side, and examine the gills. Cut away one gill arch, place it in water, and examine with a dissecting microscope. The spaces between the gills are called **gill slits,** or **gill clefts.** Attached to the lower edge of the operculum is the **branchiostegal membrane,** supported by rays of cartilage. This membrane serves as a one-way valve allowing water to pass out of the opercular opening but preventing its return.

A lateral line extends along each side of the whole body of the perch. The lateral line is essentially a system of water-filled canals that communicate by means of pores with the water in which the fish swims. The system is believed to register vibratory currents made both by moving objects in the water and by the swimming movements of the fish itself. The system therefore functions as a sensitive "listening" device for detecting water turbulence and for discriminating between different kinds of turbulence.

Two separate dorsal fins are on the back of the perch; a **caudal fin** is on the end of the tail; and an **anal fin** is

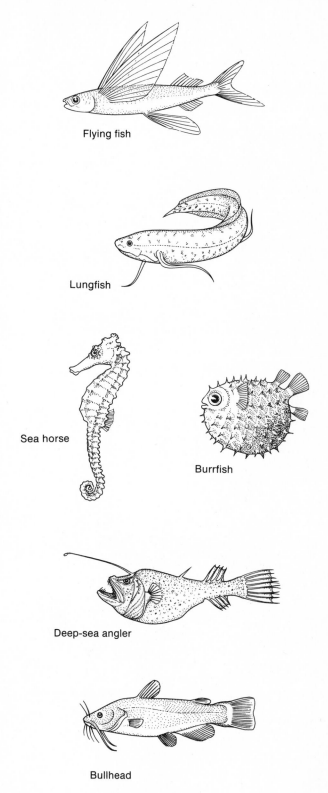

Flying fish

Lungfish

Sea horse

Burrfish

Deep-sea angler

Bullhead

FIG. 38-6
Representative bony fish.

438

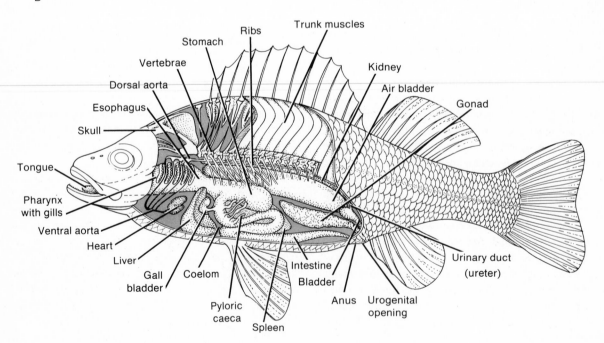

FIG. 38-7
Anatomy of yellow perch *(Perca flavescens):* (A) external anatomy and (B) internal anatomy.

on the ventral side of the tail. Just anterior to the anal fin are the anus and the **urogenital opening**. The lateral, paired fins are the **pectoral fins** behind the opercula, and the ventral, **pelvic fins** are just below them. The fins are membranous extensions of the integument supported by fin rays. All the fins except the anterior dorsal fins are flexible, being supported by soft rays. Each anterior dorsal fin has from 13 to 15 solid calcified spines, and there are one or two similar rigid spines at the anterior edge of the other fins. The fins are used in swimming, steering, and maintaining equilibrium.

The trunk and tail are covered by thin, rounded scales in lengthwise and diagonal rows. Remove a scale, mount it in a drop of water on a slide, and examine under the low power of a microscope. Note the annual growth rings. As a fish grows, the size of each scale rather than the number of scales increases. As a scale grows, concentric rings are formed. Rings formed in the fall and winter are closer together than those formed in the spring and summer. By counting the number of regions of closely spaced concentric rings, you may determine the number of winters your specimen lived. What is the approximate age of your fish?

The entire body of the fish is covered by a soft mucus-producing epidermis that facilitates easy movement of the fish in water and protects against entry of disease organisms.

2. **Internal Anatomy.** Hold the fish with the ventral side up and the head pointing away from you. Insert the point of your scissors through the body wall in front of the anus, and cut up the midline of the body to the space between the opercula. Now lay the fish on its right side (with the head on your left) in the dissecting pan. Continue to cut up around the back edge of the gill chamber to the top of the body cavity. Make another incision from the starting point of the ventral incision close to the anus, and cut upward to the top of the body cavity. Be careful not to disturb the internal organs. With a scalpel, remove the whole lateral body wall by cutting along the top of the body cavity. This procedure will expose the body organs in their normal positions.

a. *Digestive System.* Locate the reddish brown **liver** in the anterior end of the body cavity (Fig. 38-7B). Raise the lobes of the liver and find the **gall bladder** attached to the lower side. Cut the liver free from its attachment to the body, and remove it. This will expose the short **esophagus** and **stomach**. Locate the **pylorus** where the stomach and intestine join. Three tubular **pyloric caeca**, secretory or absorptive in function, attach to the intestine.

Examine the loops of the intestine, and trace it to the anal opening. Long masses of fat lie along the intestinal loops. Observe the **spleen**, attached to an internal mesentery near the stomach. It is a dark red gland that has no duct and no functional connection with the digestive system. Cut the esophagus at its anterior end and carefully remove the entire alimentary canal, from the mouth to the anus.

b. *Reproductive System.* Having removed the alimentary canal, you should be able to see the gonads and the urinary bladder.

In the female, the **ovary** lies between the intestine and air bladder. It is an epithelial sac filled with eggs. The posterior end of the ovary is tapered, and the eggs pass to the outside through the urogenital opening just behind the anus. The ovaries are paired in early stages, as they are in other vertebrates, but during development they fuse into a single organ.

In the male, the **testes** are a pair of white, elongated bodies lying just below the air bladder to which they are joined by a thin sheet of tissue, the **mesentery**. They fuse together toward the posterior end, and the sperm are passed to the outside through the urogenital opening.

c. *Air Bladder (Swim Bladder).* Locate the **air bladder** along the top of the body cavity. The bladder is filled with gases (oxygen, nitrogen, and carbon dioxide) and acts as a hydrostatic organ to adjust the specific gravity of the fish at different depths of water. By secretion or absorption of gases through blood vessels in the bladder wall, a fish makes the adjustment slowly as it moves from one depth to another.

d. *Excretory System.* Remove the air bladder from the body. Lying in the roof of the bladder, near the middle, is a large blood vessel, the **dorsal aorta**. Parallel to it is a pair of long, narrow, dark-colored kidneys. The **urinary ducts (ureters)** run along the edges of each kidney, join at their posterior ends, and empty into the **urinary bladder**. Fluid nitrogenous wastes removed from the blood are emptied by means of this excretory system through the urogenital opening.

e. *Circulatory System.* Using a point of a scissors, make a horizontal cut through the anterior wall of the body cavity in front of the liver. This will expose the **peritoneal cavity**, in which lies the two-chambered **heart**. The heart consists of a single, median, light-colored **ventricle** and a larger thin-walled **atrium (auricle)**. Behind the atrium is the **sinus venosus**. The large vessel carrying blood from the ventricle is the **ventral aorta**. It is greatly enlarged just anterior to the ventricle, forming the **conus arteriosus**. Trace the ventral aorta forward toward the gill region, and identify some of the branchial arteries. Rhythmic contractions of the ventricle force the blood through the conus arteriosus and short

Obstetrical toad

Mud puppy

American toad

Tree frog

Tiger salamander

FIG. 38-8
Representative amphibians.

ventral aorta into 4 pairs of **afferent branchial arteries**, which distribute blood to capillaries in the gill filaments for oxygenation. In the gill filaments, the blood is collected into correspondingly paried **efferent brachial arteries** leading to the dorsal aorta, which has branches to all parts of the head and body.

f. *Nervous System.* Hold the fish with the dorsal side up and the head pointing away from you. Using your scalpel, cut the skin from the skull, and scrape the skull carefully to wear away the bone. When the bone is very thin, remove the pieces with your forceps to expose the brain. Locate the **olfactory lobes** in front, the larger lobes of the **cerebrum** behind them, and the very thin **optic lobes** posterior to the cerebrum. The **cerebellum** is posterior to the optic lobes, and the **medulla** is the enlargement where the **spinal** cord joins the brain.

d. Class Amphibia

The amphibians include toads, frogs, mud puppies, and salamanders (Fig. 38-8). As the name of this class implies (Greek *amphi,* "dual"; *bios,* "life"), these animals live both on the land and in the water. Indeed, their position in the evolutionary scale is between fish and reptiles in that they were the first chordates able to live on land. They exhibit several modifications that have allowed them to adapt to a terrestrial existence. These modifications include legs, lungs, nostrils, and sense organs that function both in water and air.

Most amphibians lay their eggs in the water and have an aquatic larval stage called a *tadpole.* Some amphibians are often confused with reptiles, particularly the salamanders and newts, which look like lizards. Reptiles, however, have scales, whereas salamanders and newts have smooth, slimy skin.

Amphibians are very beneficial to human beings. For example, frogs are extensively used for laboratory dissections, human pregnancy tests, pharmacological experiments, and even fish bait. Extracts of frog skin are used to make the glue used in book bindings. More than 4 million frog legs are eaten each year. In Asia, toad skin is used for medicinal purposes; certain glands contain digitalislike secretions that increase blood pressure. In France and in tropical countries, frogs and toads have been introduced to keep insects under control.

The common leopard frog, *Rana pipiens,* was studied in detail in Exercises 6 and 7. Examine other representatives of this class, noting particularly the external adaptations that have allowed them to make the transition from the water to the land.

e. Class Reptilia

Reptiles include some of the most interesting and diverse chordates, such as the turtles, snakes, lizards, crocodiles, and alligators (Fig. 38-9). They are poikilothermic (i.e., they have variable body temperature), most are covered with scales or bony plates, and they respire by means of lungs. They were the first vertebrates to evolve that were adapted to living in dry places, the dry skin and scales retarding moisture loss from the body and allowing the animal to occupy rough land surfaces. The name of the class indicates the mode of locomotion (Latin *reptus,* from *repere,* "to creep").

Examine available representatives of the various modern reptiles, and note their great diversification in form. Note particularly the ways in which reptiles are morphologically more advanced than amphibians—ways that have better adapted them for life on land such as a dry, scaly skin to prevent desiccation and appendages (when present) suited for rapid locomotion on land or in the water.

Modern reptiles comprise only a fraction of the known orders that flourished during the Mesozoic era—the age of reptiles. During that time, reptiles were the dominant vertebrates and occupied most of the habitats available from dry uplands and deserts to marshes, swamps, and oceans.

f. Class Aves

Birds are probably the best known and most easily recognized of all vertebrates because they have feathers and are capable of flying (Fig. 38-10). No other animals have feathers, although bats (which are mammals) can fly.

Birds are considered to have a reptilian ancestry. Indeed, their early embryonic development parallels that of reptiles. Further, a basic reptilian characteristic, scales, persists on the legs of birds. Fossil remains of some of the earliest birds indicate that they had reptilelike teeth.

Examine the demonstration of various birds. These animals have a number of striking adaptive features, allowing them to occupy a wide variety of habitats. Note the following morphological modifications.

1. **Coloration** is varied and striking. Although there are birds that are entirely one color, the feathers of most are marked with spots, stripes, or bars. This **protective coloration** allows a bird to blend with the environment and thus to be less visible.

2. The **bill** is a multipurpose structure. It functions both as a mouth and as hands, being used to preen the

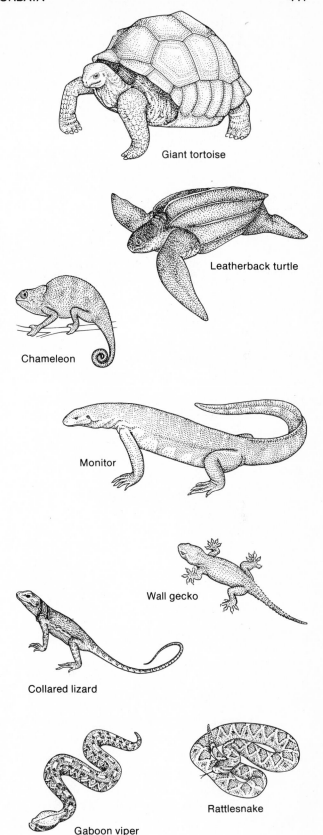

Giant tortoise

Leatherback turtle

Chameleon

Monitor

Wall gecko

Collared lizard

Gaboon viper

Rattlesnake

FIG. 38-9
Representative reptiles.

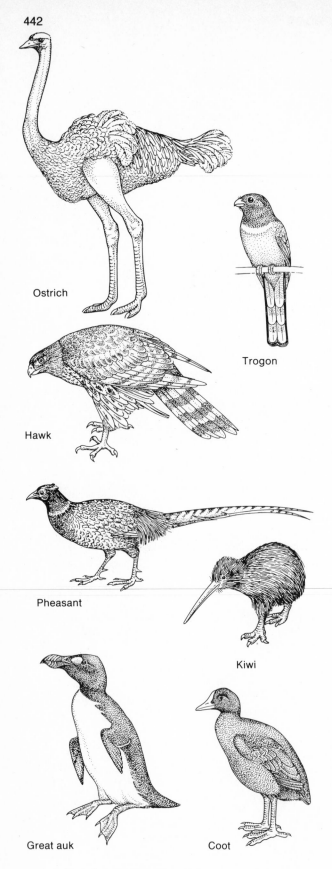

Ostrich

Trogon

Hawk

Pheasant

Kiwi

Great auk

Coot

FIG. 38-10
Representative birds.

feathers, obtain and arrange nesting materials, and even in defense. The form of the bill tells something about the food habits of the bird. For example, seed-eating birds have conical bills, those that probe into cracks and crevices for insects have slender ones, and flesh-eating species have sharp ones, and birds such as ducks that sieve food from the water have wide bills with serrated margins.

3. The **feet** are variously modified for swimming, climbing, perching, wading, and grasping.

4. The **wings** are shaped like air foils and thus supply the "lift" that keeps the bird in the air. The wings of some birds (penguins) are further modified for "flying" under water. In a few species, the wings have so degenerated that the bird is no longer capable of flight, as is true of the ostrich and kiwi.

g. Class Mammalia

Mammals are often called the "highest" animals and include rodents, monkeys, bats, horses, whales, cows, deer, and human beings (Fig. 38-11). All are covered with hair to varying degrees and are warm-blooded. They are called *mammals* because the young are nourished by milk from the mammary glands of the females. Mammals have an interesting evolution with respect to the development and care of the young. Primitive mammals, such as the duckbill platypus, resemble reptiles in that they are egg-layers. More advanced mammals, such as the marsupials (opossum and kangaroo), have limited uterine development of the young; they are born in a very immature condition and transferred to a pouch where they are suckled until they are more mature. The young of the most advanced mammals are retained in the uterus until they are in an advanced stage.

Mammals live in all kinds of habitats ranging from the tropics to the poles and from the oceans to the driest deserts. They have been able to move into these niches, and survive, because of the wide diversity in their morphological, physiological, and behavioral features.

What, for example, is the advantage of retaining the embryo in the uterus during its development?

_____

_____

_____

_____

What advantage is there in nourishing the young with milk from the mammary gland rather than with the food in the yolk of a reptilian egg?

_____

_____

_____

_____

What advantage is there in having an opposing thumb?

_____

_____

_____

_____

REFERENCES

Applegate, V. C., and J. W. Moffett. 1965. The Sea Lamprey. *Scientific American* 192(4):36–41.

Barrington, E. J. W. 1965. *The Biology of the Hemichordata and Protochordata*. W. H. Freeman and Company.

Boolootian, R. A., and K. A. Stiles. 1976. *College Zoology*. 9th ed. Macmillan.

Cochran, D. N. 1961. *Living Amphibians of the World*. Doubleday.

Gilbert, P. W. 1962. The Behavior of Sharks. *Scientific American* 207(1):60–68 (Offprint 127). *Scientific American* Offprints are available from W. H. Freeman and Company, 660 Market Street, San Francisco 94104, and 58 Kings Road, Reading RG1 3AA, England. Please order by number.

Gilliard, E. T. 1958. *Living Birds of the World*. Doubleday.

Herald, E. S. 1961. *Living Fishes of the World*. Doubleday.

Romer, A. S. 1977. The Vertebrate Body. 5th ed. Holt/Saunders.

Sanderson, I. T. 1955. *Living Mammals of the World*. Doubleday.

Storer, T. I., R. L. Usinger, R. C. Stebbins, and J. W. Nybakken. 1979. *General Zoology*. 6th ed. McGraw-Hill.

Young, J. Z. 1975. *The Life of Mammals*. 2nd ed. Oxford University Press.

FIG. 38-11
Representative mammals.

Scaly anteater

Spiny anteater

Porcupine

Aardvark

Shrew

Flying lemur

Baboon

Hyena

Funnel-eared bat

Appendixes

Use of the Bausch & Lomb Spectronic 20 Colorimeter

The Bausch & Lomb Spectronic 20 Colorimeter is an extremely versatile instrument that is useful for the spectrophotometric or colorimetric determinations of solutions.

The optical system is shown in Fig. A-1. White light is focused by a lens (1) onto an entrance slit (2), where it is collected by a second lens (3) and refocused on the exit slit (4) after being reflected and dispersed by a diffraction grating (5). Rotation of this grating by a cam (6) enables one to select various wavelengths of light in a range from 375 nm to 625 nm. The addition of a filter can extend the usable wavelength to 950 nm. After the light passes the exit slit, it goes through the sample being measured (7) and is picked up by a phototube (8). The amount of light absorbed by the sample may then be read directly on a dial.

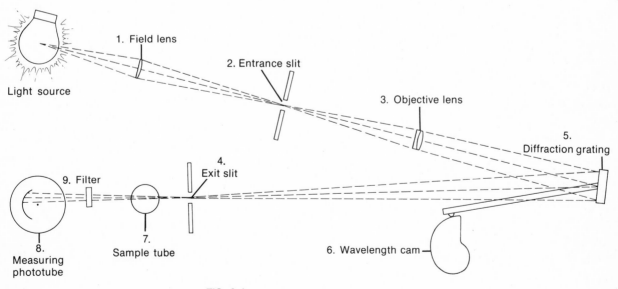

FIG. A-1
Optical system of the Spectronic 20 colorimeter.

FIG. A-2
Controls on the Spectronic 20 colorimeter.

A. COLORIMETRY

Directions for colorimetric use are as follows:

1. Rotate the wavelength control (1) shown in Fig. A-2 until the desired wavelength is shown on the wavelength dial (2). The wavelength for a given substance can be found by referring to the literature or by determining it experimentally.

2. Turn the instrument on by rotating the "0" control (3) in a clockwise direction. Allow 5 minutes for the instrument to warm up.

3. Adjust the "0" control with the cover of the sample holder closed (5) until the needle is at 0 on the transmittance scale (4).

4. Place a colorimeter tube containing water or another solvent in the sample holder, and close the cover.

5. Rotate the light control (6) so that the needle is at 100 on the transmittance scale (0.0 absorbance). This control regulates the amount of light passing through the second slit to the phototube.

6. The unknown samples may then be placed in the tube holder, and the percentage of transmittance or the absorbance can be read. The needle should always return to zero when the tube is removed. Check the 0% and 100% transmittance occasionally with the solvent tube in the sample holder to make certain the unit is calibrated.

Note: Always check the wavelength scale to be certain that the desired wavelength is being used.

The colorimetric measurements made with this apparatus employ standard matched tubes. They are selected so that variation in light transmitted through the tubes due to slight differences in diameter and wall thickness is minimal. You will be issued a set of such matched tubes. *They are to be used only for colorimetry.* The matched tubes must be handled carefully so as not to etch or scratch the surfaces exposed to the light beam. Obviously, the tubes will no longer be "matched" if scratched or etched, because such defects will cause the absorption and scattering of light.

B. SPECTROPHOTOMETRY

The method of operation for spectrophotometry is essentially the same as for colorimetry. The main difference is that the wavelength is reset for each reading, and thus a blank, or solvent, control must be readjusted at each new wavelength setting.

This procedure can be used when no information is available to determine the proper operating wavelength for an unknown substance. To do this, plot an absorption curve (absorbance versus different wavelengths) of the unknown substance (Fig. A-3). An operating wavelength may then be chosen according to the following:

1. Choose the wavelength at which the substance maximally absorbs the light (the minimum transmittance), because the greatest sensitivity will be obtained at this wavelength.

2. Do not choose wavelengths on the slope, because a small error in wavelength will cause a large error in reading.

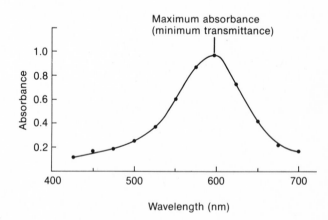

FIG. A-3
Absorption spectrum of an unknown substance.

REFERENCES

Newman, D. W. 1964. *Instrumental Methods of Experimental Biology*. Macmillan.

Umbreit, W. W., R. H. Burris, and J. F. Stauffer, 1964. *Manometric Methods*. 4th ed. Burgess.

Van Norman, R. W. 1971. *Experimental Biology*. 2nd ed. Prentice-Hall.

Spectrophotometry

Many kinds of molecules interact with or absorb specific types of radiant energy in a predictable fashion. For example, when white light illuminates an object, the color that the eye perceives is determined by the absorption by the object of one or more of the colors from the source of the white light. The remaining wavelength(s) are reflected (or transmitted) as a specific color. Thus an object that appears red absorbs the blue or green colors of light (or both), but not the red.

The perception of color, as just described is qualitative. It indicates what is happening but says nothing about the extent to which the event is taking place. The eye is not a quantitative instrument. However, there are instruments, called *spectrophotometers,* that electronically quantify the amount and kinds of light that are absorbed by molecules in solution. In its simplest form, a spectrophotometer has a source of white light (for visible spectrophotometry) that is focused on a prism or diffraction grating to separate the white light into its individual bands of radiant energy (Fig. B-1). Each wavelength (color) is then selectively focused through a narrow slit. The width of this slit is important to the precision of the measurement; the narrower the slit, the more closely absorption is related to a specific wavelength of light. Conversely, the broader the slit, the more light of different wavelengths passes through, which results in a reduction in the precision of the measurement. This monochromatic (single wavelength) beam of light, called the **incident beam** (I_0), then passes through the sample being measured. The sample, usually dissolved in a suitable solvent, is contained in an optically selected **cuvette**, which is standardized to have a light path 1 cm across. However, for special purposes, variations are available that are larger or smaller than the standard 1-cm size.

After passing through the sample, the selected wavelength of light (now referred to as the **transmitted beam,** I) strikes a photoelectric tube. If the substance in the cuvette has absorbed any of the incident light, the transmitted light will then be reduced in total energy content. If the substance in the sample container does not absorb any of the incident beam, the radiant energy of the transmitted beam will then be about the same amount as that of the incident beam. When the transmitted beam strikes the photoelectric tube, it generates an electric current pro-

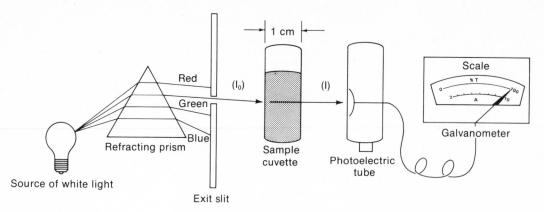

FIG. B-1
Typical photoelectric spectrophotometer.

portional to the intensity of the light energy striking it. By connecting the photoelectric tube to a device that measures electric current (a galvanometer), a means of directly measuring the intensity of the transmitted beam is achieved. In the Bausch & Lomb Spectronic 20 spectrophotometer, the galvanometer has two scales: one indicates the **% transmittance (% T)**, and the other, a logarithmic scale with unequal divisions graduated from 0.0 to 2.0, indicates the **absorbance (A)**. The term **optical density** *(OD)* may be used instead of absorbance; however, the latter term is more commonly accepted.

Because most biological molecules are dissolved in a solvent before measurement, a source of error can be due to the possibility that the solvent itself absorbs light. To assure that the spectrophotometric measurement will reflect only the light absorption of the molecules being studied, a mechanism for "subtracting" the absorbance of the solvent is necessary. To achieve this, a "blank" (the solvent) is first inserted into the instrument, and the scale is set to read 100% transmittance (or 0.0 absorbance) for the solvent. The "sample," containing the solute *plus* the solvent, is then inserted into the instrument. Any reading on the scale that is less than 100% T (or greater than 0.0 A) is considered to be *due to absorbance by the solute only*. Other instruments are available that continuously give the desired ratio between sample and blank, both visually and on a strip-chart recorder. This kind of spectrophotometer "reads" the cuvettes for the *blank* and the *sample* simultaneously. The reading that appears on the absorbance scale is therefore a ratio between the *sample* and the *blank*.

Spectrophotometers are not limited to detecting absorption of only visible light. Some also have a source of ultraviolet light (usually a hydrogen or mercury lamp), which has wavelengths that range from about 180 to 400 nm. Ultraviolet wavelengths ranging from 180 to 350 nm are particularly useful in studying such biological mole-

cules as amino acids, proteins, and nucleic acids, because each of these compounds have characteristic absorbances at different ultraviolet wavelengths. Other useful spectrophotometers have sources and suitable detectors of infrared radiation (from 780 to 25,000 nm). Numerous biological molecules can be effectively studied because of their infrared absorption spectra.

A. UNITS OF MEASUREMENT

The following terminology is commonly used in spectrophotometry.

1. Transmittance *(T):* the ratio of the transmitted light *(I)* of the sample to the incident light (I_0) on the sample.

$$T = \frac{I}{I_0}$$

This value is multiplied by 100 to derive the % T. For example,

$$T = \frac{75}{100} = 0.75$$

and

$$\% T = \frac{75}{100} \times 100 = 75\%$$

2. Absorbance *(A):* logarithm to the base 10 of the reciprocal of the transmittance:

$$A = \log_{10} \frac{1}{T}$$

For example,

1. Suppose a % T of 50 was recorded (equivalent to $T = 0.50$).

2. Then $A = \log_{10}\dfrac{1}{0.50} = \log_{10} 2.0$.

3. Thus $\log_{10} 2.0 = 0.301$ (A equivalent to a % T of 50).

Similarly a % T of 25 $= 0.602\ A$; a % T of 75 $= 0.125$ A; and so forth.

The absorbance scale is normally present along with the transmittance scale on spectrophotometers. The chief usefulness of absorbance lies in the fact that it is a logarithmic rather than arithmetic function, allowing the use of the Lambert-Beer law, which states that for a given concentration range the concentration of solute molecules is directly proportional to absorbance. The Lambert-Beer law can be expressed as

$$\log_{10}\frac{I_0}{I} = A$$

in which I_0 is the intensity of the incident light; I is the intensity of the transmitted light.

The usefulness of absorbance can be seen in the graphs shown in Fig. B-2, one graph showing the percent transmittance plotted against concentration and the other showing absorbance plotted against concentration. Using the Lambert-Beer relationship, it is necessary to plot only three or four points to obtain the straight-line relationship shown in Fig. B-2B. However, certain conditions must prevail for the Lambert-Beer relationship to hold:

Monochromatic light is used.

A_{max} is used (i.e., the wavelength maximally absorbed by the substance being analyzed).

The quantitative relationship between absorbance and concentration can be established.

The first condition can be met by using a prism or diffraction grating or other device that can disperse visible light into its spectra.

The second condition can be met by determining the absorption spectrum of the compound. This is done by plotting the absorbance of the substance at a number of different wavelengths. The wavelength at which absorbance is greatest is called the A_{max} (or λ_{max}) and is the most satisfactory wavelength to use because, on the slope, absorbance changes rapidly with slight wavelength deviations, whereas at the maximum absorbance, changes in wavelength alter absorbance less. Fig. B-3 shows an absorption spectrum of a hypothetical substance having an A_{max} of approximately 650 nm. Some compounds,

A

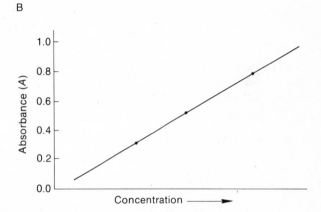

B

FIG. B-2
(A) Percent transmittance versus concentration.
(B) Absorbance versus concentration.

FIG. B-3
Determination of A_{max}

however, can have several peaks both in the visible spectrum and in the ultraviolet range. An example of this is shown in Fig. B-4 for riboflavin.

To establish the quantitative relationship between absorbance and concentration of the colored substance, it is necessary to prepare a series of standards of the substance analyzed in graded known concentrations ("color standards"). Because absorbance is *directly* proportional to concentration, a plot of absorbance versus concentration of the standard yields a straight line. Such

a plot is called a **calibration curve** or **standard curve** (Fig. B-5). After several points have been plotted, the intervening points can be extrapolated by connecting the known points with a straight line. It is not necessary to use dotted lines to indicate extrapolation on graphs; a dotted line is used in the illustration to indicate the parts of the line for which points were not determined but were presumed. When the Lambert-Beer law is followed, this is an acceptable and time-saving assumption; otherwise, points would need to be plotted throughout the entire line. In general, your graph should extend from a minimum of about 0.025 A to a maximum of about 1.0 A, or from 94% *T* to 10% *T*, this being the range of "readable" and reproducible values of absorbance. However, recall that the Lambert-Beer law operates at only certain concentrations. This is apparent in Fig. B-5 in which, at concentrations greater than 1.0 mg/ml, the curve slopes, indicating the loss of the concentration-absorbance relationship.

After a concentration curve for a given substance has been established, it is relatively easy to determine the quantity of that substance in a solution of unknown concentration by determining the absorbance of the unknown and locating it on the *y*-axis, or ordinate (Fig. B-6). A straight line is then drawn parallel to the *x*-axis, or abscissa, until it intersects with the experimental curve. A perpendicular is then dropped to the *x*-axis, the value at the point of intersection indicating the concentration of the unknown solution. In this example, the unknown absorbance is 0.32, which indicates a concentration of

FIG. B-4
Absorptions spectrum of riboflavin. (From *Experimental Biochemistry,* 2nd ed., edited by John M. Clark, Jr., and Robert L. Switzer. W. H. Freeman and Company. Copyright © 1977.)

FIG. B-5
Preparation of concentration (standard) curve.

about 0.37 mg. Concentrations are commonly expressed either as micrograms per milliliter (μg/ml) or as milligrams per milliliter (mg/ml).

If the absorbance value of the unknown is such that the line drawn parallel to the x-axis intersects the experimental curve where it is curved (Fig. B-5), then you cannot accurately determine the concentration. In this event, dilute the unknown by some factor until the absorbance readings intersect with the straight-line part of the graph where concentration is proportional to absorbance. You can then determine the unknown concentration and multiply the value by the dilution factor.

FIG. B-6
Determining concentration of "unknown."

REFERENCES

Bauman, R. P. 1962. *Absorption Spectroscopy*. Wiley.

Clark, G. L. 1961. *The Encyclopedia of Spectroscopy*. Reinhold.

Newman, D. W., ed. 1964. *Instrumental Methods of Experimental Biology*. Macmillan.

Strobel, H. 1960. *Chemical Instrumentation*. Addison-Wesley.

Van Norman, R. W. 1971. *Experimental Biology*. 2nd ed. Prentice-Hall.

Willard, H. H., L. L. Merritt, Jr., and J. A. Dean. 1964. *Instrumental Methods of Analysis*. 4th ed. Van Nostrand Reinhold.

Chromatography

Chromatographic techniques are among the most useful methods available for the separation of complex mixtures of solutes based on their selective adsorption as they are passed over such adsorbants as charcoal, starch, cellulose powders, ion-exchange resins, and filter paper. The most widely used chromatographic techniques are column chromatography on ion-exchange resins, paper-partition chromatography on filter paper, and thin-layer methods using an adsorbant bound to a supporting material such as glass. These techniques are frequently employed to isolate proteins, enzymes, lipids, hormones, plant growth substances, pigments, and other naturally occurring organic materials.

A. PAPER CHROMATOGRAPHY

Paper chromatography has revolutionized the art of detecting and identifying small amounts of organic and inorganic substances. It permits the separation of mixtures on a very small scale, which no other simple method affords. The technique has found widespread application in many areas of biology and has been used to separate and identify such substances as amino acids, carbohydrates, fatty acids, antibiotics, and many other naturally occurring substances.

To employ this technique, a small spot of the mixture to be chromatographed is placed near one end of a length of filter paper. This end of the paper is then immersed in a solvent system that is usually composed of two or more miscible substances. In **descending paper chromatography**, the solvent is contained in a trough near the top of the chromatographic chamber and is allowed to irrigate the paper by a downward flow by means of capillary action and gravity (Fig. C-1). In **ascending chromatography**, the solvent is placed at the bottom of the chamber and is allowed to rise upward the length of the paper by capillary action.

Although ascending chromatographic separation is typically used because the apparatus is quite simple, descending chromatography has the advantages of speed (the solvent flow is faster because of gravity) and of allowing for the collection of the solvent (and solute) as it runs off the paper. This permits additional analysis of solute components using other procedures.

Locating or visualizing substances that have to be separated can be done in a variety of ways. Some substances have color and thus are easily seen on the chromatogram.

Glass rod and clips holding paper

Trough to hold solvent

Solvent front

Paper

Solvent

Solvent to saturate atmosphere in chamber

ASCENDING

DESCENDING

FIG. C-1
Apparatus for ascending and descending chromatography.

For those compounds that are colorless, various procedures are employed. For example, amino acids become pink or purple spots when sprayed with ninhydrin. Reducing sugars become gray-black spots when treated with analine phthalate, and many organic substances become brown spots on a yellow background when exposed to iodine vapors.

So long as conditions such as temperature and purity of solvent are carefully regulated, it is possible not only to separate components of a mixture but to identify them. Under standardized conditions, identical substances move at characteristic rates in similar solvent systems. Thus one can calculate R_f values by comparing the distance the solvent travels with the distance the substance travels in accord with the following formula:

$$R_f = \frac{\text{distance of center of "spot" from origin}}{\text{distance of solvent front from origin}}$$

Tables of R_f values for various substances in different solvents permit preliminary identification of a substance by computing its R_f value. However, for more precise identification it is advisable to chromatograph known substances on the same sheet so that R_f values of the known and "suspected" substances can be determined under identical conditions.

B. THIN-LAYER CHROMATOGRAPHY

In thin-layer chromatography, an adsorbent is applied to a supporting material, frequently glass or aluminum, in a very thin layer. A binding agent is generally used to adhere the adsorbent to the supporting material.

In one of the more common procedures, a slurry of silica gel adsorbent, with calcium sulfate as the binder, is spread as a thin layer on a 20-cm^2 glass plate. The plates, dried to remove excess moisture, are then handled in much the same way as is paper in ascending chromatography. After separation, the spots can be scraped from the glass for detailed analysis or eluted and rechromatographed.

Separation is accomplished very quickly on thin-layer plates. Using paper chromatographic methods, the separation of some mixtures may take 24 hours. The same separation may take less than an hour when using thin-layer procedures.

REFERENCES

Heftman, E. 1975. *Chromatography*. 3rd ed. Van Nostrand Reinhold.

Kirchner, J. G. 1967. *Thin-Layer Chromatography*. Interscience.

Lederer, E., and M. Lederer. 1957. *Chromatography*. American Elsevier.

Magee, R. J. 1970. *Selected Readings in Chromatography*. Pergamon.

Stahl, E., ed. 1969. *Thin-Layer Chromatography: A Laboratory Handbook*. 2nd ed. Springer-Verlag.

Use of Live Animals
in the Laboratory

A. GENERAL PROCEDURES

If this is the first time living vertebrate animals are being used in your class, it is important that you understand the purpose in bringing these animals into the laboratory. First, there must be a genuine reason for using live animals. Second, live animals must always be treated in a humane way: never cause them unnecessary irritation or injury. Accordingly, if any organ or tissue damage may result from legitimate experimentation, the animals is first put under an anesthetic, or the nervous system is treated to make the organism insensible to pain. Avoid injurying the animal's tissues or making it bleed; such damage makes the animal less capable of "normal" reactions.

In handling organs or tissues that have been exposed or removed, use a glass hook or a small camel-hair brush moistened with Ringer's saline solution. Never handle tissues with your fingers. When you need to lay an excised organ or part down, never place it on the table, or on dry paper; place it in a watch glass or other dish and keep it moistened. Apply Ringer's solution as often as necessary while working, to keep the tissue from drying out.

Position of foramen magnum

Dissecting needle

FIG. D-1
Pithing the brain of a frog.

B. PITHING PROCEDURE

A spinal frog (one whose entire brain has been destroyed) is prepared by a procedure called **pithing**. Grasp the animal as indicated in Fig. D-1, using the thumb and fingers to secure the limbs. With the index finger, depress the snout so that the head is at a sharp angle to the body. Run the tip of the dissecting needle down the midline of the head. At a point 2 or 3 mm behind the posterior border of the eardrums, the needle should dip. This marks the location of the **foramen magnum**, a large opening in the skull through which the spinal cord emerges from the **cranium**. Place the point of a dissecting needle in this groove, and with a sharp movement force it through the skin and foramen magnum into the brain. Twist and turn the needle to destroy the brain. Halt any bleeding, and treat the pithed frog in the same way as the decerebrate animal.

C. DECEREBRATION PROCEDURE

A decerebrate frog is one in which the forebrain is no longer functional. Select a large, active frog, and grasp it firmly in the left hand, pinioning the forelimbs and hindlimbs. Position the blades of a pair of *sharp* scissors as indicated in Fig. D-2, just behind the posterior margins of the eyes. Cut quickly and cleanly to avoid excessive nerve shock. Stop any blood flow with cotton or gauze pads. Lay the animal ventral side down on a damp paper towel. Be sure to moisten the skin from time to time, as the bulk of the respiration of such animals takes place through the skin.

Forebrain

Optic lobes

Medulla oblongata

FIG. D-2
Decerebrating a frog.

REFERENCE

Steele, H. C. 1966. *The Departmental Laboratory Assistant in Biological Science*. Dorrance.

Elementary Statistical Analysis

The inherent variability of organisms, coupled with the degree of error normally encountered in most measuring systems, demands the use of some form of data evaluation before valid conclusions can be made or inferences drawn. It is particularly important that students of the biological sciences become familiar with statistical methods of handling data. The following section briefly outlines some of the basic methods used in this form of analysis.

The procedures fall into two groups. The first is concerned with those statistics that define the nature and distribution of the data. The second outlines three procedures that may be used to compare two or more sets of data. This introduction to statistical methods is not to be regarded as complete, nor is it expected to substitute for formal training in this area. Wherever possible, the student should supplement the information given by use of the references listed at the end of this appendix.

A. DEFINING THE DATA

In order to define a sample of data, one must have some knowledge of the central tendencies and degree of dispersion of the data. The statistics usually used for this purpose are the arithmetic mean, the standard deviation, and the confidence interval of the mean.

1. Arithmetic Mean

The mean $(\overline{X})$ is computed by summing (Σ) the individual sample measurements (x_i) and dividing by the total number of measurements (N):

$$\overline{X} = \frac{\Sigma X_i}{N}$$

2. Standard Deviation

The mean of a group of data gives little information concerning the distribution of the data about the mean. Obviously, different numerical values can give the same mean value. For example:

$$\text{Set 1: 32, 32, 36, 40, 40} \quad \overline{X} = 36$$
$$\text{Set 2: 2, 18, 24, 36, 100} \quad \overline{X} = 36$$

The means for both sets of figures are identical. Yet the variation from the mean in Set 2 is so great as to make the average meaningless. The standard deviation is a measure of data dispersion about the mean. The range covered by the mean plus or minus ($\pm$) one standard deviation includes about 68% of the data on the basis of which the mean was calculated. The range covered by the mean $\pm$ two standard deviations will include approximately 95% of the data. The calculation of the standard deviation is summarized below:

1. Compute the arithmetical mean $(\overline{X})$ by summing (Σ) the individual measurements (x_i) and dividing by the total number of measurements (N): $\overline{X} = \Sigma x_i / N$.
2. Calculate the deviation from the mean for each measurement: $(x_i - \overline{X})$.
3. Square each of the individual deviations from the mean: $(x_i - \overline{X})^2$. This allows one to deal with positive values.
4. Determine the sum of the squared deviations: $\Sigma(x_i - \overline{X})^2$.
5. Calculate the standard deviation(s) of the sample, using the formula

$$s = \sqrt{\frac{\Sigma(x_i - \overline{X})^2}{N - 1}}$$

A sample set of standard deviation measurements is shown in Table E-1, where

Number of individual measurements $(N) = 10$
Arithmetical means $(X) = 220/10 = 22$
Degrees of freedom $(\overline{N} - 1) = 9$

$$s = \sqrt{\frac{\Sigma(x_i - \overline{X})^2}{N - 1}} = \sqrt{\frac{42}{9}} = \sqrt{4.66} = 2.16$$

3. Confidence Interval for a Sample Mean

The confidence interval (C) for a sample mean equals the standard deviation of the sample divided by the square root of the sample number (N) and multiplied by a factor (t) that is determined by the probability level desired and the value of the sample number:

$$C = \pm t\left(\frac{s}{\sqrt{N}}\right)$$

It is highly improbable that a sample mean, based on a relatively small series of data, will correspond exactly to the true mean calculated from an infinitely large sample of the population. It is necessary, therefore, to define a range within which the true mean might be expected to lie. To define this range—the confidence interval—the standard error of the mean $(\text{S.E.}\overline{X})$ must be known. The standard error equals the standard deviation divided by the square root of the number in the sample:

$$\text{S.E.}\overline{X} = \frac{s}{\sqrt{N}}$$

The confidence interval is then calculated by multiplying the $\text{S.E.}\overline{X}$ by t, whose value depends on the number in the sample $N)$, and the level of probability selected. Normally, a probability or significance level of 0.05 is accepted in biological studies. This implies that in only 5% of the samples taken separately from a given population would the parameters defined by the sample *fail* to have significance.

The t values may be obtained from the t table (Table E-2). These values are listed in columns for 0.10, 0.05, and 0.01 probability levels. Note that it is necessary to have a value for the number of degrees of freedom (D.F.) of the sample. In this case, the D.F. for the sample equals the number in the sample minus one $(N - 1)$.

B. COMPARISON OF DATA

1. Standard Error of the Difference of Means

The standard error of the difference of means is computed by using the formula

$$\text{S.E.}\overline{X}_1 - \overline{X}_2 = \sqrt{\frac{s_1}{N_1} + \frac{s_2}{N_2}}$$

where s_1 and s_2 represent the standard deviations of two different groups, N_1 and N_2 represent the number of individuals in each group (preferably at least 20), and $\overline{X}_1$ and $\overline{X}_2$ are the respective means. Using this formula, if the difference between the two means is *larger than two times* the standard error of the difference, it can be concluded that the difference between the groups was not

TABLE E-1
Sample calculation of the standard deviation.

Observation number	Individual measurement (x_i) of stem length (mm)	Deviation from mean $(x_i - \bar{X})$	$(x_i - \bar{X})^2$
x_1	20	-2	4
x_2	24	$+2$	4
x_3	22	0	0
x_4	19	-3	9
x_5	26	$+4$	16
x_6	22	0	0
x_7	24	$+2$	4
x_8	20	-2	4
x_9	22	0	0
x_{10}	21	-1	1
	TOTAL = $220 = \Sigma x_i$	0	$42 = \Sigma(x_i - \bar{X})^2$

TABLE E-2
Significance limits of student's t distribution.

(n) degrees of freedom	Confidence levels		
	0.10	0.05	0.01
1	6.314	12.706	63.657
2	2.920	4.303	9.925
3	2.353	3.182	5.841
4	2.132	2.776	4.604
5	2.015	2.571	4.032
6	1.943	2.447	3.707
7	1.895	2.365	3.499
8	1.860	2.306	3.355
9	1.833	2.262	3.250
10	1.812	2.228	3.169
11	1.796	2.201	3.106
12	1.782	2.179	3.055
13	1.771	2.160	3.012
14	1.761	2.145	2.977
15	1.753	2.131	2.947
16	1.746	2.120	2.921
17	1.740	2.110	2.898
18	1.734	2.101	2.878
19	1.729	2.093	2.861
20	1.725	2.086	2.845
21	1.721	2.080	2.831
22	1.717	2.074	2.819
23	1.714	2.069	2.807
24	1.711	2.064	2.797
25	1.708	2.060	2.787
26	1.706	2.056	2.779
27	1.703	2.052	2.771
28	1.701	2.048	2.763
29	1.699	2.045	2.756
30	1.697	2.042	2.750
40	1.684	2.021	2.704
60	1.671	2.000	2.660
120	1.658	1.980	2.617
∞	1.645	1.960	2.576

Adapted from Table III of Fisher and Yates, *Statistical Tables for Biological, Agricultural, and Medical Research*, Oliver & Boyd, Edinburgh.

due to chance alone, but was due to the treatment given. It can be further concluded that similar plants or animals under similar treatment could be expected to respond in a similar manner.

2. Student's *t* Test

The student's *t* test is used to determine whether, within a selected degree of probability, two groups of data represent samples taken from the same or different populations of data. In other words, it is used to determine if two groups of data are significantly different. This test uses both the means and standard deviations of the two samples. It is calculated as

$$t = \frac{(\bar{X}_1 - \bar{X}_2)\left(\sqrt{\dfrac{N_1 N_2}{N_1 + N_2}}\right)}{\sqrt{\dfrac{(N_1 - 1)(s_1^2) + (N_2 - 1)(s_2^2)}{N_1 + N_2 - 2}}}$$

where s_1 and s_2 represent standard deviations of two different groups, N_1 and N_2 represent the number of individuals in each group, and $\bar{X}_1$ and $\bar{X}_2$ are the respective means.

The calculated *t* value is then compared to the value in the *t* table (Table E-2) at the probability level chosen (usually 0.05) and at the combined degrees of freedom of the two samples ($N_1 + N_2 - 2$). If the value for *t* is *less* than that found in the table, then the two groups of data are not considered significantly different at the chosen level of probability. If the *t* value *exceeds* that in the table, then the two groups of data may be considered significantly different.

3. Wilcoxon Test

This test, although mechanically easier to carry out than the student's *t* test, should only be used on small amounts of data—such as in a preliminary study—to help determine if a particular experiment is worth pursuing.

Basically, this test employs a ranking system. A simple example, given below, is a comparison of the pulse rate *(PR)* between normal male and females to test for sexual differences.

The hypothesis to be tested (H_0—the null hypothesis) is

$$PR \; ♀ = PR \; ♂$$

that is, there is no difference in heart rate (in terms of pulse beat) between males and females.

a. Raw Data

Sex	Pulse Rate					
♂	74	77	78	75	72	71
♀	80	83	73	84	82	79

b. Calculation of Means

$$\Sigma \; ♂ = 447; \; \bar{X} = 74.5$$
$$\Sigma \; ♀ = 481; \; \bar{X} = 81.7$$

c. Ranking of Data

(1) Rank the data in an order of increasing magnitude. Underline all values from the group having the smaller mean. In this example, it is the males.

(2) Also write the rank number under the data, beginning with 1 for the smallest value and proceeding to the largest value. Again, underline the rank number corresponding to the male values.

71	72	73	74	75	77	78	79	80	82	83	84
1	2	3	4	5	6	7	8	9	10	11	12

(3) Next, reorder the rank numbers by sex, and add them up. If there is no real difference in pulse rate between sexes, then the sum of rank numbers should be equal.

$$♂ \quad 1 + 2 + 4 + 5 + 6 + 7 = 25$$
$$♀ \quad 3 + 8 + 9 + 10 + 11 + 12 = 53$$

d. Computing *U*

In this case, the sums of the rank numbers are different. But is there a significant difference between males and females? To determine this, the statistical value *U* must be determined:

$$U = W_1 - \tfrac{1}{2} n_1 (n_1 = 1)$$

where $W_1 =$ the total of the rank numbers belonging to the group with the smallest mean (i.e., the males: $W_1 = 25$).

$n_1 =$ the number of individuals (or measurements) in the group having the smallest mean (i.e., the males: $n_1 = 6$)

Thus:

$$U = 25 - \tfrac{1}{2} \cdot 6 \, (6 + 1)$$
$$= 25 - 21$$
$$= 4$$

e. Determining Significance

1. Refer to Table E-3 (Wilcoxon table for unpaired data).

TABLE E-3
Wilcoxon distribution (with no pairing). The numbers given in this table are the number of cases for which the sum of the ranks of the sample of size n_1 is less than or equal to W_1.

n_1	n_2	$C_{n_1 n_2}$	0	1	2	3	4	5	6	7	8	9	10	11	12	13	14	15	16	17	18	19	20
			\multicolumn{21}{c}{Values of U, where $U = W_1 - \frac{1}{2}n_1(n_1 + 1)$}
3	3	20	1	2	4	7	10	13	16	18	19	20											
3	4	35	1	2	4	7	11	15	20	24	28	31	33	34	35								
4	4	70	1	2	4	7	12	17	24	31	39	46	53	58	63	66	68	69	70				
3	5	56	1	2	4	7	11	16	22	28	34	40	45	49	52	54	55	56					
4	5	126	1	2	4	7	12	18	26	35	46	57	69	80	91	100	108	114	119	122	124	125	126
5	5	252	1	2	4	7	12	19	28	39	53	69	87	106	126	146	165	183	199	213	224	233	240
3	6	84	1	2	4	7	11	16	23	30	38	46	54	61	68	73	77.	80	82	83	84		
4	6	210	1	2	4	7	12	18	27	37	50	64	80	96	114	130	146	160	173	183	192	19.	203
5	6	462	1	2	4	7	12	19	29	41	57	76	99	124	153	183	215	247	279	309	338	363	386
6	6	924	1	2	4	7	12	19	30	43	61	83	111	143	182	224	272	323	378	433	491	546	601
3	7	120	1	2	4	7	11	16	23	31	40	50	60	70	80	89	97	104	109	113	116	118	119
4	7	330	1	2	4	7	12	18	27	38	52	68	87	107	130	153	177	200	223	243	262	278	292
5	7	792	1	2	4	7	12	19	29	42	59	80	106	136	171	210	253	299	347	396	445	493	539
6	7	1716	1	2	4	7	12	19	30	44	63	87	118	155	201	253	314	382	458	539	627	717	811
7	7	3432	1	2	4	7	12	19	30	45	65	91	125	167	220	283	358	445	545	657	782	918	1064
3	8	165	1	2	4	7	11	16	23	31	41	52	64	76	89	101	113	124	134	142	149	154	158
4	8	495	1	2	4	7	12	18	27	38	53	70	91	114	141	169	200	231	264	295	326	354	381
5	8	1287	1	2	4	7	12	19	29	42	60	82	110	143	183	228	280	337	400	466	536	607	680
6	8	3003	1	2	4	7	12	19	30	44	64	89	122	162	213	272	343	424	518	621	737	860	994
7	8	6435	1	2	4	7	12	19	30	45	66	93	129	174	232	302	388	489	609	746	904	1080	1277
8	8	12870	1	2	4	7	12	19	30	45	67	95	133	181	244	321	418	534	675	839	1033	1254	1509

Note that it has three columns labeled $n_1, n_2, C_{n_1 n_2}$; and Value of U.

2. *The values of n_1 and n_2 in the data are 6 and 6.* Refer to this combination in the first column of the table. The corresponding figure in the $C_{n_1 n_2}$ column is 924.

3. Run along the U columns to $U = 4$, and then down the $U = 4$ column to the row corresponding to $C_{n_1 n_2} = 924$. The value at these intersecting points is 12. This value represents the number of possible rank totals that would be less than or equal to ($\leq$) 25.

4. Suppose we consider that if an event occurs less than 5 times out of 100 (5/100 or 50/1000, $P = .05$) it occurred, not as a result of chance, but as a result of the treatment, or in this case, was due to the difference in sex.

The value of 12 in the U column represents a probability of 12 times out of 1000 (1.2/100 or $P = 0.012$). This value is considerably lower than the 5/100 that we will accept for considering that the difference in pulse rate is based on the difference in sex. Therefore, we would reject the hypothesis that

$$PR\ \male\ =\ PR\ \female$$

and would say that the difference in pulse rates is significant and results from the difference in sex.

C. CHI-SQUARE ANALYSIS

The statistical test most frequently used to determine whether data obtained experimentally provide a good fit, or approximation, to the expected or theoretical data, is relatively simple to carry out. Basically, this test can be used to determine if any deviations from the *expected values* are due to chance alone or to factors or circumstances other than chance.

The formula for chi square (X^2) is

$$X^2 = \Sigma \left[\frac{(O - E)^2}{E} \right]$$

where O = the **observed** number of individuals
E = the **expected** number of individuals
and Σ = the summation of all values of $(O - E)^2/E$ for the various categories of phenotypes

The following example shows how this type of analysis can be applied to genetics data. It can be used in many other analyses as long as numerical data are used and not percentages or ratios.

TABLE E-4
Summary of the calculations of chi squares for the hypothetical cross given.

Phenotype	Genotype	O	E	(O − E)	(O − E)²	(O − E)²/E
Tall	T−	84	82.5	1.5	2.25	0.027
Dwarf	tt	26	27.5	− 1.5	2.25	0.082
Total		110	110.0	0		0.109

TABLE E-5
Distribution of χ^2.

n	Probability													
	.99	.98	.95	.90	.80	.70	.50	.30	.20	.10	.05	.02	.01	.001
1	.00016	.00063	.00393	.0158	.0642	.148	.455	1.074	1.642	2.706	3.841	5.412	6.635	10.827
2	.0201	.0404	.103	.211	.446	.713	1.386	2.408	3.219	4.605	5.991	7.824	9.210	13.815
3	.115	.185	.352	.584	1.005	1.424	2.366	3.665	4.642	6.251	7.815	9.837	11.345	16.268
4	.297	.429	.711	1.064	1.649	2.195	3.357	4.878	5.989	7.779	9.488	11.668	13.277	18.465
5	.554	.752	1.145	1.610	2.343	3.000	4.351	6.064	7.289	9.236	11.070	13.388	15.086	20.517
6	.872	1.134	1.635	2.204	3.070	3.828	5.348	7.231	8.558	10.645	12.592	15.033	16.812	22.457
7	1.239	1.564	2.167	2.833	3.822	4.671	6.346	8.383	9.803	12.017	14.067	16.622	18.475	24.322
8	1.646	2.032	2.733	3.490	4.594	5.527	7.344	9.524	11.030	13.362	15.507	18.168	20.090	26.125
9	2.088	2.532	3.325	4.168	5.380	6.393	8.343	10.656	12.242	14.684	16.919	19.679	21.666	27.877
10	2.558	3.059	3.940	4.865	6.179	7.267	9.342	11.781	13.442	15.987	18.307	21.161	23.209	29.588

Source: Table IV of Fisher and Yates: Statistical Tables for Biological, Agricultural and Medical Research, published by Longman Group, Ltd., London (previously published by Oliver & Boyd, Edinburgh) and by permission of the authors and publishers.

1. Example of Chi-Square Analysis

In a cross of tall maize (corn) plants to dwarf plants, the F_1 generation consisted entirely of tall plants. The F_2 generation consisted of 84 tall and 26 dwarf plants. The question we want to answer is whether this F_2 data fits the expected 3:1 monohybrid ratio. Using the data given in Table E-4, chi square was calculated.

$$X^2 = \Sigma \left[\frac{(O - E)^2}{E} \right]$$
$$= \Sigma [0.027 + 0.082]$$
$$X^2 = 0.109$$

What does this chi-square value of 0.109 mean? Consider that if the observed values were exactly equal to the expected values (i.e., $O = E$) then we would have a perfect fit, and X^2 would equal 0. Thus if you obtain a small value of X^2, this would indicate a close agreement of the observed and expected ratios, whereas a large value for X^2 would indicate marked deviation from the expected ratios. However, deviations from the expected values are always bound to occur due to chance alone. The question is "Are the observed deviations within the limits expected by chance?"

Statisticians have generally agreed, for these types of studies, on the arbitrary limits of 1 chance in 20 (probability = 0.05 = 5 %) for making the distinction between acceptance or rejection of the data as fitting the expected ratio.

The chi-square value for a two-term ratio (i.e., 3:1) that corresponds to a 0.05 or 1 in 20 probability is 3.841. Therefore, you would expect to obtain this value, *due to chance deviations only,* in only 5% of similar trials if the hypothesis is true. When X^2 for this two term ratio is larger than 3.841, then the probability that the variation is due to chance alone is less than 5% or 1 in 20. You would therefore *reject* the hypothesis that the observed and expected ratios are in close agreement.

In our example, X^2 was 0.109, which is considerably less than 3.841. Thus we can say that the variation between the observed and expected values *was* due to chance alone and accept the data as fitting the 3:1 ratio.

Where did we obtain the value 3.841? Mathematicians have developed a variety of statistical tables. Table E-5 is an example of a table of chi-square values. The table is set up so that probability *(P)* values extend across the top, and "degree of freedom" (D.F.) values are down the left margin. The number of degrees of freedom in tests of genetic ratios is *generally always one less than the number of classes* in the ratio being analyzed. Thus in tests of such ratios as 1:1 or 3:1 there is one degree of freedom, a test of a 1:2:1 ratio would have two degrees of freedom, and a test of a 1:2:1:2:4:2:1:2:1 would have eight degrees of freedom. The general idea of degrees of freedom can be exemplified by the situation encountered by a small boy when he is putting on his shoes. He has two shoes, but only one degree of freedom. Once one shoe is filled by a foot, right or wrong, the other shoe is automatically committed to being right or wrong too. Similarly, in a two-place table, one value can be filled arbitrarily, but the other is then fixed by the fact that the total must add up to the precise number of observations made in the experiment, and the deviations in the two classes must compensate for each other. When there are four classes, any three are usually free, but the fourth is fixed. Thus, when there are four classes, there are usually three degrees of freedom.

In our example, we have two classes in the ratio (i.e., 3:1) and therefore have one degree of freedom when we interpret the chi-square table. Look at the one-degree-of-freedom row under the 0.05 probability column, and you will find the value 3.841. This number represents the **maximum value** for chi square that you should be willing to accept and yet consider the deviations observed as due to chance alone. If you were willing to accept a P value representing 1 chance in 10, what value of chi square would you accept as maximum?

In our example, chi square was calculated to be 0.109. Looking across the one-degree-of-freedom line on Table E-5, we find that this value falls between the 0.70 ($X^2 = .148$) and the 0.80 ($X^2 = .0642$) columns. This says that the probability that the deviations we obtained from the expected values could be attributed to chance alone is between 70 and 80%. That is, if we were to repeat the study 100 times, we would obtain deviations as large as those observed about 70% of the time (i.e., 7 out of every 10 experiments). We can thus reasonably regard this deviation as simply a sampling, or chance, error.

REFERENCES

Alder, H. L., and E. B. Roessler. 1968. *Introduction to Probability and Statistics*. 4th ed. W. H. Freeman and Company.

Simpson, G. G., A. Roe, and R. C. Lewontin. 1960. *Quantitative Zoology*. Harcourt Brace.

Snedecor, G. W. 1956. *Statistical Methods*. 5th ed. Iowa State College Press.

Sokal, R. R., and F. J. Rohlf. 1969. *Biometry*. W. H. Freeman and Company.

Steel, R. G. D., and J. H. Torrie. 1960. *Principles and Procedures of Statistics*. McGraw-Hill.

Radioisotopes

The nuclei of atoms are composed of neutrons and protons. In any single element, the nuclei contain the same number of protons. Some nuclei, however, may contain a *different number of neutrons* and thus have a different atomic mass. Atoms having nuclei with the same number of protons but different numbers of neutrons are called **isotopes**. Most isotopes are stable. However, others have certain combinations of protons and neutrons that make them unstable. Such isotopes tend to reach a stable state and in the process emit a distinctive type of radiation. During the disintegration of such isotopes, called **radioisotopes**, three types of radiation may be emitted:

Alpha (α) rays are particles consisting of two neutrons and two protons each. Thus, alpha rays are basically charged helium atoms.

Beta (β) rays are electrons emitted by some nuclei. The energy levels of these electrons may vary and produce hard beta radiation (highly charged electrons) or soft beta radiation (low-charged electrons). Phosphorus-32 is an example of a hard beta emitter; carbon-14 is a soft beta emitter.

Gamma (γ) rays are electromagnetic radiation and closely resemble X rays. Cobalt-60 is an example of a gamma emitter.

Because of the constant loss of particles, radioisotopes are said to "decay." The amount of radioactive material that remains will therefore be reduced with time. The rate of decay is known for many radioisotopes and is expressed as the **half-life** of the isotope. Half-life is the length of time it takes for a radioactive substance to lose half of its radioactivity. For example, the half-life of uranium-238 is 4,500,000,000 years; phosphorus-32 is 8.0 days.

Because radiation is damaging to human tissues, any radioactive materials used in the laboratory must be handled with extreme caution. Radioisotopes should be handled with the same care as harmful bacteria or strong acids. Remember, your "senses" cannot detect radiation. You *must* use proper techniques and follow certain rules.

SAFETY PRECAUTIONS IN THE USE OF RADIOISOTOPES

1. *Do not* eat, drink, smoke, chew gum, or apply cosmetics in the laboratory.

2. Wear an apron or laboratory coat.

3. To guard against contamination, place some disposable material (such as aluminum) over the table top on which you are working.

4. *Never* pipet any radioactive material by mouth. Use the special pipets provided by the instructor.

5. Discard paper, and other materials used, in the container designated for this purpose.

6. Never pour radioactive liquids into the standard drain. Pour them into the "waste" jar provided by the instructor.

7. Wash hands thoroughly before leaving the laboratory and after any suspected contact with radioactive material.

8. If you should spill radioactive material, notify your instructor immediately.

9. Clean up immediately after the experiment. Wash all contaminated equipment, and set it aside to be checked by the instructor for radioactivity.

REFERENCES

Chase, G. D., and J. L. Rabinowitz. 1967. *Principles of Radioisotope Methodology*. 3rd ed. Burgess.

Van Norman, R. W. 1971. *Experimental Biology*. 2nd ed. Prentice-Hall.

Wang, C. H., and D. L. Willis. 1965. *Radiotracer Methodology*. Prentice-Hall.

Mendel's Laws of Inheritance

Gregor Mendel was an Austrian monk trained in the science of mathematics. He began his studies of heredity in 1857 using the common garden pea. His choice of pea plants was based on the fact that they were readily available, easy to grow, and grew rapidly. Furthermore, different varieties had distinctly different traits that "bred" true and reappeared year after year. Lastly, the pistil and stamens in the flower are entirely enclosed by the petals. Thus the flower typically self-pollinates (and thus self-fertilizes); accidental cross-pollination could not occur and confuse the experimental results. In Mendel's own words (a truism that holds even today), "The value and utility of any experiment are determined by the fitness of the material to the purpose for which it is used."

Mendel chose 2 variants for each of 7 different traits (form of the seed, color of the seed, position of the flower, flower color, form of the pod, color of the pod, and stem length). For each trait, Mendel noted the apparent loss of one alternate characteristic in the next generation. For example, when he crossed short plants with tall plants, only tall plants were found in the next generation (also called the Filial 1 or F_1 generation). When these F_1 progeny were allowed to self-pollinate, both parental types reappeared in the succeeding, or F_2, generation. Furthermore, Mendel noted a consistent 3:1 ratio of tall plants to short plants. This 3:1 ratio is frequently called the **monohybrid** ratio; *hybrid* refers to the heterozygosity of the particular trait in the offspring or parents. Thus, in the above example (and for all others he tested), the trait was not lost in the F_1 generation, but was "masked" in some fashion such that it did not express itself. The trait that was expressed is **dominant** and that which is hidden, or not expressed, is **recessive**.

Mendel's research suggested to him that those "factors" (now called **genes**) that determined various traits were transmitted from generation to generation in a predictable manner. From his findings, Mendel suggested that each gene for a given trait could exist in 2 alternative forms (now called **alleles**) that were responsible for the phenotype expressed. Thus, plants or animals that expressed only one phenotype (either dominant or recessive) through several generations were considered to be

FIG. G-1
Types of gametes produced in homozygous and heterozygous crosses.

homozygous (or pure breeding) for that trait. Organisms that produced 2 phenotypes were **heterozygous** (or hybrid).

Today we know that the gametes are the physical link between 2 generations and that homozygous individuals produce only one type of gamete, whereas heterozygous organisms produce 2 types of gametes and in equal numbers.

From his experiments involving the transmission of single characteristics, Mendel formulated his first law of inheritance—the **law of segregation**. This law says that, in sexually reproducing organisms, there are factors (genes) that come together at fertilization and segregate at meiosis. The alleles involved do this without losing their identity; that is, they show no changes in the offspring, which thus rules out any consideration involving a "blending" theory of inheritance.

Mendel's second law, the **law of independent assortment**, evolved from his experiments involving crosses between individuals differing in two gene pairs. For example, if you cross a homozygous plant with smooth, yellow seeds with one having wrinkled, green seeds, the F_1 generation results in plants having smooth, yellow seeds. In this cross, what is the genotype for each of the parents for each of the traits considered?

In the space below, show the cross, gametes, and genotype and phenotype for the F_1 plants.

When the F_1 plants were self-fertilized, they gave rise to an F_2 generation divided into 5 phenotypic classes as follows:

9/16 of the population were smooth and yellow

3/16 of the population were wrinkled and yellow

3/16 of the population were smooth and green

1/16 of the population were wrinkled and yellow

This ratio is referred to as a **dihybrid ratio**, where *dihybrid* is defined as being heterozygous in terms of the 2 pair of factors, or alleles, being studied. In the space below, diagram the cross just described. Show the phenotype and genotype of the F_1 plants, the gametes produced by the F_1 plants, the phenotype and genotype of the F_2 plants and the dihybrid ratio.

Interestingly, one can still demonstrate the validity of Mendel's first law of segregation if you consider the data for only one pair of genes at a time. For example, if you combine all the smooth seeds (9/16 + 3/16 = 12/16) and all the wrinkled seeds (3/16 + 1/16 = 4/16), you obtain a 12/16:4/16 or 3:1 monohybrid ratio. Thus you again demonstrate that gene pairs act independently of one another and are not changed in their transmission from one generation to another. This indeed was the basis for Mendel's second law of inheritance.

Although Mendel's career as a "geneticist" was cut short by a beetle that devastated his pea crops and by being appointed head of the monastery, he left us with several important concepts, including his 2 laws of inheritance and the fact that results of various crosses are mathematically predicatable.

REFERENCES

Lerner, I. M., and W. J. Libby. 1976. *Heredity, Evolution, and Society.* 2nd ed. W. H. Freeman and Company.

Raven, A. W. 1965. *The Evolution of Genetics.* Academic Press.

Stern, C., and E. R. Sherwood. 1966. *The Origin of Genetics.* W. H. Freeman and Company.

Stine, G. J. 1973. *Laboratory Exercises in Genetics.* Macmillan.

Culture of *Drosophila*

A. LIFE CYCLE OF *DROSOPHILA*

There are 4 distinct stages in the life cycle of the fruit fly (Fig. H-1): egg, larva, pupa, and adult. At 25°C, a fresh culture of *Drosophila* will produce new adults in 9 or 10 days: about 5 days in the egg and larval stages and 4 days in the pupal stage. The adult flies may live for several weeks. *Drosophila* cultures should not be exposed to high temperatures (e.g., 30°C), because such exposure results in sterilization or death of the flies, nor to low temperatures (e.g., 10°C), because it prolongs the life cycle (perhaps 57 days) and reduces viability.

1. Egg

The adult *Drosophila* female starts to deposit eggs on the second day after emergence from the pupa. Each egg is about 0.5 mm long and is ovoid in shape and white in color. Extending from its anterior end are 2 thin stalks that expand into flattened, spoonlike terminal parts. Embryonic development of the egg takes about one day at 25°C.

2. Larva

The larva is white, segmented, and wormlike. It has black mouth parts (jaw hooks) in a narrowed head region, but no eyes and so is completely blind. The larva also lacks appendages and must literally eat and push its way through its environment. It breathes by trachea and has a pair of conspicuous spiracles (air pores) both at the anterior end and at the posterior end of the body.

The larval stage in the *Drosophila* life cycle is one of rapid eating and growing. It consists of 3 subdivisions called **instars**. The first and second instars terminate in molts. Each molt consists of a complete shedding of the skin and mouth parts of the larva and is the mechanism by which the animal grows. The third instar terminates

476

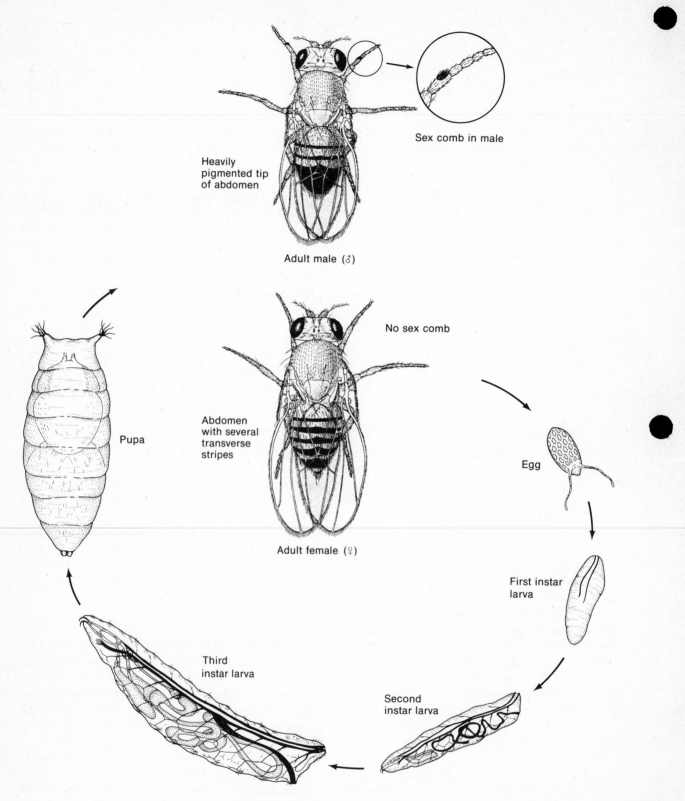

Sex comb in male

Heavily
pigmented tip
of abdomen

Adult male (♂)

No sex comb

Abdomen
with several
transverse
stripes

Egg

Pupa

Adult female (♀)

First instar
larva

Third
instar larva

Second
instar larva

FIG. H-1
Life cycle of *Drosophila melanogaster.*

in pupation. Just before pupation, the animal ceases to feed, crawls to some relatively dry surface, and everts its anterior spiracles. The larval stage takes about 4 days at 25°C for completion, at which time the third instar is about 4.5 mm long.

3. Pupa

The pupal stage is considered a reorganizational stage of the fly's life cycle in which most larval structures are destroyed and adult structures are developed from embryonic tissues called **anlagen** (imaginal discs). These embryonic tissues have been lying dormant in the animal since their differentiation in the egg stage. The animal pupates within the last larval skin, which is at first soft and white but slowly hardens and darkens in color. The transformation that takes place in the pupa results in the development of the body form and structures of the adult (**imago**). The pupal stage takes about four days at 25°C to be complete, at which time the adult fly emerges from the puparium (pupal case).

4. Adult

The adult stage is considered the reproductive stage of the life cycle. The fly emerges from the puparium by forcing its way through the anterior end. At first the adult fly is greatly elongated, with its wings unexpanded. Within an hour, however, the wings expand and the body gradually attains the more rounded form typical of an adult. The adult is also relatively light in color when it first emerges, but within the first few hours it darkens to its characteristic adult colors.

Adult *Drosophila* mate about six hours after emerging from the puparium. The sperm are then stored in the spermathecae and ventral receptacles of the female and are released gradually into the oviduct as eggs are produced and passed through the oviduct into the vagina. As stated earlier, the female begins to deposit eggs about two days after it has emerged. It may deposit as many as 50 to 75 eggs per day for the first few days. Thereafter, its egg production decreases with time. The average lifespan of adult flies is 37 days at 25°C.

B. CULTURE MEDIUM

A number of media have been developed for the culture of *Drosophila*. However, the easiest to use are the "instant media" available from many biological supply houses. A concentrated medium requires only the addition of water to be immediately usable. No cooking is necessary.

Pour the medium into chemically clean bottles. These bottles may be of any size, but 4-ounce (120 ml), wide-mouthed bottles or half-pint milk bottles are satisfactory. (It is best to transfer the mixture to a beaker for pouring. None of the medium should come into contact with the neck of the bottle.) Fill the bottles with medium to a depth of about 1 inch (2.5 cm). Then place a piece of *nonabsorbent paper such as brown wrapping paper* in each bottle so that it extends down into the medium (a double piece of paper is more satisfactory). The paper should be about an inch wide and should extend upward to a point about one-half inch (12 mm) below the neck of the bottle. This paper provides a dry place on which the larvae can pupate. Stopper the bottles with cotton plugs (such as those used in bacteriology) or with disposable foam plugs, which are more convenient. Sterilize the bottles in an autoclave at 20 pounds pressure for 20 minutes. At the same time, it is wise to sterilize other materials that you may wish to use in handling flies. Before placing the flies in the cooled bottles of medium, shake a small amount of dry yeast on the medium. The yeast will grow and serve as food for the developing fly larvae.

C. ETHERIZATION OF FLIES

It is necessary to etherize flies in order to keep them inactive while they are being examined and when they are being transferred into culture bottles for matings. The etherizing bottle can consist of any small container that has an opening the same size as that of the culture bottle and a tight-fitting cork. Into the bottom of the cork, tack a pad of cotton. Just before employing the technique outlined below (Fig. H-2), douse the cotton with a few dropperfuls of ether.

1. Shake the flies down into the bottom of the culture bottle by tapping the bottle on a rubber pad on a desk.

2. Remove the cotton plug from the culture bottle and, in its place, *quickly* insert the empty etherizing bottle. Make certain you have blown any residual fumes from the etherizing bottle before you invert it over the culture bottle.

3. Reverse the position of the two bottles so that the etherizer is now on the bottom.

4. Hold the 2 bottles firmly together and shake the flies from the culture bottle into the etherizer. This is best done by tapping the sides of the culture bottle horizontally

478

A. Gently tap the culture bottle to force the flies to the bottom.

B. Remove the cotton plug and in its place quickly insert the etherizing bottle.

C. Reverse the two bottles so that the etherizer is now on the bottom. Shake the flies into the etherizer.

D. Remove the culture bottle and quickly replug. Simultaneously plug the etherizer with its cork.

E. Transfer the flies to a white card. Examine them with a hand lens or dissecting microscope. Move flies around with a toothpick.

FIG. H-2
Procedure for etherizing flies.

so that the flies are dislodged and fall into the etherizer. Make certain you do not shake the food loose in the culture bottle.

5. After you have shaken the flies into the etherizer, remove the culture bottle and quickly replug it. Simultaneously plug the etherizer with its cork. The cotton on the cork should feel *moist* with ether but not wet.

6. Observe the flies in the etherizer. Thirty seconds after they have stopped walking around, pour them out onto your counting plate. If the flies have been overetherized (killed), their wings will be extended at right angles to their bodies.

7. Normally, the flies will remain etherized from 5 to 10 minutes. If they begin to awaken on the plate, they can be reetherized as follows: On the inner surface of a petri dish, tape a piece of paper toweling. Moisten the paper toweling with ether, and place the petri dish over the flies to form an etherizing chamber.

D. DISTINGUISHING THE SEX

Examination of the external genitalia under magnification is the best means of distinguishing the sex of flies. Only male flies exhibit darkly colored external genitalia, which are visible on the ventral side of the tip of the abdomen. The following characteristics, illustrated in Fig. 17-1, may also be helpful in distinguishing males from females:

1. *Size:* Females are usually larger than males.

2. *Shape:* The abdomen of the male is round and blunt, whereas that of the female is sharp and protruding. The abdomen of the male is relatively narrow and cylindrical, whereas that of the female is distended and appears spherical or ovate.

3. *Color:* Black pigment is more extensive on the abdomen of the male than on that of the female. On the male, the markings extend completely around the abdomen and meet on the ventral side. On the female, the pigment is present only in the dorsal region.

4. *Sex Combs:* Only males have a small tuft of black bristles called a *sex comb* on the anterior margin at the basal tarsal joint of each front leg. Magnification is necessary to see the sex combs.

E. ISOLATING VIRGINS

Females of *D. melanogaster* can store and use sperm from one insemination for a large part of their reproductive lives. As a result, only virgin females should be used in making crosses. Females of this species can mate 6 hours after they have emerged from the puparium. Therefore, a procedure must be followed that will ensure the collection of females that are no more than 6 hours old. A number of possible procedures are available to you, depending on your preference and the accessibility of the laboratory.

If the laboratory is generally accessible,

1. Shake out and discard into the morgue (a bottle containing ethanol, oil, or detergent) all adult flies (10 or more days after the introduction of the parental flies). This step should be done early in the morning (8–10 A.M.) for most efficient results.

2. Return to the laboratory within 4 to 6 hours, and examine the newly hatched flies. The females in this group may be presumed to be virgin and can be used in experimental matings.

If the laboratory is not generally accessible,

1. Collect darkened pupae from the paper or sides of the bottle with a fine camel-hair brush.

2. Turn each pupa so that the legs are visible through the pupal case. Examine under high power the upper most or proximal joint of the tarsi of the front legs. The presence of sex combs indicates a male.

3. Collect the pupae that are *without* sex combs, hence female, and place them individually in fresh culture bottles. After the flies have hatched from their pupal cases, examine them to be certain that no male pupae have accidentally been placed in a culture. All the flies that are female can be used in experimental matings.

REFERENCE

Levine, L. and N. M. Schwartz. 1973. Laboratory Exercises in Genetics. Mosby.